Data Compression and Error Control Techniques with Applications

Data Compression and Error Control Techniques with Applications

Edited by

V. Cappellini

Dipartimento di Ingegneria Elettronica
Università di Firenze
and Istituto di Ricerca sulle Onde Elettromagnetiche
Consiglio Nazionale delle Ricerche
Florence, Italy

 1985

ACADEMIC PRESS
Harcourt Brace Jovanovich, Publishers
London   Orlando   San Diego   New York
Austin   Montreal   Sydney   Tokyo   Toronto

ACADEMIC PRESS INC. (LONDON) LTD.
24–28 Oval Road
LONDON NW1 7DX

United States Edition published by
ACADEMIC PRESS, INC.
Orlando, Florida 32887

British Library Cataloguing in Publication Data

Data compression and error control techniques
    with applications.
    1. Data compression (Computer science)
    I. Cappellini, V.
    001.64'42   QA76.9.D33

Library of Congress Cataloging in Publication Data
Main entry under title:

Data compression and error control techniques with
    applications.

    Includes bibliographies and index.
    1. Data compression (Telecommunication)   2. Coding
theory.   3. Error-correcting codes (Information theory)
I. Cappellini, Vito.
TK5102.5.D336   1985   001.64'4   85-6016
ISBN 0–12–159260–X (alk. paper)
ISBN 0–12–159261–8 (paperback)

85 86 87 88   9 8 7 6 5 4 3 2 1

Contents

v

Chapter 3   Data Compression Techniques
G. Benelli, E. Del Re, V. Cappellini, and F. Lotti

Chapter 4   Channel Models and Channel Coding
G. Benelli and C. Bianciardi

Chapter 8   Hardware Implementation of Data Compression and Error Control Techniques
V. Cappellini and E. Del Re

Chapter 9   Applications of Data Compression and Error Control Techniques
V. Cappellini

Appendix 1   Finite Fields: A Brief Survey

Appendix 2   Computer Programs for the Implementation of Data Compression and Error Control Techniques

List of Contributors

Numbers in parentheses indicate the pages on which the authors' contributions begin.

G. Benelli (33, 83, 109, 157, 185), Dipartimento di Ingegneria Elettronica, Università di Firenze, 50139 Florence, Italy

C. Bianciardi (83, 109), Ministero Pubblica Istruzione, Siena, Italy, and Dipartimento di Ingegneria Elettronica, Università di Firenze, 50139 Florence, Italy

V. Cappellini (1, 33, 109, 157, 221, 251), Dipartimento di Ingegneria Elettronica, Università di Firenze, and Istituto di Ricerca sulle Onde Elettromagnetiche, Consiglio Nazionale delle Ricerche, 50139 Florence, Italy

E. Del Re (33, 157, 185, 221), Dipartimento di Ingegneria Elettronica, Università di Firenze, 50139 Florence, Italy

G. Longo (11), Dipartimento di Elettrotecnica Elettronica Informatica, Università di Trieste, 34127 Trieste, Italy

F. Lotti (33, 185), Istituto di Ricerca sulle Onde Elettromagnetiche, Consiglio Nazionale delle Ricerche, 50127 Florence, Italy

A. Sgarro (11), Istituto di Matematica and DEEI, Università di Trieste, 34127 Trieste, Italy

List of Contributors

Preface

Since the pioneering work by C. E. Shannon, who founded the mathematical theory of communication, or information theory, in 1948, many source codes (data compression techniques) and channel codes (error control techniques, i.e., techniques for correcting and/or detecting channel errors) have been defined and applied.

The first applications of data compression and error control techniques were mainly in the area of space digital telemetry or military communications. Subsequently, and especially in the past decade, the applications have been widely extended to satellite telecommunication systems, ground telephony, telemetry and data transmission systems to increase the efficiency of the communication link by, e.g., data and/or bandwidth reduction or by reducing the probability of error.

In this book, the theory of data compression and error control coding is presented, together with a description of their implementation and application in many areas of communications and signal or image processing. The book is divided into three main parts. The first part (Chapters 1, 2, 4 and Appendix 1) is essentially tutorial in character and summarizes the basic aspects and relationships for the different types of source and channel codes. In the second part (Chapters 3, 5 and 6), the most important practical techniques of data compression and error control coding are derived from the preceding general theory, and efficiency comparisons are presented. In the third part (Chapters 7, 8, 9 and Appendices 2 and 3), software and hardware implementation problems are considered, and useful computer programs and specific hardware realizations are described. Next, their impact in research, operational and industrial areas is outlined, and several applications to space digital telemetry, speech compression and vocoders, digital processing and transmission of facsimile and television images, space digital communications, data transmission, biomedicine and remote sensing are presented.

It is hoped that the approach adopted in this book, with the inclusion of the theoretical aspects of the subject as well as the practical implementation procedures with the main applications — involving several authors for the different parts — will be of interest to students, researchers, practising engineers and technical managers.

Indeed the close co-operation of the research groups working in these fields at the Electrical Engineering Departments of the Universities of Florence and Trieste and at the Istituto di Ricerca sulle Onde Elettromagnetiche (IROE) of Consiglio Nazionale delle Ricerche (CNR) in Florence has made the writing of this book possible. Individual experiences and joint research efforts were utilized in bringing together the theoretical developments and practical applications included in the book.

Other institutes, laboratories and firms have assisted our research on a number of specific subjects. In particular, we acknowledge the helpful contributions to practical implementations and applications of data compression and error control techniques made by CSELT, Torino, Italy; LINKABIT Inc., San Diego, California; TRT, Paris, France; and Telettra SpA, Milan, Italy.

Finally, the help of the technical staff at the Department of Electrical Engineering of Florence University and at the IROE, and in particular of Mrs. C. Bacci, F. Meiners, C. Mealli, A. Nozzoli, C. Rescic, P. Poli, D. Tirelli, and L. Zuccagnoli, was invaluable for the preparation of the final manuscript and figures.

Florence, Italy   V. CAPPELLINI

Chapter 1

Information Sources and Communication Channels

V. CAPPELLINI

Dipartimento di Ingegneria Elettronica
Università di Firenze
and Istituto di Ricerca sulle Onde Elettromagnetiche,
Consiglio Nazionale delle Ricerche
Florence, Italy

1.1 Introduction

In 1948 C. E. Shannon initiated the *mathematical theory of communication,* or *information theory*. He proposed an objective measure of information and formally defined information sources and channels. On the basis of entropy (of a source) and capacity (of a channel), he proposed two basic theorems which set precise bounds to the accurate representation and errorless transmission of data. When there are no limitations on resources (time, computing power, etc.), then (1) the code word length for optimal source codes is approximately equal to (but not less than) the source entropy, and (2) arbitrarily accurate transmission through a channel can be achieved at rates not beyond the channel capacity [1, 2].

Many practical source codes (or *data compression techniques*) and channel codes (or *error control techniques*, i.e., techniques for correcting and/or detecting channel errors) have been defined, tested and applied since the pioneering work of Shannon. It is therefore important to review the fundamental aspects of information theory as they apply to the information sources and communication channels in this chapter and to other topics (as the two basic theorems) in Chapters 2 and 4.

1

DATA COMPRESSION AND ERROR CONTROL
TECHNIQUES WITH APPLICATIONS

1.2   Information Sources and Source Models

Information sources can be described in terms of probabilistic models, which are suitable for representing the most part of actual messages (signals, images, data, etc.).

Let us consider a simple discrete information source, called a *finite memoryless source* (FMS), $A = \{a_1, a_2, \ldots, a_q\}$, where $a_1, a_2, \ldots, a_q$ are the *source symbols or letters* (*source alphabet*). Each symbol a_i has a fixed probability $p(a_i) = p_i$, according to a defined probability distribution $P = \{p_1, p_2, \ldots, p_q\}$ [1–3].

The amount of information $H_i(a_i)$ connected to the symbol a_i is assumed to be related to the logarithm of the inverse of its probability p_i

$$H_i(a_i) = c \log_D (1/p_i) \tag{1.1}$$

where c and D are suitable constants. The *average amount of information* provided by the source A is defined as the addition of the $H_i(a_i)$ terms weighted by the corresponding probabilities p_i; that is,

$$H(A) = \sum_{i=1}^{q} p_i \log_D \frac{1}{p_i} = - \sum_{i=1}^{q} p_i \log_D p_i \tag{1.2}$$

which is called the *entropy of the source*. In general, it is assumed that $D = 2$, and the entropy is representing the average number of binary units (bits) per symbol. Other more complex source models can be defined as sources with memory (Markov sources) (see Chapter 2).

For the preceding discrete information sources, the nth-order extension A^n can be defined: The new symbols or letters of A^n are n-tuples of symbols a_i. Thus, A^n has q^n symbols. The entropy of A^n can easily be related to the entropy of A. For instance, in the case of an FMS source A, the entropy of A^n is given by (Section 2.7)

$$H(A^n) = nH(A) \tag{1.3}$$

It is important to point out that the preceding sources of discrete type can indeed also represent continuous sources such as signals and images. A time signal $f(t)$ can be sampled with a *sampling interval* T_s (*sampling theorem*) as

$$T_s \leq 1/2\nu_M \tag{1.4}$$

where ν_M is the maximum signal-spectrum frequency [4]. The obtained samples $f(nT_s) = f(n)$ can hence be quantized, that is, expressed as a multiple of an amplitude *quantization interval* Δ. A set of discrete amplitude values $f_1(n), = \Delta, f_2(n) = 2\Delta, \ldots, f_q(n) = q\Delta$ are, therefore, obtained, which correspond to the preceding source symbols a_i:

$$a_i = f_i(n), \qquad i = 1, 2, \ldots, q \tag{1.5}$$

In a similar way, an image $f(x, y)$ can be sampled with a *space sampling interval* X:

$$X \leq 1/2v_{xM}, \qquad X \leq 1/2v_{yM} \qquad (1.6)$$

where v_{xM} and v_{yM} are the maximum space frequencies regarding, respectively, the x and y axes [4]. The obtained space samples $f(n_1, n_2) = f(n_1 X, n_2 X)$ can hence be quantized as in the preceding and expressed as a multiple of an amplitude quantization interval. Discrete amplitude values $f_i(n_1, n_2)$ are obtained, again corresponding to the source symbols a_i,

$$a_i = f_i(n_1, n_2), \qquad i = 1, 2, \ldots, q \qquad (1.7)$$

1.3 Discrete Channel Models

A common and general block diagram of a communication system is represented in Fig. 1.1 [5]. In this scheme, the information source messages are first transformed by the *source encoder* to obtain a compact representation (optimal source codes can be defined as having a minimum code word length; see Chapter 2). The data coming from the source encoder (usually binary data) enter the *channel encoder*, which protects the remaining useful data from the channel noise (see Chapter 4). Hence, the coded data enter the modulator. The splitting channel encoder/modulator is fundamental in this diagram (and in our model) because the channel-encoder operation is a discrete-time operation, while the modulator performs a continuous-time operation.

Without loss of generality, we suppose that M messages may emerge from the source encoder. Each message has a duration equal to T sec, and it may

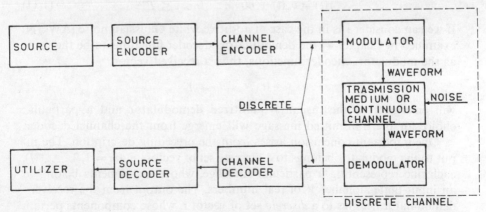

FIG. 1.1. General block diagram of a communication system. (From Viterbi and Omura [5].)

be formed by k source symbols belonging to an alphabet $A = \{a_1, a_2, \ldots, a_q\}$. Hence $M = q^k$, $q \geq 2$.

The channel encoder may be viewed as a mapping from this discrete set of M messages to a discrete set of vectors, each of $N \leq M$ real numbers as components.

If now

$$\mathbf{v}_m = (v_{m1}, v_{m2}, \ldots, v_{mN}), \qquad m = 1, 2, \ldots, M$$

is such a vector representing a particular message, the aim of the modulator is to associate a finite-energy signal $v_m(t)$, $0 \leq t \leq T$ to this message for the transmission through the continuous channel. In fact, from the *Gram–Schmidt* procedure [6], it is possible to represent the M signals $v_m(t)$ as linear combinations of $N \leq M$ basis functions $\Phi_i(t)$ such that

$$\int_0^T \Phi_j(t)\Phi_k(t)\, dt = \delta_{kj} = \begin{cases} 1, & \text{if } j = k \\ 0, & \text{if } j \neq k \end{cases} \tag{1.8}$$

i.e., such that the $\Phi_i(t)$, $i = 1, 2, \ldots, N$, are orthonormal. In this way, we can write

$$v_m(t) = \sum_{i=1}^N v_{mi}\Phi_i(t), \qquad m = 1, 2, \ldots, M \tag{1.9}$$

and

$$v_{mi} = \int_0^T v_m(t)\Phi_i(t)\, dt, \qquad i = 1, 2, \ldots, N \tag{1.10}$$

Now, the transmitted waveform $v_m(t)$ may be corrupted by the transmission-medium noise, which can be modeled by a function $n(t)$ in this case. Therefore the input to the receiver–demodulator can be expressed as

$$r(t) = v_m(t) + n(t), \qquad 0 \leq t \leq T \tag{1.11}$$

If we can consider [as in the case of additive white Gaussian noise (AWGN) examined in Chapter 4] the demodulator–decoder functions to be the same as the modulator–encoder functions, then a received vector

$$\mathbf{r} = (r_1, r_2, \ldots, r_N)$$

will emerge from the (usually) quantized demodulator and a particular choice for the transmitted message will emerge from the channel decoder.

One important conclusion arises from the preceding description. The input to the modulator belongs to a *discrete* set of vectors v_m $(m = 1, 2, \ldots, M)$, each one representing a particular message, whose components belong to an input finite-alphabet V of real numbers. The output from the receiver–demodulator belongs to a *discrete* set of vector $\mathbf{r}$, whose components pertain to an output finite alphabet R of real numbers (depending on the quantization rules actually used). Now, if we consider the modulator and the demodulator together with the transmission medium as *the channel*, this *compound* channel is a *discrete channel*.

In what follows, we refer to this discrete channel as the fundamental *basis model* for the examined transmission-channel models. The discrete channel model is then described by a probability measure of the set of **r** vectors for each **v** vector input.

DEFINITION The discrete channel is memoryless (DMC) if the channel output symbol depends *only* on the corresponding channel input symbol. Then, in our notations, the discrete channel will be *memoryless* if

$$P(\mathbf{r}, v_m) = \prod_{i=1}^{N} P(r_i \,|\, v_{mi}) \qquad (1.12)$$

or the probability that **r** will be received when v_m has been transmitted is equal to the product of the conditional probabilities related to their components r_i and v_{mi} (channel output and input symbols). In particular, this memoryless channel will be described entirely by the $P(r_i \,|\, v_{mi})$ conditional probabilities between channel input and output alphabets (the so-called transition probabilities). Moreover, if (1.12) is not valid for any v_{mi} and r_i, the channel is not memoryless.

Without going into details about memory arising (see Chapter 4), we can affirm that the discrete channel is with *memory* (DCWM) if the current channel output depends statistically not only on the corresponding input but also on prior inputs and outputs. Finally, it should be noted that the discrete-channel model is only a particular model choice among other possible models. However, it seems a proper choice, if we consider that, for example, memory arises not only from the transmission-medium noise but also from the modulator–demodulator (MODEM) system actually used.

1.4 The Memoryless Discrete-Channel Capacity

In this section we recall some definitions and notations on probabilistic models and on mutual information and capacity, well known from information theory.

1.4.1 The Probabilistic DMC Model

For sake of simplicity, we can denote the DMC input alphabet with $A = \{a_1, a_2, \ldots, a_q\}$ and the DMC output alphabet with $B = \{b_1, b_2, \ldots, b_j\}$, $q \geq 2$, $j \geq 2$, each alphabet being formed by a finite number (q and j, respectively) of letters. In fact, referring to the block diagram of Fig. 1.1, too, the channel encoder is simply a "mapping" from the alphabet A to an alphabet V of real numbers and in the same way the channel-decoder function can be viewed as a mapping from the finite real numbers alphabet R to the finite letters alphabet B.

Now, it is customary to call the set $\{a_1, a_2, \ldots, a_q\}$ the sample space of the channel input and to define the ensemble (or probability space), denoted by I, the channel-input sample space and its probability assignment $P(a_r)$, $r = 1, 2, \ldots, q$ (or the probability of each alternative $a_1, a_2, \ldots, a_q$). Likewise, the set $\{b_1, b_2, \ldots, b_j\}$ will be the channel-output sample space and Θ the channel-output ensemble. An arbitrary particular input (or output) is denoted by the same, but small, letter i (or θ). Moreover, the set of pairs $\{(a_r, b_s)\}$, $1 \le r \le q$ and $1 \le s \le j$, is called the joint sample space, and likewise, this joint sample space with a joint probability assignment $P(i, \theta)$ is called the joint $I\Theta$ ensemble.

According to Bayes's rule on conditional probabilities, it is known that the joint probability of the pair (a_r, b_s)

$$P(a_r, b_s) = P(b_s|a_r)P(a_r) = P(a_r|b_s)P(b_s)$$
$$1 \le r \le q, \quad 1 \le s \le j \qquad (1.13)$$

results, first, from the product of the conditional probability $P(b_s|a_r)$ that, given the input $i = a_r$, the output is $\theta = b_s$ by the probability $P(a_r)$ that the input is $i = a_r$ and, second, likewise. Then the set of conditional probabilities $P(b_s|a_r) = P_{rs}$, $1 \le s \le j$, $1 \le r \le q$, describes completely the discrete memoryless channel model, and P_{rs} can be viewed as the elements of a matrix (the *channel matrix*). Moreover, it is obvious that the probability $P(b_s)$ of a certain channel output is given by

$$P(b_s) = \sum_{r=1}^{q} P(a_r, b_s), \qquad P(a_r) = \sum_{s=1}^{j} P(a_r, b_s), \qquad (1.14)$$

Equation (1.14) is usually utilized, given the channel-input ensemble $I = \{a_r, P(a_r)\}$, $r = 1, 2, \ldots, q$, and the channel matrix of the DMC $P(b_s|a_r) = P_{rs}$, $r = 1, 2, \ldots, q$, $s = 1, 2, \ldots, j$, in order to estimate the probability of each output alternative.

1.4.2 Information and Capacity in the DMC Model

Following this line, it is known that $P(a_r)$ is also called the *a priori* probability of the input alternative a_r and that $P(a_r|b_s)$ is called the *a posteriori* probability of the same input (because the output b_s has been observed hereafter). Hence, also from (1.13) it is customary to affirm that the *mutual information* provided by the occurrence of b_s about the alternative a_r is given by[†]

$$I(a_r; b_s) = \log[P(a_r|b_s)/P(a_r)] = \log[P(b_s|a_r)/P(b_s)],$$
$$r = 1, 2, \ldots, q \qquad (1.15)$$

which can be viewed as the difference between the *a priori* and the *a posteriori* uncertainties about the input alternative a_r.

In fact, the *self-information* of the same input alternative a_r is defined as (Section 1.2)

$$I(a_r) = \log[1/P(a_r)], \qquad r = 1, 2, \ldots, q \qquad (1.16)$$

which can be viewed as the *a priori* uncertainty about the alternative a_r or as the information we need to resolve this uncertainty. Moreover, the *conditional self-information* of a_r after the observation of the output b_s is defined as

$$I(a_r|b_s) = \log[1/P(a_r|b_s)], \qquad r = 1, 2, \ldots, q \qquad (1.17)$$

Now, as for the definition of the source entropy (Section 1.2), the *average* amount of uncertainty of the input ensemble I or the quantity

$$H(I) = \sum_{r=1}^{q} P(a_r)I(a_r) = \sum_{r=1}^{q} P(a_r)\log\frac{1}{P(a_r)} \qquad (1.18)$$

is called the *a priori* input ensemble *entropy*, and the *average* amount of uncertainty of the input ensemble I *after* the observation of the output Θ or the quantity

$$H(I|\Theta) = \sum_{r=1}^{q}\sum_{s=1}^{j} P(a_r, b_s)I(a_r|b_s) = \sum_{r=1}^{q}\sum_{s=1}^{j} P(a_r, b_s)\log\frac{1}{P(a_r|b_s)} \qquad (1.19)$$

is called the *a posteriori* input ensemble *entropy*.

Then, by averaging (1.15) and from (1.18) and (1.19), the quantity

$$I(I; \Theta) = H(I) - H(I|\Theta) = \sum_{r=1}^{q}\sum_{s=1}^{j} P(a_r, b_s)\log\frac{P(a_r, b_s)}{P(a_r)P(b_s)} \qquad (1.20)$$

is called the *average mutual information* of the joint input–output ensemble (I, Θ), and it is expressed as the difference between the *a priori* and the *a posteriori* average uncertainties.

Moreover, from (1.13) and (1.14) it could be shown that it would be possible to write

$$I(I; \Theta) = H(\Theta) - H(\Theta|I) \qquad (1.21)$$

[†] The base of the logarithm in (1.15) and in what follows is 2, as usual. The numerical value of I is consequently defined as the number of bits of information (Section 1.2).

where $H(\Theta)$ has been called the average equivocation of the output Θ and $H(\Theta|I)$ the average equivocation of the output Θ, *given the input I.*

For a discrete memoryless channel (DMC), the following is unambiguous:

DEFINITION   The average mutual information $I(I; \Theta)$ given by (1.20) or (1.21), when it is maximized over the input probability assignment $P(I)$, is called the DMC *capacity.*

Then the DMC capacity C is defined as

$$C \triangleq \max_{P(I)} I(I; \Theta) \qquad (1.22)$$

1.4.3   Some General Remarks

At this point, it seems advisable to recall some known conclusions of information theory about the preceding subjects.

1.4.3.1   DMC Matrix

Equation (1.14) forms an equation system on the unknown output probabilities $P(b_s)$, $s = 1, 2, \ldots, j$, which can be evaluated given the input probability $P(a_r)$, $r = 1, 2, \ldots, q$, and the *channel matrix*

$$P = \begin{vmatrix} P_{11} & \cdots & P_{1j} \\ \vdots & & \vdots \\ P_{q1} & \cdots & P_{qj} \end{vmatrix}, \qquad P_{rs} \triangleq P(b_s|a_r) \qquad (1.23)$$

where each matrix row corresponds to a channel input and each matrix column to a channel output. Note that the sum $\sum_{s=1}^{j} P_{rs} = 1$. (The sum of the elements of each row is equal to one because, given an input, a certain output must occur.) Moreover, given $P(b_s)$ and P_{rs} in (1.14), it could not be possible to yield $P(a_r)$ [namely, the system (1.14) could not be reversed]. Finally, we observe that by means of Bayes's rule the so-called *reverse probabilities* $P(a_r|b_s) = P(b_s|a_r)P(a_r)/P(b_s)$ can be obtained from (1.13).

1.4.3.2   A priori and a posteriori Entropies

The quantity $H(I)$ given by (1.18) can be viewed also as the average number of bits needed to represent a channel-input letter and the quantity $H(I|\Theta)$ given by (1.19) can be viewed as the average number of bits needed to represent the same input *after* the observation of the output. Hence, it is a natural conclusion that we gain an average number of $|H(I) - H(I|\Theta)| = I(I; \Theta)$ bits of information by observing a single-channel output (the mutual information).

1.4.3.3   The Signum of I(I; Θ)

If $I(I; \Theta)$ can be viewed as the average number of information bits gained by the output observation, the question arises if it is a real gain, or if $I(I; \Theta)$

is either greater than or equal to or less than zero. It is an important and an encouraging conclusion of the information theory that $I(I;\Theta) \geq 0$. It is $I(I;\Theta) = 0$ iff $P(a_r, b_s) = P(a_r)P(b_s)$ [see also (1.20)] or iff channel inputs and outputs are statistically independent (as it is obvious). Hence, generally the output observation gives us some information.

1.4.3.4 Noiseless Channels

A noiseless channel is such that one channel output is originated by a single channel input without ambiguity. Hence, in the channel matrix P, given by (1.23), any column (which represents a particular channel output) will have one and only one non-zero element. In these conditions, when an output b_s is observed, it is known which input has been transmitted; namely, all the $P(b_s|a_r)$ are zero or one.

Then from (1.19) it follows that, for a noiseless channel, $H(I|\Theta) = 0$. It is an obvious conclusion if we think that the mutual information $I(I;\Theta)$ must coincide with $H(I)$, the *a priori* uncertainty, for a noiseless channel.

1.4.3.5 Mutuality of $I(I;\Theta)$

From (1.20) and (1.21) it emerges that $I(I;\Theta) = I(\Theta;I)$ or that it is possible to interchange input and output without changing the mutual information. This "mutuality" of mutual information suggests that the preceding arguments could be applied to any joint ensemble of statistically dependent random variables other than the channel inputs and outputs.

1.4.3.6 Mutual Information and Capacity

From (1.20) it emerges that $I(I;\Theta)$ is dependent on $P(I)$, the channel input probability assignment. On the contrary, the channel capacity C, as defined from (1.22), does not depend on $P(I)$ but only on the transition probabilities $P(b_s|a_r)$ that specify the channel model. It is an obvious conclusion if we consider that C has been reached for the *particular* choice of $P(I)$ that maximizes $I(I;\Theta)$.

1.4.3.7 Capacity and Memory

The definition (1.22) is unambiguous only for discrete memoryless channels, and it could be shown that the maximum value of $I(I;\Theta)$, namely, C, must exist in the DMC case. Now, it is known also that, roughly, C can be viewed as the *maximum* average amount of information that can be transmitted over the DMC.

The question arises if a channel with memory (DCWM) with the same average error rate of a DMC has a capacity either less than, or equal to or greater than that of DMC itself. Even though definition (1.22) is not applicable to a DCWM, however, we can affirm that memory *increases* capacity (see Chapter 4).

1.4.3.8 The Channel nth Extension

The so-called channel nth extension is a channel model such that its input symbols and its output symbols are sequences, each formed by n input symbols and n output symbols of the original channel model. The channel nth extension matrix has elements each of which is formed by the product of the corresponding transition probabilities of the original channel. Moreover, it can be shown that the mutual information $I(I^n; \Theta^n)$ of the nth extension is n times the mutual information $I(I; \Theta)$ of the original channel; i.e., $I(I^n; \Theta^n) = nI(I; \Theta)$.

References

1. Shannon, C. E. (1948). A mathematical theory of communication, *Bell Syst. Tech. J.* **27**, 379–423, 623–656.
2. Shannon, C. E., and Weather, W. (1949). "The Mathematical Theory of Communication." Univ. Illinois Press, Champaign-Urbana, Illinois.
3. Abramson, N. (1963). "Information Theory and Coding." McGraw-Hill, New York.
4. Cappellini, V., Constantinides, A. G., and Emiliani, P. (1978). "Digital Filters and Their Applications." Academic Press, London.
5. Viterbi, A. J., and Omura, J. K. (1979). "Principles of Digital Communications and Coding." McGraw-Hill, New York.
6. Gallager, R. G. (1968). "Information Theory and Reliable Communication." Wiley, New York.

Chapter 2

Source Coding

G. LONGO

Dipartimento di Elettrotecnica
Elettronica Informatica
Università di Trieste
Trieste, Italy

A. SGARRO

Istituto di Matematica
and
DEEI
Università di Trieste
Trieste, Italy

2.1 Introduction

For our purposes, information sources will be described in terms of probabilistic models, e.g., as generators of random variables or random processes [1]. Such models are not appropriate in most real-world communication situations (e.g., when the information sources are human beings), but engineering experience has shown that the special needs of data transmission and storage are often met satisfactorily by such models. Morever, those models can take advantage of existing rich and sophisticated mathematical tools. Rather, problems may arise when the theoretical results obtained for the models have to be interpreted and transferred to the actual transmission and storage systems. In fact, models are *not* the systems they represent but are simplified versions thereof. In the next section we describe the simplest model for an *information source* [1–3].

11

DATA COMPRESSION AND ERROR CONTROL
TECHNIQUES WITH APPLICATIONS

2.2   The Finite Memoryless Source

DEFINITION 2.2.1   A finite memoryless source (FMS) is a sequence of independent realizations $x_1, x_2, \ldots$ of a random variable (rv) X which takes its values in a finite set $A = \{a_1, a_2, \ldots, a_K\}$ (the *alphabet* of the source) according to a fixed probability distribution (pd) $P = \{p_1, p_2, \ldots, p_K\}$, where

$$p_i = \Pr\{X = a_i\}, \qquad 1 \le i \le K \tag{2.1}$$

$$\sum_{i=1}^{K} p_i = 1, \qquad\qquad p_i > 0, \quad 1 \le i \le K \tag{2.2}$$

Several remarks are in order.

REMARK 2.2.1   The construction of any source model is essentially made by the user (or users) of the source, e.g., the choice of the size K and of the *letters* (or messages) $a_1, a_2, \ldots, a_K$ of the alphabet depends on (1) the resources (computational facilities, time, and money) and (2) the fidelity requirements of the user. In particular, it is the user's decision which makes a_i different from a_j ($1 \le i, j \le K, i \ne j$). On the other hand, a_i might correspond to several outputs of the real source which another user might consider convenient to reflect into distinct letters in his own model. This fact is general, and although it is customary to speak about "information sources", it would be more realistic to speak about "source–user" pairs. Also, remember that what really matters is the size K of A and not the particular "names" a_i of the letters.

REMARK 2.2.2   The user also assigns the probabilities p_i to the letters a_i. This assignment can be the outcome of a statistical estimate or the expression of a subjective appraisal. Again, different users might give different probabilities to the *same* letters.

It is apparent that the choice of a model may not be a simple matter. Also, it may happen that the model adopted at the beginning has to be changed later.

EXAMPLE 2.2.1   Even a normal die can be considered as an information source. User U_1 can model the die as follows $A_1 = \{1, 2, 3, 4, 5, 6\}$, $P_1 = \{\frac{1}{6}, \frac{1}{6}, \frac{1}{6}, \frac{1}{6}, \frac{1}{6}, \frac{1}{6}\}$. User U_2 is interested only in the parity of the result, hence $A_2 = \{\text{even}, \text{odd}\}$, $P_2 = \{\frac{1}{2} + \varepsilon, \frac{1}{2} - \varepsilon\}$, where $\varepsilon > 0$ comes from user U_2's subjective feeling that the die is biased.

2.3   A More General Model for Finite Sources

Consider a sequence $X_1, X_2, \ldots$ of random variables each of which takes its values in the same finite alphabet $A_K = \{a_1, a_2, \ldots, a_K\}$. The statistical behavior of these random variables is described by the following probability assignment:

$$\Pr\{X_{t_1} X_{t_2} \cdots X_{t_k} = a_{i_1} a_{i_2} \cdots a_{i_k}\}, \tag{2.3}$$

where $t_1 < t_2 < \cdots < t_k$ and k are arbitrary positive integers, and $i_1, i_2, \ldots, i_k$ are k (not necessarily distinct) integers between 1 and K. In practice, however, the source models are much simpler, as the infinite description (2.3) reduces to a finite one.

2.3.1 The Markov Source

A finite Markov source M on the alphabet A_K is defined as follows. At each time instant M outputs a letter a_i of A_K, which is selected with a probability that depends (only) on the previous letter output. These "transition probabilities" are constant in time. Putting

$$\Pr\{X_t = a_j | X_{t-1} = a_i\} = p_{ij} \tag{2.4}$$

the source is completely specified by A_K, the stochastic matrix $\Gamma = \{p_{ij}\}$ and an initial probability distribution P_1 on A_K, which rules the selection of the first source output. The term stochastic matrix means that the following relations hold:

$$p_{ij} \geq 0, \qquad \sum_{j=1}^{K} p_{ij} = 1, \qquad 1 \leq i \leq K \tag{2.5}$$

We remark that our Markov sources can be identified with *Markov chains*, the letters being the states of the chain.

REMARK 2.3.1 More generally the current letter is output by the information source according to a probability which depends on the m previous letters; m is some fixed nonnegative integer, called the *memory* of the source. The FMS has memory zero, the Markov source has memory m.

EXAMPLE 2.3.1 Consider the following Markov source ($m = 1$), $A_3 = \{a, b, c\}$,

$$\Gamma = \begin{bmatrix} \frac{1}{3} & \frac{1}{3} & \frac{1}{3} \\ \frac{1}{4} & \frac{1}{2} & \frac{1}{4} \\ \frac{1}{4} & \frac{1}{4} & \frac{1}{2} \end{bmatrix}$$

$P_1 = \{\frac{3}{11}, \frac{4}{11}, \frac{4}{11}\}$. This means that the initial letter is output according to P_1 and that each subsequent letter according to whatever row of Γ is in order. Thus, the probability of the sequence $abbca\ldots$ is $\frac{3}{11} \cdot \frac{1}{3} \cdot \frac{1}{2} \cdot \frac{1}{4} \cdot \frac{1}{4} \cdots$. All of this can be conveniently illustrated by a *transition graph* (Fig. 2.1) on which the circles represent the letters (states) and each transition is represented by an arrow labelled with the corresponding transition probability. Here P_1 is

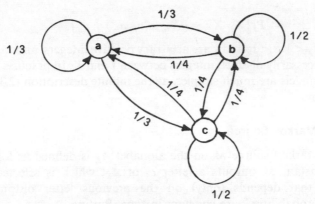

FIG. 2.1. Example of a transition graph.

the pd for the rv X_1 (first letter). The pd for X_2 is given by $P_2 = P_1 \cdot \Gamma$ (matrix product) and in general the pd for X_n is given by $P_n = P_{n-1} \cdot \Gamma = P_1 \cdot \Gamma^{n-1}$. In our case it is seen that $P_1 = P_2 = \cdots = P_n$ for all n's; i.e., the source is *stationary*. If we choose an initial pd P'_1 different from P_1, this is no longer true, since the equation in P

$$P\Gamma = P \tag{2.6}$$

has the unique solution $P_1 = \{\frac{3}{11}, \frac{4}{11}, \frac{4}{11}\}$. However, irrespective of the initial pd P'_1, the sequence $P'_1, P'_1\Gamma, P'_1\Gamma^2, \ldots$ can be seen to converge to P_1, which is consequently called the *asymptotic* pd of the source. This behaviour is typical of a large class of Markov sources called *ergodic Markov sources*. They are characterized by the existence of a unique asymptotic pd and by the possibility of eventually reaching any state from any state. If for some positive integer N the entries of Γ^N are all positive, then the source is ergodic and vice versa; in our example $N = 1$ [notice that for all N's Γ^N is a stochastic matrix whose (i, j) entry is the probability of passing from letter a_i to letter a_j in N steps]. The asymptotic pd of an ergodic Markov source is the unique solution of (2.6).

If we deal with an information source which is not digital (discrete) to start with, there are ways to convert it into digital based on sampling and quantizing (see Section 1.2). In this chapter, we are only interested in the discrete source created by this analog-to-digital conversion; see, however, Section 2.10 for a brief account of rate-distortion theory.

Note that in sampling and quantizing there is some freedom, which can be used to make the discrete source as convenient as possible, i.e., suitable for subsequent processing (PCM, Δ modulation . . .). At this point, it might be necessary to translate the symbols $a_1, a_2, \ldots, a_K$ of the discrete source into a different alphabet, e.g., a binary one.

2.4 Representation of the Source Messages I

In this section we are interested in the most rudimentary form of source encoding, i.e., the simple translation of the source messages into sequences of symbols from a given alphabet. In this context, this alphabet will be called the *secondary alphabet*, whereas the source alphabet will also be called *primary*. For the time being, the statistics of the source are not taken into account.

Let $B = \{b_1, \ldots, b_D\}$ be the secondary alphabet. To each letter a_i of A we associate a sequence $\mathbf{w}_i$ of letters from B, which is called the *code word* for a_i. Moreover, to each sequence $a_{i_1} a_{i_2} \ldots a_{i_n}$ of messages output by the source in n successive time instants (for any integer $n \geq 1$), we associate the juxtaposition $\mathbf{w}_{i_1} \mathbf{w}_{i_2} \ldots \mathbf{w}_{i_n}$ of the corresponding code words.

The set $C_K = \{\mathbf{w}_1, \ldots, \mathbf{w}_K\}$ is a *code* for the single letters of the source, and we are interested in *uniquely decipherable* codes, which allow us to uniquely reconstruct the primary sequence $a_{i_1} \ldots a_{i_n}$ from the sequence $\mathbf{w}_{i_1} \ldots \mathbf{w}_{i_n}$. A more precise definition follows.

DEFINITION 2.4.1   A uniquely decipherable (ud) code over B for the single letters of A is a set $\{\mathbf{w}_1, \ldots, \mathbf{w}_K\}$ such that if $a_{i_1} \ldots a_{i_m}$ and $a_{j_1} \ldots a_{j_n}$ are both encoded into the same secondary sequence $b_{l_1} \ldots b_{l_t}$, then

(i) $m = n$

(ii) $a_{i_s} = a_{j_s}$ for all s, $1 \leq s \leq n$

It is obvious that a necessary condition for C_K to be ud is that all of its words be distinct. This implies that if D is small (in most applications $D = 2$), the code words cannot all be "short". More precisely, if $l_i = |\mathbf{w}_i|$ is the *length* of $\mathbf{w}_i$ (i.e., the number of D-ary symbols in it), then the following theorem holds.

THEOREM 2.4.1   (KRAFT–MCMILLAN INEQUALITY)   If C_K is a ud code on B, then its lengths satisfy

$$\sum_{i=1}^{K} D^{-l_i} \leq 1 \tag{2.7}$$

PROOF   Set $\sum_{1}^{K} D^{-l_i} = T$ and consider the nth power $T^n = [\sum_{1}^{K} D^{-l_i}]^n$. Here T^n will contain powers of D^{-1} from 0 to nl, where l is the greatest code word length. Let N_j be the coefficient of power D^{-j} in T^n ($N_j \geq 0$),

$$T^n = \sum_{j=0}^{nl} N_j D^{-j} \tag{2.8}$$

Now notice that N_j coincides with the number of secondary sequences of length j, which are derived from primary n-tuples. This number cannot be

larger than the number of distinct secondary sequences, which is D^j, since
the code is ud: $N_j \leq D^j$. Substituting in (2.8) and summing yields

$$T^n \leq nl + 1$$

for all n's. This can only be true if $T \leq 1$.   Q.E.D.

REMARK 2.4.1   The lengths l_i of a code satisfy (2.7) but are not enough
for the code to be ud. For example, the binary code $C_4 = \{0, 00, 111, 101\}$
over $B = \{0, 1\}$ is obviously not ud.

The binary code $C_2 = \{01, 011\}$ is ud $(T = \frac{3}{8})$ since 0 marks the beginning
of all code words (0 acts as a "comma"). However, we see that in decoding
C_2 011 is recognized as soon as it ends, whereas 01 is recognized with a *delay*
of one symbol. In some cases, this decoding delay is not upperbounded. For
example, the binary code $C_3 = \{1, 10, 00\}$ is ud $(T = 1)$, but a sequence
made by a 1 followed by a run of zeros cannot be decoded until the next 1
is received, which can take an arbitrary length of time. Once the next 1 appears, however, decoding is performed in an unambiguous way.

There exists a class of ud codes which do not suffer from this drawback,
namely, the class of *prefix codes*, which are instantaneously decodable (i.e.,
each code word is identified as soon as it ends).

DEFINITION 2.4.2   A *prefix condition code* (or simply *prefix code*) is a code
in which no code word is a prefix (initial part) of a longer code word.

EXAMPLE 2.4.1   The following codes are prefix: $C_4 = \{0, 11, 100, 101\}$;
$C_7 = \{0, 2, 10, 110, 111, 112, 12\}$. Here C_4 is binary; C_7 is ternary.

A convenient representation of D-ary codes is offered by D-ary trees.

2.4.1 D-ary Code Trees

Given any D-ary rooted tree, we label the branches stemming from each
internal node with the symbols $0, 1, \ldots, t \, (1 \leq t \leq D - 1)$, e.g., clockwise.
These branch labels allow the association of a D-ary sequence to each tree
node.

(1)   To the tree root we associate the empty sequence λ
(2)   To each (internal or external) node we associate the ordered sequence
of the labels corresponding to the branches connecting the root to that node
(see Figs. 2.2 and 2.3 for examples).

It is obvious that the code words of any D-ary code C_K can be associated
to K nodes of some convenient D-ary tree. Such nodes are the *code nodes*
for C_K. Once the code nodes are marked on the chosen tree, we can delete
those branches that are not used to going from the root to any code node.

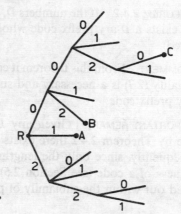

FIG. 2.2. Labelling a ternary tree. Here $R \rightarrow \lambda$, $A \rightarrow 1$, $B \rightarrow 02$ and $C \rightarrow 0020$.

What is left is the *code tree*. See Fig. 2.3 for an example referring to the ternary (nonprefix) code $C_8 = (0, 00, 11, 2, 21, 210, 211, 212)$. The tree on the left can be used to embed the code nodes. The code tree is then shown on the right.

REMARK 2.4.2 In the code tree of a prefix code all code nodes are external. Conversely, given any (finite) D-ary tree, the labels of its external nodes are the words of a D-ary prefix code.

We now state the following important result.

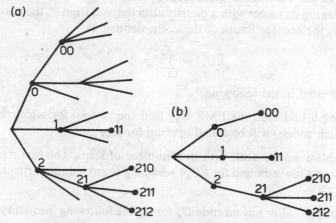

FIG. 2.3. Ternary (nonprefix) code C_8: (a) the tree used to embed the code nodes and (b) the code tree.

THEOREM 2.4.2   If the numbers $D, l_1, l_2, \ldots, l_K$ satisfy inequality (2.7), then there exists a D-ary prefix code whose words have lengths $l_1, \ldots, l_K$ (proof omitted).

COMMENT   From this theorem it can be deduced that the Kraft–McMillan inequality (2.7) is a necessary and sufficient condition for the existence of a D-ary prefix code.

IMPORTANT REMARK   Given any D-ary ud code, its lengths satisfy (2.7); hence by Theorem 2.4.2 there exists a prefix code having the same lengths. Consequently, since only the lengths of its code words serve to assess the goodness of a code (see Section 2.5), the search for good ud codes can be carried out within the subfamily of prefix code.

2.5   Representation of the Source Messages II

So far in representing the source messages via a code alphabet, we were only concerned about the ud property, i.e., the fidelity of the mapping. However, in real data transmission or storage, the *cost* of the representation is also involved. The cost is a nonnegative function which, in general, depends on the code letter being transmitted or stored. It is often the case, however, that the cost is the same for all code letters and that it is additive. For the sake of simplicity we shall make this assumption throughout and identify the cost of a code word with its length (number of symbols).

Let $C_K = \{w_1, w_2, \ldots, w_K\}$ be a (prefix) D-ary code for the FMS $G_K = \{A, P\}$ (see Section 2.2) and let $l_i = |w_i|$ be the length of code word w_i. Since the length of the code word generated by the source coder is a random variable L taking its values with a distribution derived from P, the parameter of interest is the *average length* of the code, defined as

$$\bar{l}(C_K) = \sum_{i=1}^{K} l_i p_i \tag{2.9}$$

We are interested in the following.

PROBLEM 2.5.1   Given the FMS G_K, find the code(s) for which $\bar{l}(G_K)$ is minimal. Such code(s) will be called *optimal* for G_K.

This problem will be dealt with in a number of steps. The first step consists of finding a lower bound for $\bar{l}(C_K)$ when C_K is any ud (in particular prefix) code.

THEOREM 2.5.1   For any ud code C_K for G_K the following inequality holds:

$$\bar{l}(C_K) \geq - \sum_{i=1}^{K} p_i \log_D p_i \tag{2.10}$$

PROOF   Consider the K numbers $\{D^{-l_i}\}_{i=1}^K$ and set $A = \sum_{i=1}^K D^{-l_i}$. By the relation (2.7) $A \le 1$. The numbers $\{D^{-l_i}/A\}_{i=1}^K$ are a pd, e.g., Q over the alphabet A, hence we can use the fact that the informational divergence $D(P\|Q)$ between P and Q is nonnegative (Remark 2.5.4); this yields

$$D(P\|Q) = \sum_{i=1}^K p_i \log_D \frac{p_i}{l_i} A \ge 0 \qquad (2.11)$$

The inequality (2.10) now follows easily, keeping in mind that $\log_D A \le 0$.

Q.E.D.

DEFINITION 2.5.1   The quantity on the right in (2.10),

$$H_D(p_1, p_2, \ldots, p_K) = H_D(P) = H_D(G_K) = - \sum_{i=1}^K p_i \log_D p_i \qquad (2.12)$$

is called the D-ary entropy of P or of G_K. If $D = 2$, the specification of D is usually omitted and the binary entropy is called simply entropy. The D-ary entropy is measured in D-its and the entropy in bits. Obviously $H(P) = H_D(P) \log_2 D$.

REMARK 2.5.1   An application of the inequality $D(\cdot \| \cdot) \ge 0$ to the probability distributions P and $U = \{1/K, 1/K, \ldots, 1/K\}$ yields

$$D(P \| U) = \sum_{i=1}^K p_i \log_D \frac{p_i}{1/K} = \log K - H_D(P) \ge 0 \qquad (2.13)$$

with equality if and only if) $p_i = 1/K$ $(i = 1, \ldots, K)$ i.e., when the source pd is uniform. Of course $H_D(P)$ is a positive quantity, but if we allow some of the source letters to have zero probability, then $H_D(P) = 0$ iff all letters but one have zero probability (it is assumed that $p \log_D p$ is zero if p is zero).

REMARK 2.5.2   The entropy of a source can be interpreted as (1) the average quantity of uncertainty as to what letter the source is going to generate and (2) the average quantity of *information* provided by a source letter. In the present approach, however, no such interpretation is needed, and the entropy comes out in a natural way in the context of a well-defined coding problem. The role of entropy will be made even more transparent in what follows.

One natural question about Theorem 2.5.1 is whether inequality (2.10) is tight. The following theorem gives a partial answer.

THEOREM 2.5.2   For any FMS G_K there exist prefix codes for which

$$\bar{l}(C_K) < H_D(G_K) + 1 \qquad (2.14)$$

PROOF   To each p_i in P we associate an integer l_i' defined by

$$D^{-l_i'} \le p_i < D^{-l_i'+1}$$

which is always possible. Notice that the numbers l'_i satisfy the Kraft inequality (Theorem 2.4.1), as seen by summing over i in the first inequality. Hence a prefix code C_K can be constructed whose code words have lengths $l'_1, \ldots, l'_K$. Now passing to the D-ary logarithms, multiplying by p_i and summing over i in the second inequality, we readily get (2.14)   Q.E.D.

REMARK 2.5.3   The proof of Theorem 2.5.2 is constructive and the resulting code is called the Shannon–Fano code.

REMARK 2.5.4   The informational divergence, called also cross entropy or relative entropy, is defined as

$$D(P \| Q) = \sum_{i=1}^{K} p_i \log \frac{p_i}{q_i} \qquad (2.15)$$

We make the continuity conventions $0 \log(0/a) = 0 \log(0/0) = 0$, $a \log(a/0) = +\infty$ $(a > 0)$. We have $D(P \| Q) \geq 0$, $D(P \| Q) = 0$ if and only if $P = Q$. To prove this it is enough to use the obvious inequality $\ln x \leq x - 1$, which expresses the fact that the natural logarithm lies below its tangent at point $(1, 0)$. By substituting $1/y$ instead of x we obtain the relation we need: $\ln y \geq 1 - 1/y$, with equality only for $y = 1$.

2.6   The Huffman Code

In general the Shannon–Fano code is not optimal. The optimal (i.e., minimal average length) code for any given FMS G_K is obtained by a construction due to Huffman, which we now illustrate.

Consider first the binary case $(D = 2)$ and assume that the letters a_i of A are ordered in such a way that $p_1 \geq p_2 \geq \cdots \geq p_K$.

The construction of Huffman codes is based on the following *reduction procedure*: from G_K we construct a reduced source G_{K-1} defined by

$$G_{K-1} = \begin{bmatrix} a'_1 & a'_2 & \cdots & a'_{K-1} \\ p'_1 & p'_2 & \cdots & p'_{K-1} \end{bmatrix} \qquad (2.16)$$

where $a'_i = a_i$, $p'_i = p_i$ $(i = 1, 2, \ldots, K - 2)$, $p'_{K-1} = p_{K-1} + p_K$, i.e., a'_{K-1} is obtained by merging a_{K-1} and a_K.

PROPERTY 2.6.1   If $C^*_{K-1} = \{w'_1, w'_2, \ldots, w'_{K-1}\}$ is an optimal code for G_{K-1}, then $C^*_K = \{w_1, w_2, \ldots, w_{K-1}, w_K\}$ with $w_i = w'_i$ $(i = 1, 2, \ldots, K - 2)$, $w_{K-1} = w'_{K-1}00, w_K = w'_{K-1}01$,[†] is an optimal code for G_K.

The same reduction procedure can be applied to G_{K-1} (possibly after a permutation of its letters so that they have nonincreasing probabilities), to

---

† o denotes juxtaposition.

obtain G_{K-2}, and then to $G_{K-2},\dots$, until we get a binary source G_2 for which an optimal code is obviously $C_2^* = \{0,1\}$. From C_2^*, going backward, we can easily construct $C_3^*, C_4^*, \dots, C_K^*$. Each of these codes is a prefix code.

EXAMPLE 2.6.1   Consider the following source

$$G_5 = \begin{bmatrix} a_1 & a_2 & a_3 & a_4 & a_5 \\ 0.4 & 0.2 & 0.2 & 0.1 & 0.1 \end{bmatrix} \tag{2.17}$$

The accompanying table illustrates the successive reduced sources leading to G_2. The optimal code for G_2 is $\{0,1\}$; optimal codes for G_3, G_4, and G_5 are $C_3^* = \{1,00,01\}$, $C_4^* = \{1,01,000,001\}$, and $C_5^* = \{1,01,000,0010,0011\}$, respectively.

G_5	P_5	P_4	P_3	P_2
a_1	0.4	0.4	0.4	0.6
a_2	0.2	0.2	0.4	0.4
a_3	0.2	0.2	0.2	
a_4	0.1	0.2		
a_5	0.1			

As seen from this example, the assignment of the code words to the source letters is to some extent arbitrary, because the digits 0 and 1 can be appended to either of the code words being extended. Thus, with reference to example (2.6.1), the same construction can lead to the following Huffman codes for G_5:

$$\{0,10,111,1101,1100\}, \qquad \{1,01,000,0011,0010\}, \quad \text{etc.}$$

A similar ambiguity and code multiplicity occurs also in the construction of the Shannon–Fano code. In the case of Huffman codes, however, a more basic ambiguity may arise, namely, the code word lengths are not uniquely determined by the source pd.

EXAMPLE 2.6.2   Consider the same source G_5 as in Example 2.6.1 and construct a Huffman code according to the accompanying table. Optimal codes for G_2, G_3, G_4, and G_5 are $\{0,1\}$, $\{1,00,01\}$, $\{00,01,10,11\}$, and

G_5	P_5	P_4	P_3	P_2
a_1	0.4	0.4	0.4	0.6
a_2	0.2	0.2	0.4	0.4
a_3	0.2	0.2	0.2	
a_4	0.1	0.2		
a_5	0.1			

$\{00, 10, 11, 010, 011\}$, respectively. While in example 2.6.1 the probability resulting from merging was listed as low as possible among the probabilities of the new reduced source, here we have listed it as high as possible.

As a result, the code word lengths are more uniform than in the previous case (although the average length is always the same, namely 2.2).

REMARK 2.6.1 Huffman codes can also be constructed over a D-ary alphabet $(D > 2)$, where G letters are merged in the first reduction and D at each subsequent reduction. Here

$$G = 2 + R_{D-1}(K - 2) \qquad (2.18)$$

where $R_{D-1}(K - 2)$ is the remainder of the division of $K - 2$ by $D - 1$.

Also in this case the algorithm works "backward" starting from the optimal code for a source with D letters, which is $\{0, 1, \ldots, D - 1\}$.

2.7 Asymptotic Results

Since a Huffman code C_K^* is prefix, its average length satisfies inequality (2.10); since it is optimal, it satisfies (2.11),[†]

$$H_D(G_K) \leq \bar{l}(C_K^*) < H_D(G_K) + 1 \qquad (2.19)$$

Inequalities (2.19) were obtained for codes whose words are given to the single letters of the source. We might also conceive codes for *blocks* of n source letters. This corresponds to the construction of the nth order extended source.

[†] From now on we shall omit the subscript D unless we wish to stress the base of the logarithms.

DEFINITION 2.7.1   Given the FMS $G = \{A, P\}$ (see Definition 2.2.1), its nth order extended source G^n is an FMS whose alphabet is the nth Cartesian power A^n of $A^\dagger$ and whose pd P^n is the nth memoryless extension of $P = \{p_1, p_2, \ldots, p_K\}$; thus if $\mathbf{a} = a_{i_1} a_{i_2} \ldots a_{i_n} \in A^n$, then

$$P^n(\mathbf{a}) = p_{i_1} p_{i_2} \cdots p_{i_n} \tag{2.20}$$

LEMMA 2.7.1   The entropy $H(G^n)$ of the extended source is n times the entropy $H(G)$ of the original source.

PROOF

$$H(G'') = - \sum_{a \in A^n} P^n(\mathbf{a}) \log P^n(\mathbf{a})$$

$$= \sum_{a_{i_1} \in A} \sum_{a_{i_2} \in A} \cdots \sum_{a_{i_n} \in A} (p_{i_1} p_{i_2} \cdots p_{i_n}) \log(p_{i_1} p_{i_2} \cdots p_{i_n})$$

$$= \left(- \sum_{a_{i_1} \in A} p_{i_1} \log p_{i_1} \right) \sum_{a_{i_2} \in A} p_{i_2} \cdots \sum_{a_{i_n} \in A} p_{i_n}$$

$$+ \sum_{a_{i_1} \in A} p_{i_1} \left(- \sum_{a_{i_2} \in A} p_{i_2} \log p_{i_2} \right) \cdots \sum_{a_{i_n} \in A} p_{i_n} + \cdots$$

$$+ \cdots \sum_{a_{i_1} \in A} p_{i_1} \sum_{a_{i_2} \in A} p_{i_2} \cdots \left(- \sum_{a_{i_n} \in A} p_{i_n} \log p_{i_n} \right)$$

$$= H(G) + H(G) + \cdots + H(G) = nH(G) \quad \text{Q.E.D.} \tag{2.21}$$

The codes for G^n assign code words to its single letters, i.e., to n-tuples of letters of G. Hence, the average code word length $\bar{l}^{(n)}$ is the length of such code words averaged with P^n and the appropriate generalization of the average length as defined by (2.9) is $\bar{l}^{(n)}/n$, which represents the average code word length per source letter. Based on Lemma 2.7.1 we now prove that by coding sufficiently long blocks we can make $\bar{l}^{(n)}/n$ as close as wished to the source entropy $H(G)$.

THEOREM 2.7.1   Given any FMS G, for any positive integer n there exist codes for which

$$H(G) \leq [\bar{l}^{(n)}/n] < H(G) + (1/n) \tag{2.22}$$

PROOF   Apply (2.12) to $G^n = G_{K^n}$ to get

$$H(G^n) \leq \bar{l}(C_{K^n}) = \bar{l}^{(n)} < H(G^n) + 1$$

for some code C_{K^n}. Using Lemma 2.7.1 and dividing by n, we get the thesis. Q.E.D.

$\dagger$ This means that the "letters" of A^n are the K^n n-tuples of letters from $A = \{a_1, a_2, \ldots, a_K\}$.

We state explicitly that encoding blocks of length n might imply an exponential growth of the complexity of the encoding procedure. There exist codes, however, whose complexity grows only linearly with n. Such codes are suboptimal for any given n.

2.8   A More General Encoding Procedure

So far we have considered encoding fixed-length blocks of source letters into code words of variable length. There exists, however, a more general encoding which consists in assigning variable-length code words to "messages" consisting of source letter blocks which have different lengths. The choice of such messages is of course very important and has to be made in such a way that the stream of letters from the source is always encodable (i.e., it is possible to chop any infinite source sequence into a sequence of messages).

It is not required *a priori* that the primary sequence be *uniquely encodable*, but it is obviously required that the code be *uniquely decodable*. It is, however, convenient to impose that the code also be uniquely encodable. This point will be rediscussed in the next paragraph in the particular case of variable-length to fixed-length codes.

For this general class of variable-length to variable-length codes (provided they are both uniquely encodable and uniquely decodable) the important parameter is the *compression ratio*, which is defined as

$$\text{Average length of messages/Average length of code words} \qquad (2.23)$$

In the particular case of fixed-to-variable-length codes (e.g., Huffman codes) the compression ratio is given by $n/\bar{l}^{(n)}$, (see Theorem 2.7.1). A good code should have a large compression ratio.

2.9   Variable Length-to-Block Encoding

Variable length-to-block encoding provides good compression ratios for *skew sources* (a skew source is one for which the probabilities of some letters very much exceed those of the others). We offer the following examples.

EXAMPLE 2.9.1   (Run length encoding). Consider the following binary memoryless source

$$G_2 = \begin{bmatrix} 0 & 1 \\ 0.9 & 0.1 \end{bmatrix} \qquad (2.24)$$

We encode the binary sequence output by G_2 in two stages as follows: we first count the number of zeroes between two successive ones; then we encode these numbers (called "run lengths") into binary code words. For instance,

Source sequence	Run lengths	Code I	Code II
1	0	000	0000
01	1	001	0001
001	2	010	0010
...		...	
			:
...			
0000001	6	110	0110
0000000	7	111	1

Notice that Code I is variable-to-block, hence, obviously ud. Code II is variable-to-variable, but it is ud also.

Consider for instance the source sequence 000100000110000000000000100-000000001. The run lengths are 3, 5, 0, 7 + 4, 7 + 3. The code word sequences are

Code I: 011   101   000   111   100   111   011

Code II: 0011   0101   0000   1   0100   1   0011

To define a variable-to-variable (in particular a variable-to-block) code it is necessary to assign a *message set* $W(T) = \{\mathbf{m}_1, \mathbf{m}_2, \ldots, \mathbf{m}_T\}$ for the given source, where $\mathbf{m}_i$ is some sequence of source letters. Whenever the source encoder recognizes message $\mathbf{m}_i$, it outputs the corresponding code word $\mathbf{w}_i = \phi(\mathbf{m}_i)$. For this procedure to work without encoding delay it is necessary that $W(T)$ be *proper* and *complete*.

DEFINITION 2.9.1   A message set $W(T)$ is proper when $\mathbf{m}_i$ is not a prefix of $\mathbf{m}_j$ for $i \neq j$, and $W(T)$ is complete if any infinite source sequence has a prefix which belongs to $W(T)$.

We shall now restrict our attention to variable-to-fixed-length codes and to message sets which are proper and complete. Such sets verify certain properties.

PROPERTY 2.9.1 $W(K) = \mathscr{A} = \{a_1, a_2, \ldots, a_K\}$, i.e., the source alphabet, is the only proper and complete message set of size K.

PROPERTY 2.9.2   If $W(T)$ is a proper and complete message set of size T and $\mathbf{m}^* \in W(T)$, then the set

$$W(T + K - 1) = \{W(T) - \mathbf{m}^*\} \bigcup_{a \in \mathscr{A}} \mathbf{m}^* a \qquad (2.25)$$

is a proper and complete message set of size $T + K - 1$, which is called the extension of $W(T)$ via $\mathbf{m}^*$.

PROPERTY 2.9.3   If $W(T)$ is a proper and complete message set of size T, then

$$T = K + n(K - 1) \tag{2.26}$$

for some integer $n \geq 0$.

It is obvious that $W(T)$ is given the product-type probability distribution

$$Q(\mathbf{m}_i) = \prod_{j=1}^{|m_i|} P(a_{i_j}) \tag{2.27}$$

where $\mathbf{m}_i = a_{t_1} \ldots a_{t_{|m_i|}}$.

Assume now that $W(T)$ has been chosen, and let D be the cardinality of the secondary alphabet. Any finite output sequence of the source can be segmented into elements of $W(T)$ because the latter is complete. On the other hand, the properness of $W(T)$ implies that only one partition of the sequence into elements of $W(T)$ is possible.

Now consider any w_i in $W(T)$ and assign to it a D-ary sequence $\Phi(w_i)$ of length $M = 2 + [\log_D T]$ ($[y]$ is the greatest integer less than or equal to y). The first letter of Φ is the digit 1, the remaining $1 + [\log_D T]$ are the expansion of i to the base D (i is the index of w_i). The sequence $\Phi(w_i)$ is the code word for w_i in this variable-length-to-block encoding.

The code rate, measured in bits, is

$$R(T) = M \log D / E[L(w)] \tag{2.28}$$

where $E[x]$ is the expected value of the random variable x and $L(w)$ the length of w, is a good measure of the efficiency of the coding scheme, since it is proportional to the average number of code digits per source letter.

It has been proved by Turnstall [3] that for any admissible size $T = k + n(k - 1)$ the following algorithm yields the complete and proper word set $W(T)$ which minimizes the code rate.

ALGORITHM 2.9.1   Let $W^*(K) = \{a_1, \ldots, a_k\}$. Let $W^*(k + (k - 1))$ be the complete and proper word set of size $(k + (k - 1))$ which is formed by extending $W^*(k)$ with the most probable word in $W^*(k)$. Let $W^*(k + 2(k - 1))$ be the complete and proper word set of size $(k + 2(k - 1))$ obtained by extending $W^*(k + (k - 1))$ with the most probable word in $W^*(k + (k - 1)) \ldots$. Continue this procedure, i.e., form $W^*(k + n(k - 1))$ by extending $W^*(k + (n - 1)(k - 1))$ with its most probable word ($n = 1, 2, \ldots$).

We omit the proof of the optimality of algorithm 2.9.1. More formally, for any admissible T, define the minimal code rate

$$R_{\min}(T) = \min_{W(T)} [M \log D / E(L(w))] \tag{2.29}$$

where the minimal is taken over all word sets of size T and $M = 2 + [\log_D T]$ as before. Then as $T \to \infty$ it can be shown that $R_{\min}(T)$ tends to the source entropy,

$$\lim_{T \to \infty} R_{\min}(T) = H_2(P) \qquad (2.30)$$

This result is the variable-length-to-block version of Shannon's coding theorem for finite memoryless sources.

2.10 Block Codes and Rate-Distortion Theory

The use of variable-length codes can lead to practical shortcomings. Actually, if the source message rate and the channel transmission rate are constant, the output of a variable-length encoder should be stored in a buffer memory before transmission lest a rate mismatch occurs and some information gets lost (when long code words are generated corresponding to unlikely source messages). With probability one, however, any finite-capacity buffer overflows sooner or later and some information again is lost. Consequently, we should be wary when using variable-length codes for transmission. They are better suited for information storage.

One way out is to resort to block codes, i.e., source codes which encode source blocks of length n by means of code words of constant length l.

DEFINITION 2.10.1 A (n, l) block code for the FMS $\mathscr{G}_K$ consists of two functions: f (the encoder), which maps n-tuples of the primary alphabet $\mathscr{A}$ into l-tuples of the secondary alphabet $\mathscr{B}$; and ϕ (the decoder), which maps l-tuples from $\mathscr{B}$ into n-tuples from $\mathscr{A}$. The rate of (f, ϕ) is defined as $R = (1/n)\log\|f\|$, where $\|f\|$ is the number of distinct code words. The error probability of (f, ϕ) is defined as

$$P_e = \Pr\{\phi(f(\mathbf{X})) \neq \mathbf{X}\} \qquad (2.31)$$

where $\mathbf{X}$ is the random n-length output of $\mathscr{G}$.

IMPORTANT REMARK The choice of the secondary alphabet $\mathscr{B}$ is of no consequence in assessing the performances of the code (error probability and rate). In the real systems, $\mathscr{B}$ is chosen to meet practical requirements; often $\mathscr{B}$ is binary. Similarly, what matters is the number $\|f\|$ of distinct code words and not what they look like. For economy's sake their length l is chosen as the smallest integer such that $D^t \geq \|f\|$, or $l \cong nR/\log D$, for R fixed in advance (here $D = |\mathscr{B}|$ and logs are to the base 2).

Now if our block codes have to be uniquely decipherable (i.e., $P_e = 0$), then they perform very poorly compared with variable-length codes, since their (average) length must be at least $n\,(\log K/\log D)$ (to ensure that the number D^l of distinct code words is not less than K^n) and $\log K$ is strictly greater than the source entropy $H^\dagger$. We can therefore give up the requirement that $P_e = 0$ in order to get a smaller code word length.

It is not obvious that there exist block codes for which (1) P_e is reasonably small and (2) the code word length is approximately equal to $nH/\log D$. That such codes exist is an important result of information theory which is based on the following asymptotic property: when n tends to infinity, among the $K^n = 2^{n \log K}$ primary n-sequences from $\mathscr{G}_K$ there are approximately 2^{nH} (the "typical" sequences) which are almost equally probable and whose overall probability tends to 1. Conversely, the overall probability of any set of less than 2^{nH} primary n-tuples tends to 0. Encoding then may consist in giving distinct code words to the typical sequences and any of those code words to the nontypical ones. In decoding we always decode into a typical sequence. This yields the following performances:

(1)   The probability of error (which equals the probability of the nontypical sequences) tends to 0;

(2)   the length of the code words is approximately $nH/\log D$.

Conversely, if the code word length is less than $nH/\log D$ the error probability cannot be made to approach 0; rather it approaches 1 as n approaches infinity.

In dealing with source coding, we have so far assumed that the user needs a *perfect* reproduction of the source output. Hence, the performance of a source coder has been assessed by the probability of erroneous decoding, which makes all mistakes equally serious. In several practical cases, however, errors can be more or less serious (e.g., reproducing 33 with 43 is worse than with 34). Therefore, a more flexible performance measure is needed. Moreover, in some cases the user is not interested in a perfect reproduction of the data and such a reproduction may not be possible (e.g., when an analogue source feeds a discrete channel). What is wanted is not an error measure, but rather a *distortion measure*.

Let $\mathscr{G}_K$ be a finite memoryless source with alphabet $\mathscr{A} = \{a_1, \ldots, a_K\}$ and pd $P = \{p_1, \ldots, p_K\}$. Consider a *reproduction alphabet* $\mathscr{R} = \{r_1, \ldots, r_H\}$ which is the one that the user reads ($\mathscr{R}$ may coincide with $\mathscr{A}$). Now a distortion measure of order k ($k = 1, 2, \ldots$) is defined as a function $d_k(\mathbf{a}, \mathbf{r})$ which associates a nonnegative real number to the pair of k-tuples $\mathbf{a} \in \mathscr{A}^k$ and $\mathbf{r} \in \mathscr{R}^k$; this number can be interpreted as the distortion (cost, loss, etc.) when $\mathbf{a}$ is reproduced by $\mathbf{r}$.

$\dagger$ Of course, $H = \log K$ if the source distribution is uniform, but then no compression is possible.

There are two problems with distortion measures, (1) the choice of $d_k(\cdot,\cdot)$ may be difficult and is a matter of taste, art and experience; (2) if a function $d_k(\cdot,\cdot)$ reflects reality adequately it may be difficult to handle mathematically; conversely a simple function may be of no practical significance. As an example of problem (2), by far the greatest part of studies in this field deal with "averaging" functions of the form

$$d_k(\mathbf{a},\mathbf{r}) = \frac{1}{k}\sum_{i=1}^{k} d(a_i,r_i), \qquad k = 1,2,\ldots \tag{2.32}$$

and we shall conform to this (notice that $d(\cdot,\cdot)$ is actually $d_1(\cdot,\cdot)$, i.e., a distortion measure for the *single letters* of $\mathscr{A}$ and $\mathscr{R}$).

If we are to use a distortion measure, definition (2.10.1) of block codes must be modified somehow, namely:

DEFINITION 2.10.2 A (k,l) block code for the FMS $\mathscr{G}_K$ with reproduction alphabet $\mathscr{R}$ consists of two functions: f (the encoder), which maps k-tuples of the primary alphabet $\mathscr{A}$ into l-tuples of the secondary alphabet $\mathscr{B}$; and ϕ (the decoder), which maps l-tuples of $\mathscr{B}$ into k-tuples of $\mathscr{R}$. The rate of (f,ϕ) is defined as $1/k \log \|f\|$; its average distortion is

$$\bar{d}_k = E d_k(\mathbf{X}, \phi f(\mathbf{X})) \tag{2.33}$$

Now let $\{p(\mathbf{a}), \mathbf{a} \in \mathscr{A}^k\}$ be the pd on the k-tuples output by the source (since the latter is memoryless, $p(\mathbf{a})$ is simply a product of probabilities) and let $\{p(\mathbf{a},\mathbf{r}), \mathbf{a} \in \mathscr{A}^k, \mathbf{r} \in \mathscr{R}^k\}$ be a joint pd on the pairs $(\mathbf{a},\mathbf{r})$ which is completely arbitrary except that its marginal on $\mathscr{A}^k$ coincides with $p(\cdot)$,

$$\sum_{\mathbf{r}} p(\mathbf{a},\mathbf{r}) = p(\mathbf{a}) \qquad \text{for all} \quad \mathbf{a}$$

From $\{p(\mathbf{a})\}$, $\{p(\mathbf{a},\mathbf{r})\}$, and $q(\mathbf{r}) \triangleq \sum_{\mathbf{a}} p(\mathbf{a},\mathbf{r})$ we can compute the *conditional* probability distributions

$$p(\mathbf{a}/\mathbf{r}) \triangleq p(\mathbf{a},\mathbf{r})/q(\mathbf{r}), \qquad q(\mathbf{r}/\mathbf{a}) \triangleq p(\mathbf{a},\mathbf{r})/p(\mathbf{a})$$

as well as the *mutual information* $I(\mathbf{A};\mathbf{R})$ between the random k-dimensional variables $\mathbf{A}$ and $\mathbf{R}$:

$$I(\mathbf{A};\mathbf{R}) \triangleq \sum_{\mathbf{a}}\sum_{\mathbf{r}} p(\mathbf{a},\mathbf{r}) \log \frac{q(\mathbf{r}/\mathbf{a})}{q(\mathbf{r})}$$

$$= \sum_{\mathbf{a}}\sum_{\mathbf{r}} p(\mathbf{a},\mathbf{r}) \log \frac{p(\mathbf{a}/\mathbf{r})}{p(\mathbf{a})} \tag{2.34}$$

Here $I(\mathbf{A};\mathbf{R})$ is interpreted as the average quantity of information provided on $\mathbf{A}$ by a realization of $\mathbf{R}$ (or conversely). In accordance with this interpretation, it turns out that $I(\mathbf{A};\mathbf{R})$ is nonnegative and that it vanishes if and only if $\mathbf{A}$

and **R** are independent. This interpretation is backed by the theory of information channels (see Chapter 1), where the mutual information between the input and the output of a channel is used to measure the *capacity* of the channel, i.e., the maximum rate at which information can be reliably transmitted through the channel.

The joint pd $p(\mathbf{A}; \mathbf{R})$ allows us to compute the *average distortion*

$$\bar{d}_k = \sum_{\mathbf{a}} \sum_{\mathbf{r}} p(\mathbf{a}, \mathbf{r}) d_k(\mathbf{a}, \mathbf{r}) \tag{2.35}$$

between the source k-tuples and their reproductions. We can now require that $\bar{d}_k$ be not greater than a given threshold d; in other words, d is the greatest average distortion that we are prepared to tolerate. The condition

$$\bar{d}_k \leq d \tag{2.36}$$

defines the set

$$\mathcal{D}_k(d) = \{\{p(\mathbf{a}, \mathbf{r})\} : \bar{d}_k \leq d\} \tag{2.37}$$

of those joint probability distributions $p(\mathbf{a}, \mathbf{r})$ (having of course $p(\mathbf{a})$ as marginal on $\mathcal{A}^k$) which satisfy inequality (2.36) when substituted in (2.35). It sometimes happens that $\mathcal{D}_k(d)$ is empty (if d is too small), but in general it contains an infinite number of probability distributions. We choose one according to an economy criterion, namely, minimizing the mutual per-letter information $1/k \; I(\mathbf{A}; \mathbf{R})$. Correspondingly we define (for all $d \geq 0$)

$$R_k(d) \triangleq \min_{\mathcal{D}_k(d)} \frac{1}{k} I(\mathbf{A}; \mathbf{R}) \tag{2.38}$$

which is called the *rate-distortion function*. If, however, $\mathcal{D}_k(d)$ is empty we set $R_k(d) = +\infty$.

However formal the definition (2.38) may look, the rate-distortion function has a paramount practical significance, which we now illustrate. First, however, it is important to notice that for a discrete memoryless source $R_k(d) = R_1(d)$ for all k's. Hence, we can omit the k index. Figure 2.4 illustrates a typical $R(d)$ curve. The function is monotonically decreasing between $d = 0$ and $d = d_{max}$. Here d_{max} is a value for the average distortion which can be obtained without coding effort, e.g., by guessing the source output. Consequently $R(d) = 0$ for all $d > d_{max}$. Here $R(d)$ describes the optimal performance of the block codes of definition (2.10.2); for any value of d there exist codes such that

(1) the average distortion is approximately d and
(2) the length of the code words is approximately $nR(d)/\log D$.

Conversely, if the code word length is less than $nR(d)/\log D$ the average distortion remains greater than d.

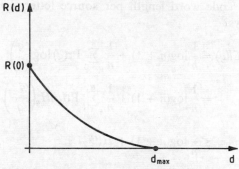

FIG. 2.4. Typical $R(d)$ curve.

2.11 Universal Coding

The assumption, made so far, that the statistics of the information source are completely known, is unrealistic in several practical cases. Moreover, it can happen that the source statistics vary in time and it is not possible to keep track of them with great accuracy. This lack of knowledge can be formalized by saying that the source $\mathscr{G}$ belongs to some source *class* $\mathscr{S}$, which is completely known although the individual source at work is not. So the problem arises to encode $\mathscr{G}$ in such a way that the code be efficient, in some sense, irrespective of the actual source within $\mathscr{S}$. It is not obvious that this problem can be solved, hence the existence of *universal codes* for particular source classes is a nontrivial result. Actually, universal codes exist in specific cases, when the source must be reproduced faithfully and when a certain amount of distortion is tolerated.

We illustrate the concept of universal coding through a simple though significant example. A binary source $\mathscr{G}_2$ has to be block-to-variable-length encoded using binary code words; it is known that $\mathscr{G}_2$ is stationary and memoryless but $p = \Pr(1)\ (0 < p < 1)$ is unknown. Let n be the length of the primary blocks; each code word consists of two parts: (1) a prefix which specifies the weight (number of ones) of the block, and (2) a suffix which identifies the block within the set of the blocks having that weight. The resulting code is uniquely decipherable.

The weight g of any block ranges between 0 and n, hence $\log(n + 1)$ binary symbols are sufficient to specify g (notice that the length of this prefix is constant). There are $\binom{g}{n}$ n blocks of weight g, hence $\log\binom{g}{n}$ binary digits are needed to specify the block within its set. Thus, the length of the code word for a block of weight g is

$$l(g) = \log(n + 1) + \log\binom{g}{n} \tag{2.39}$$

Now the average code word length per source letter, $1/n\, El(g)$, is upper-bounded as follows

$$\frac{1}{n}\,El(g) = \frac{1}{n}\log(n+1) + \frac{1}{n}\sum_{g=0}^{n}\Pr(g)\log\binom{g}{n}$$

$$= \frac{1}{n}\log(n+1) + \frac{1}{n}\sum_{g=0}^{n}\Pr(g)H_n\!\left(\frac{\mathscr{G}_2}{g}\right)$$

$$\leq \frac{1}{n}\log(n+1) + H(\mathscr{G}_2) + \frac{2}{n} \tag{2.40}$$

where $H_n(\mathscr{G}_2/g)$ is the conditional entropy of an n-block from $\mathscr{G}_2$ given its weight g, which is not greater than the unconditional entropy $H_n(\mathscr{G}_2) = nH(\mathscr{G}_2)$.

Hence, when n tends to infinity, $1/n\log(n+1) + (2/n)$ goes to zero and this code tends to be as good as an optimal (Huffman) code constructed for the real source in hand. The construction of our code, on the other hand, does not assume knowledge of p. Note, however, that for small values of n the Huffman code for the specific source might outperform the code illustrated earlier.

References

1. Shannon, C. E. (1984). A mathematical theory of communication, *Bell Syst. Tech. J.* **27**, 379–423, 623–656.
2. Gallager, R. (1968). "Information Theory and Reliable Communication." Wiley, New York.
3. Longo, G. (1980). "Teoria dell' Informazione." Boringhieri, Torino, Italy.
4. Shannon, C. E. (1959). Coding theorems for a discrete source with a fidelity criterion, *IRE Nat. Conv. Rev.* **4**, 142.
5. Berger, T. (1971). "Rate Distortion Theory." Prentice-Hall, Englewood Cliffs, New Jersey.

Chapter 3

Data Compression Techniques

G. BENELLI and E. DEL RE

Dipartimento di Ingegneria Elettronica
Università di Firenze
Florence, Italy

V. CAPPELLINI

Dipartimento di Ingegneria Elettronica
Università di Firenze
and Istituto di Ricerca sulle Onde Elettromagnetiche,
Consiglio Nazionale delle Ricerche
Florence, Italy

F. LOTTI

Istituto di Ricerca sulle Onde Elettromagnetiche
Consiglio Nazionale delle Ricerche
Florence, Italy

3.1 Introduction

In this chapter, a detailed description is given of the most important data compression techniques for digital communication systems. A schematic representation of a digital communication link is shown in Fig. 3.1, in which the source output is assumed to be a signal, which has been sampled, quantized and encoded in a finite alphabet (digital signal). The task of the source encoder is that of transmitting the data coming from the source into a more

33

DATA COMPRESSION AND ERROR CONTROL
TECHNIQUES WITH APPLICATIONS

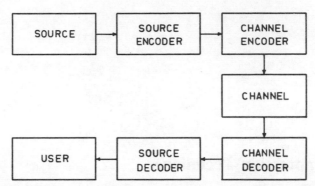

FIG. 3.1. Schematic representation of a digital communication link.

suitable form for an efficient transmission. This is obtained *by reducing the amount of redundancy* and hence also *the required transmission bandwidth.*

In many applications, in fact, the transmission of numerical data is accomplished by means of pulse code modulation (PCM) or similar techniques, which require in general a bandwidth proportional to the product of the number of samples per second by the number of bits necessary to represent each sample. Therefore, a reduction in the total amount of bits per second emitted by the source encoder has the consequence of reducing the necessary transmission rate or the total transmission time.

The redundancy reduction techniques usually exploit the intrinsic correlation of the source messages while a non-correlated or random sequence of messages which don't contain redundancy cannot, in general, be compressed. The theoretical approach to the source encoding problem given in Chapter 2 shows the importance of knowing the source output statistics for the design of efficient and optimal algorithms which minimize the average number of bits at the encoder output. However, in most practical applications the source statistics are not well known, or they are not stationary. In these cases, there is the problem of designing optimal algorithms which remain efficient during the time evolution of the signal.

In this chapter, particular emphasis is given to those techniques which do not require exact knowledge of the source statistics for a good performance. Moreover, for each *basic* algorithm, various types of adaptive techniques are described that partially solve the problems of input signals that are non-stationary.

The third block in Fig. 3.1 (*error control coding*) represents the encoding of compressed data in such a way as *to reintroduce a suitable redundancy* to protect the encoded signal against the degradation introduced by the channel noise. Automatic error detection and in some cases error correction can be achieved by this technique which is called *channel encoding* and is described in detail in Chapters 4 and 5. Channel encoding is in fact useful and often necessary after source encoding, because the compressed data are, in general, very sensitive to the communication channel noise, due to the low residual correlation and to the particular synchronization technique used to decode the signals at the receiver.

3.2 Data Compression by Means of Predictors and Interpolators

A class of algorithms very easy to be hardware implemented is that of *predictors* and *interpolators*. The technique used in the prediction methods consists of utilizing the information of some previous samples, while in the interpolation methods the knowledge of both past and future samples is used to estimate the current sample value.

In the most widely applied methods, a prefixed tolerance band is placed around the estimated values and a comparison is made with the actual sample, which will be transmitted only if it lies out of the tolerance band, or otherwise it is considered as redundant and discarded.

Figure 3.2 shows the block diagram of a typical data compression system using prediction or interpolation techniques. The non redundant samples (i.e., the samples for which the prediction or interpolation fails) are fed into a buffer memory, to be reorganized in their time distribution, with the insertion of the *time position identification* (synchronization), necessary for the reconstruction of the original data from the compressed samples.

Therefore, the important role of the buffer is to store the incoming aperiodic samples, so that they can be sent out at a uniform rate. In this way, while at the input of the buffer we have *bit compression*, at its output we can also have *bandwidth compression*.

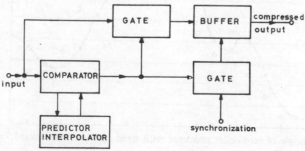

FIG. 3.2. Block diagram of typical data compression system using prediction or interpolation.

3.3 The Prediction Method

Let us now examine in more detail some of the most largely applied algorithms of compression using the prediction method. More specifically, the polynomial prediction, which is a finite difference technique, is described by means of an N-th order polynomial which can be passed through $(N + 1)$ data points. Predicted data are obtained by extrapolation of the polynomial, one unit at a time. A polynomial

$$y(t) = a_0 + a_1 t + a_2 t^2 + \cdots + a_N t^N \tag{3.1}$$

may be fitted to the data points by means of the difference equation [1, 2, 3].

$$y_{pn} = y_{n-1} + \Delta y_{n-1} + \Delta^2 y_{n-1} + \cdots + \Delta^N y_{n-1} \tag{3.2}$$

where $y_n = y(t_n)$ and $t_n = nT$. Here T is the sampling period and y_{pn} the predicted sample at time instant t_n, y_{n-1} the sample value at the sampling instant prior to t_n, $\Delta y_{n-1} = y_{n-1} - y_{n-2}$, and $\Delta^N y_{n-1} = \Delta^{N-1} y_{n-1} - \Delta^{N-1} y_{n-2}$.

The value of N corresponds to the order of the prediction algorithm; with $N = 0$, we obtain the zero-order predictor and with $N = 1$ the first-order predictor.

3.3.1 Zero-Order Predictors

We first describe a simple algorithm, called *zero-order predictor with fixed aperture*. In the zero-order predictor (ZOP) only the last sample y_{n-1} is utilized for the prediction of the sample y_n at the n-th instant, i.e.,

$$y_{pn} = y_{n-1} \tag{3.3}$$

In the fixed aperture mode, the range of the data is subdivided into a set of fixed bands with amplitude 2Δ (Fig. 3.3). If the predicted and the actual

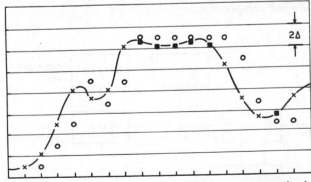

FIG. 3.3. Principle of zero-order predictor with fixed aperture: transmitted, $\times$; predicted, $\bigcirc$; non-transmitted, $\blacksquare$.

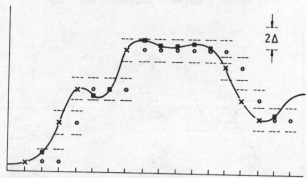

Fig. 3.4. Principle of zero-order predictor with floating aperture: transmitted, ×; predicted, ○; non-transmitted, ■.

samples lie in the same band, then y_n is not transmitted. In the latter case, the sample y_{n+1} is compared with y_{pn} and so on.

To obtain a more flexible algorithm, the tolerance bands can be made variable; in this case the zero-order predictor with *floating aperture* is obtained (Fig. 3.4). Also, in this algorithm the predicted sample is given by (3.3), but the aperture of amplitude 2Δ is placed about the last transmitted sample. If the actual sample y_n lies in this tolerance band, then it is not transmitted and the next sample y_{n+1} is compared again with the last transmitted sample and so on.

The zero-order predictors are very simple to implement for both hardware and software; at the same time they present a good efficiency for many classes of signals.

3.3.2 First-Order Predictors

In the *first-order predictor* (FOP) algorithm with *floating aperture*, two samples are utilized to perform the prediction of the actual sample (Fig. 3.5). The first two samples y_0 and y_1 are transmitted and a straight line is drawn through them, placing a tolerance aperture with amplitude 2Δ about the obtained line. If the actual sample y_n is within this aperture, it will not be transmitted and the line will be extrapolated for a subsequent time interval and so on. Conversely, when the actual sample y_n lies outside the tolerance band, the prediction fails; then the sample y_n is transmitted, and a new straight line is utilized, constructed using the last point on the previous prediction line and y_n.

Some different modifications of this basic algorithm can be introduced to improve its performance. For example, in order to reduce the effects of the

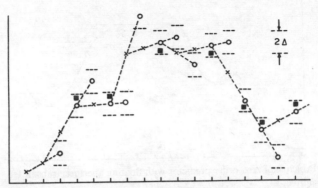

Fig. 3.5. Principle of first-order predictor with floating aperture: transmitted, ×; predicted, O; non-transmitted, ■.

channel noise on the reconstructed signal, the algorithm in Fig. 3.6 can be used [4]. In this case, the transmitted sample is the last predicted one each time the prediction fails. This particular method strongly reduces the distortion produced by the channel noise, as it is described in Chapter 6.

The predictors with order higher than one are rarely used in practical applications due to many reasons. In particular, these algorithms are often unstable and very sensitive to any disturbance and noise.

3.4 Adaptive Predictors

In the previous methods, the prediction of the actual sample was performed using a fixed procedure, i.e., by considering fixed predictor coefficients. Nevertheless, in many cases a sufficient knowledge of the source to be pro-

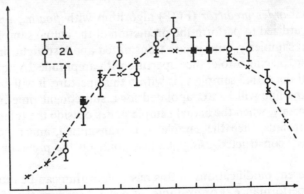

Fig. 3.6. Principle of modified first-order predictor with floating aperture: transmitted, ×; predicted, O; non-transmitted, ■.

cessed is not available and the predictive coefficients can often be difficult to choose. In these cases, it is convenient to utilize a prediction algorithm of *adaptive* type [5-7]. In these algorithms, the prediction coefficients are changed according to the *time evolution* of the signal. Adaptive algorithms present a more complex implementation, but offer good performance for a large class of signals. In the following section we describe two types of these adaptive algorithms.

3.4.1 Linear Adaptive Prediction

In the linear adaptive prediction, the predicted sample $y_p(t_n)$ is evaluated as a linear weighting of the M preceding samples

$$y_p(t_n) = \sum_{j=1}^{M} \beta_j y(t_{n-j}) \tag{3.4}$$

where β_j are weighting coefficients. The reconstructed data are represented by an $x(t_j)$ time series, which is the addition of $y(t_j)$ and an error sequence $\varepsilon(t_j)$, this error sequence $\varepsilon(t_j)$ being either the prediction error or zero depending on whether or not the prediction error falls within a given threshold value Δ. If $\varepsilon(t_j)$ is zero (the prediction error falls within the Δ value), the actual sample is not transmitted. Assuming that the process is a *stationary Gaussian time series with zero mean*, the weighting coefficients β_j can be determined so that the mean square prediction error

$$\sigma^2(M,N) = \frac{1}{N} \sum_{k=1}^{N} \left[y(t_{n-k}) - \sum_{j=1}^{M} \beta_j(M,N) y(t_{n-k-j}) \right]^2 \tag{3.5}$$

is minimized, where M is the *prediction memory* (M represents the number of preceding samples which are memorized by the predictor) and N the *learning period* (N represents the number of samples which the predictor uses to learn the time evolution of the signal). It can be useful to examine the utilization of the autocorrelation curve for the learning period definition. A particular case can be represented by periodic signals for which we exactly know the period value.

Differentiating (3.5) with respect to β_j ($j = 1, 2, \ldots M$) and equating to zero, we obtain (with $y_n = y(t_n)$)

$$\frac{1}{N} \sum_{1}^{N} 2 \left[y_{n-k} - \sum_{1}^{M} \beta_j(M,N) y_{n-k-j} \right] y_{n-k-i} = 0$$

$$\sum_{1}^{M} \left[\beta_j(M,N) \sum_{1}^{N} y_{n-k-j} y_{n-k-i} \right] = \sum_{1}^{N} y_{n-k} y_{n-k-i} \tag{3.6}$$

$$(i = 1, 2, \ldots, M)$$

Let

$$r_M = r(i, j) = \frac{1}{N} \sum_{1}^{N}{}_k y_{n-k-i} y_{n-k-j}, \qquad i, j = 1, 2, \ldots, M$$

$$\tag{3.7}$$

$$g_M = r(i, 0) = \frac{1}{N} \sum_{1}^{N}{}_k y_{n-k} y_{n-k-i}, \qquad i = 1, 2, \ldots, M$$

Using (3.7), (3.6) can be written in matrix form

$$\beta_{M,N} = r_M^{-1} g_M \tag{3.8}$$

where r_M is the determinant of the matrix.

Relation (3.8) represents a linear system of N equations and M unknowns (β_j) which uniquely solves the problem in the cases in which r_M is nonzero.

It is best to select an N value that is not too large, in order to permit the predictor to adapt itself to the statistical evolution of the data, and not too small, in order to have a good mean in (3.5).

3.4.2 Non-Linear Adaptive Prediction

Due to the fact that the receiver (or *decompressor*) must use, in reconstructing the data series, the predicted data which in general contain some error, it is best that the compressor in transmission use predictions of the nontransmitted samples. The mean square prediction error now to be minimized can be set in the form

$$\sigma_c^2(M, N) = \frac{1}{N} \sum_{k=M+1}^{M+N} \left[y(t_k) - \sum_{j=1}^{M} \beta_j(M, N) x(t_{k-j}) \right]^2 \tag{3.9}$$

where

$$x(t_k) = \begin{cases} y(t_k) & \text{if } \left| y(t_k) - \sum_{j=1}^{M} \beta_j(M, N) x(t_{k-j}) \right| > \Delta \\ \sum_{j=1}^{M} \beta_j(M, N) x(t_{k-j}) & \text{if } \left| y(t_k) - \sum_{j=1}^{M} (M, N) x(t_{k-j}) \right| \leq \Delta \end{cases} \tag{3.10}$$

The minimization of (3.9) is usually performed by methods such as *steepest descent* [8], because the system obtained by the direct method $(\partial \sigma_c^2(M, N)/\partial \beta_j = 0, \ j = 1, 2, \ldots, M)$ is nonlinear. The initial values of the β_j coefficients, when the steepest descent algorithm is used, can be the values computed in the application of linear prediction using the same M and N.

3.5 Interpolators

These algorithms differ from the corresponding ones with prediction because they utilize both past and future samples to perform a prediction of the actual sample. The most interesting algorithms of this class are the zero- and first-order interpolators [1–3].

3.5.1 Zero-Order Interpolators

In the *zero-order interpolators* (ZOI) a tolerance aperture with amplitude 2Δ is placed about the actual sample $y(t_n)$, as shown in Fig. 3.7. An analogous tolerance band is placed about $y(t_{n+1})$. Then two different cases can occur:

(1) the two tolerance bands have a part in common (intersection band);
(2) the tolerance bands are separate and do not have any part in common.

In the first situation, each horizontal line in the intersection band is distant less than Δ from the points $y(t_n)$ and $y(t_{n+1})$; therefore the sample $y(t_n)$ can be represented by the mean value of the intersection band with an error less than Δ and $y(t_n)$ is not transmitted.

In the second case, the sample $y(t_n)$ is transmitted and utilized as the first point for the next prediction. In the first case, the sample $y(t_{n+2})$ is taken into account and a tolerance band is placed about it. If this tolerance band

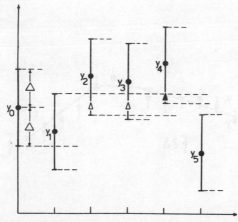

FIG. 3.7. Principle of zero-order interpolator (the samples $y(t_n)$ are indicated as y_n): interpolated, $\triangle$; transmitted, $\blacktriangle$; non-transmitted, $\bullet$.

has a common part with the intersection band formed using $y(t_n)$ and $y(t_{n+1})$, the sample $y(t_{n+1})$ is considered as correctly predicted and a new intersection band is formed as the intersection of the tolerance bands placed around $y(t_n)$, $y(t_{n+1})$ and $y(t_{n+2})$. At the receiver, each non-transmitted sample is replaced by the mean value of the intersection band.

3.5.2 First-Order Interpolators

In the *first-order interpolator* (FOI), as in the first-order predictor, the prediction of the actual sample is performed by using straight lines. Let us consider two samples $y(t_n)$ and $y(t_{n+1})$, as shown in Fig. 3.8. Two straight lines are drawn, which connect the point $y(t_n)$ with $y(t_{n+1}) + \Delta$ and $y(t_{n+1}) - \Delta$, respectively. These two lines form the angle ϕ_{n+1}. Two new straight lines are then defined which connect the pairs of points: $y(t_n), y(t_{n+2}) + \Delta$ and $y(t_n)$, $y(t_{n+2}) - \Delta$; and form an angle ϕ_{n+2}.

If the two angles ϕ_{n+1} and ϕ_{n+2} have a non-zero intersection angle, the sample $y(t_{n+1})$ is considered as predicted in a correct way and it is not transmitted.

At the receiver, the predicted sample $y(t_{n+1})$ is replaced by the mean value of the intersection band. When the sample $y(t_{n+1})$ is not predicted, the process starts again, taking $y(t_{n+1})$ or $y(t_{n+2})$ as first point in the prediction chain. In the first case, i.e., when $y(t_{n+1})$ is assumed as the first point for the prediction, the algorithm is called the *joined line segment method*. In the latter case, the algorithm is called the *disjoined line segment method*. This second method is more stable and less sensitive to channel errors than the *joined* one.

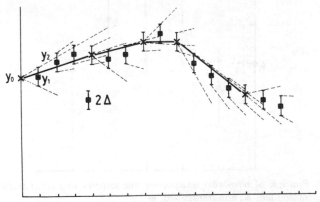

FIG. 3.8. Principle of first-order interpolator (joined line segment): interpolation range, ---; reconstructed curve, ——; transmitted, ×; non-transmitted, ■.

3.6 Differential Pulse Code Modulation

The differential pulse code modulation (DPCM) technique has many applications and has received great attention for its efficiency and flexibility in many cases [8–13]. The block diagram of a DPCM system is shown in Fig. 3.9. The predicted sample y_{pn} is generated through a linear weighting of the M past samples y_n according to

$$y_{pn} = \sum_{i=1}^{M} a_i y_{n-i} \tag{3.11}$$

where a_i are the weighting coefficients. The predicted samples can be obtained in general by using any of the prediction algorithms discussed in Section 3.3. The difference $e_n = y_n - y_{pn}$ between the present sample and the predicted one is quantized in steps of amplitude Δ and encoded for transmission in a code word L_w bits long. If the correlation of the input signal is high, provided that the weighting coefficients are correctly chosen, DPCM generally achieves a higher efficiency with respect to PCM. In general, if an equal number of bits is used, the signal-to-quantization-noise ratio is higher than for PCM. Alternatively the same signal-to-quantization noise ratio is obtained in DPCM by means of a lower number of bits than in PCM.

The gain G in the signal-to-quantization-noise ratio of DPCM with respect to PCM can be expressed as [12]

$$G = E[y_n^2]/E[e_n^2] = E[y_n^2]/E[(y_n - y_{pn})^2] \tag{3.12}$$

where $E[\cdot]$ is the statistical expectation operator.

In general, the variance of the difference $y_n - y_{pn}$ is lower than that of the signal y_n and an effective improvement of the signal-to-quantization-noise ratio using DPCM is achieved. To maximize G, it is necessary to choose suitable coefficients a_i of the predictor (3.11) to minimize the variance of the difference e_n.

The DPCM technique is of appreciable efficiency for stationary signals. When nonstationary signals are to be processed and the prediction becomes

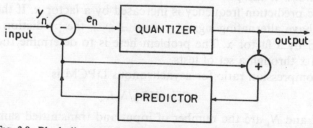

FIG. 3.9. Block diagram of differential pulse code modulation system.

nonadequate, large peak errors in the reconstructed data may result. To avoid these errors, two strategies can be followed [13, 14]:

(1) Use of *adaptive quantization step amplitude* Δ, which is changed according to the signal evolution. The Δ value becomes small when the signal is slowly varying and, vice-versa, it is increased when the signal has quick variations.

(2) Use of *adaptive prediction*. In this case, a learning capability in determining the set of coefficients a_i in (3.11) is introduced. The coefficients a_i are determined in order to minimize the mean squared error of the predicted sample values, given by

$$\sigma^2(M, N) = \frac{1}{N} \sum_{k=1}^{N} \left[y_{n-k} - \sum_{i=1}^{M} a_i(M, N) y_{n-k-i} \right]^2 w_k \qquad (3.13)$$

where N is the size of the learning set and w_k are weights used to assign a relative importance to each past situation of the predictor.

For the basic and adaptive DPCMs the compression ratio is given by

$$C_b = L_p/L_w \qquad (3.14)$$

where L_p is the PCM word length and L_w is the DPCM word length.

A higher efficiency can be obtained by using variable word length DPCM. If we know the amplitude distribution of y_n, Huffman encoding can be applied (see Chapter 2). The mean compression ratio is now

$$C_b = L_p/\bar{L}_H \qquad (3.15)$$

where $\bar{L}_H$ is the mean word length of the Huffman encoding. This method can achieve good efficiency in terms of exact reconstruction of the signal and compression ratio [15]. However, its implementation is, in general, complex and the necessary knowledge of the statistical distribution of the signal can be a difficult condition to meet.

Another modification of DPCM is the asynchronous DPCM [16]. With this algorithm, the length M of the prediction interval is determined by the signs and values of the past m differences e_n between the predicted and the actual values. If the past m differences have the same sign and maximum value, the prediction frequency is increased by a factor x. If the past m differences have alternating signs $(- + - + \cdots)$, the prediction frequency is decreased by a factor x. The problem here is to determine the best values of m and x through a set of tests.

The compression ratio for asynchronous DPCM is

$$C_b = NL_p/N_t L_w \qquad (3.16)$$

where N and N_t are the number of input and transmitted samples, respectively.

3.7 Delta Modulation

Delta modulation (DM) can be considered as a particular case of DPCM with a 1 digit code [17, 18]. Also in DM the changes in the signal amplitude between consecutive sampling instants are transmitted in place of the absolute signal amplitude. These changes are sent in the form of binary pulses.

A typical block diagram of a DM encoder is represented in Fig. 3.10. The input signal $i_0(t)$ is sampled at a frequency v_s and at each sampling instant $i_0(t)$ is compared with the signal $i_1(t)$ coming from an integrator network.

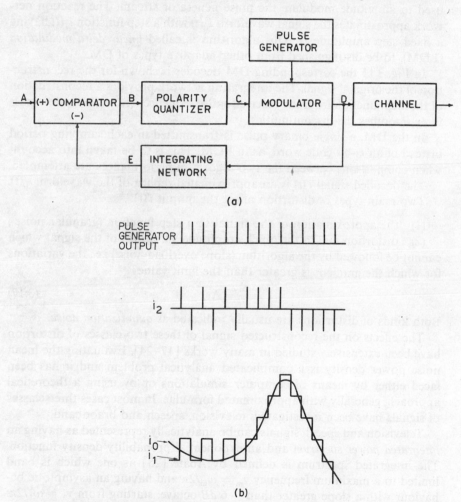

Fig. 3.10. Delta modulation: (a) block diagram of the system; and (b) waveforms in the different points of the system. A: i_0, B: $i_0 - i_1$, C: $(i_0 - i_1)/|i_0 - i_1|$, D: i_2, E: i_1.

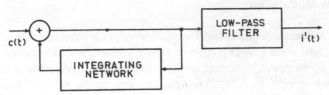

FIG. 3.11. Delta modulation decoder.

The sign of the difference $i_0(t) - i_1(t)$, evaluated in the quantizer unit, is used to amplitude modulate the pulse generator stream. The reaction network approximates the signal waveform $i_0(t)$ with a step function $i_1(t)$ having a fixed step amplitude Δ. This algorithm is called *linear delta modulation* (LDM), to be distinguished from other adaptive types of DM.

In Fig. 3.11 the corresponding DM decoder is shown for the reconstruction of the original signal. The integrating network provides a reconstruction of the step function from the received pulse sequence $c(t)$, while the low-pass filter smoothes the discontinuities.

In the DM, a single binary pulse is transmitted in each sampling period instead of an m-bit code word, as in PCM. This is to be taken into account when comparisons between the two algorithm performances are attempted.

The decoded signal $i'(t)$ is an approximated replica of the waveform $i_0(t)$. Two main types of distortion affect the output $i'(t)$:

(1) the approximation of the signal to a step function (granular noise);
(2) distortion due to the quick amplitude variations of the signal which cannot be followed by the algorithm (slope overload noise) i.e., the variations for which the gradient is greater than the limit value

$$G = \Delta v_s \tag{3.17}$$

Both kinds of distortions are usually indicated as *quantization noise*.

The effects on the reconstructed signal of these two classes of distortion have been extensively studied in many works [17–24]. Evaluating the mean noise power density is a complicated analytical problem and it has been faced either by means of computer simulations or by using a theoretical approach, generally with approximated formulae. In most cases three classes of signals have been investigated: television, speech and braodband.

Television and speech signals can be analytically represented as having an *integrated power spectrum* and an exponential probability density function. The integrated spectrum is defined by Abate [25] as one which is band limited to a maximum frequency $v_m = \omega_m/2\pi$ and having an asymptotic behaviour with a slope greater than $-6 \, dB$/octave; starting from $v_1 = \omega_1/2\pi$:

$$G(\omega) = \left(\omega_1 \tan \frac{\omega_m}{\omega_1} \right)^{-1} \left[1 + \left(\frac{\omega}{\omega_1} \right)^2 \right]^{-1} \tag{3.18}$$

The broadband signals can be approximated by a band limited uniform power spectrum $F(\omega)$ with a maximum frequency v_m, i.e.,

$$F(\omega) = 1/\omega_m \qquad (3.19)$$

and having a Gaussian probability density function.

Let P_d be the mean power of the input signal derivative; as a first approximation

$$P_d = \left\langle \left[\frac{i(rT) - i[(r-i)T]}{T} \right] \right\rangle \qquad (3.20)$$

The *slope loading* factor s is then defined as

$$s = \Delta v_s / \sqrt{P_d} \qquad (3.21)$$

This factor depends on the delta modulation characteristics through the Δ and v_s parameters and the signal amplitude variations.

Some interesting results on the behaviour of quantization noise are reported by Abate [25] where the signal-to-noise ratio is shown as a function of s. From these results it can be seen that a value of s always exists which maximizes the S/N ratio. This corresponds to the optimum choice of the product Δv_s. The maximum signal-to-noise ratio increases with the ratio v_s/v_m.

The quantization noise sensitively changes with s even for small variations of this parameter. This makes LDM very critical with respect to the choice of the sampling rate and the step amplitude.

In order to improve the accuracy and the efficiency of LDM, several methods have been studied and developed. These methods utilize the information carried out by the recent pulse history to change the value of the DM parameters. An important class of algorithms operates in changing the step amplitude Δ, while a second class of adaptive DM bases its adaptivity on the sampling interval changes.

3.8 Amplitude Adaptivity

Several methods have been proposed to adapt the amplitude of the step to the dynamic distribution of the signal. Depending on the criteria adopted to vary the Δ value, the adaptive DM algorithms are subdivided into three classes:

(1) *instantaneous compounding,*
(2) *syllabic compounding* and
(3) *hybrid compounding.*

In the instantaneous compounding DM the Δ value is evaluated at any instant $t_n = nT$ $(n = 0, 1, \ldots)$, according to a fixed rule, based on the sequence of the previous pulse sign(s). Typical examples of instantaneous compounding DM are the *high information DM* (HIDM) and the *constant factor DM* (CFDM).

3.8.1   The High Information DM

To clarify the operating principle of the class of adaptive algorithms let us examine in some detail the HIDM, first proposed by Winkler [26]. The step amplitude is increased when a given number n of consecutive pulses have the same (binary) value, and it is decreased in the other case. The simplest method consists of using two consecutive pulses to vary the Δ amplitude.

Figure 3.12 represents the behaviour of HIDM with $n = 2$, when applied to a step function. The criterion followed to implement the algorithm is described in the Table 3.1.

A little more sophisticated scheme, which requires one more memory cell, is indicated in Table 3.2, where the signs of the first three pulses are utilized to define the Δ variation criteria, in order to reduce overshoots and oscillations in the presence of discontinuities, thus giving slope overload noise.

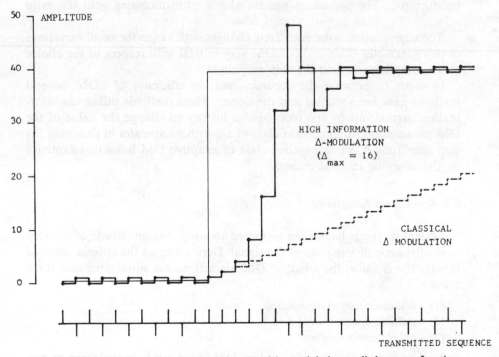

FIG. 3.12. Typical behaviour of high information delta modulation applied to a step function.

TABLE 3.1. A typical rule for the variation of the step amplitude in an HIDM having a memory of two bits.

Pulse sign sequence	Past difference bits	Next step amplitude	Next pulse sign
+ + or − −	0	×2	Unchanged
+ − or − +	1	÷2	Changed

3.8.2 The Constant Factor DM

The CFDM uses the signs of the previous and actual pulses to change the amplitude of Δ_n at the instants $t_n = nT$, according to the following rule:

$$\begin{cases} \Delta_n = \Delta_{n-1}P, & \text{if} \quad b_n = b_{n-1} \\ \Delta_n = \Delta_{n-1}Q, & \text{if} \quad b_n \neq b_{n-1} \end{cases} \tag{3.22}$$

where P and Q are constant factors, and b_n and b_{n-1} are the pulse signs; $Q = P = 1$ gives the case of LDM.

Jayant assumes $PQ \leq 1$ to assure the stability of the decoded signal. This inequality has the sense of a nonsymmetrical rate of change of Δ while its value is increasing or decreasing.

The parameter P is generally chosen to be greater than 1 to follow quick amplitude variations of the signal, while Q must be set less than 1 in order to improve the algorithm behaviour during the quiescent periods.

Jayant [25] showed that the best choices for P and Q are

$$1 < P_{opt} < 2$$
$$PQ_{opt} = 1 \tag{3.23}$$

and, for the class of speech signals, by means of simulations, he obtained

$$P_{opt} \cong 1.5 \tag{3.24}$$

TABLE 3.2. A typical rule for the variation of the step amplitude in an HIDM having a memory of three bits.

Pulse sign sequence	Past difference bits	Next step amplitude	Next pulse sign
+ + + or − − −	0 0	×2	Unchanged
+ + − or − − +	0 1	÷2	Changed
+ − + or − + −	1 1	÷2	Changed
+ − − or − + +	1 0	Constant	Unchanged

3.8.3 Syllabic Compounding DM

The operating principle of such a class of algorithms is presented here by the detailed description of the method of *continuously variable slope* DM (CVSD) [18, 28].

The Δ step amplitude variation is based on the examination of a sequence of a prefixed number N of output pulses stored in a shift register. The pattern of N equal consecutive pulse signs is considered as a probable slope overload situation, whilst the occurrence of some sign changes in the sequence indicates with high probability a quiescent or a "well followed" signal.

Figure 3.13a shows the schematic diagram of the encoder, where the adaptation logic, according to the preceding criteria, issues a control signal C_n which is equal to 1 in the case of slope overload detection and equal to 0 otherwise. The output n of the filter is obtained following the formula

$$\Delta_n = \Delta_{n-1} \exp(-\alpha T) + C_n \cdot G[1 - \exp(-\alpha T)] \qquad (3.25)$$

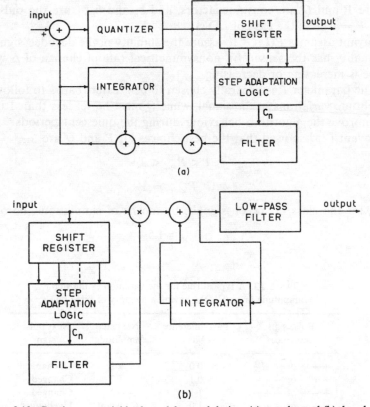

(a)

(b)

FIG. 3.13. Continuous variable slope delta modulation: (a) encoder and (b) decoder.

During the well-behaved periods ($C_n = 0$) the step amplitude Δ_n is decreased with a syllabic time constant $1/\alpha$ and a lower boundary of Δ_{min}. When $C_n = 1$, the constant factor G modifies the step amplitude, increasing its value, but not beyond an upper boundary Δ_{max}. The decoder (Fig. 3.13b) is mainly a dual replica of the encoder.

3.8.4 Hybrid Compounding DM

In this technique, especially used in speech processing, Δ_n is given by

$$\Delta_n = \Delta_{n-1}\delta_n \qquad (3.26)$$

where δ_n is the instantaneous step amplitude.

The initial value of the step amplitude, Δ_0, is periodically recomputed at syllabic intervals T_s, according to the average slope energy E during the preceding T_s, i.e.,

$$\Delta_0 = cE \qquad (3.27)$$

with c being a prefixed constant.

The evaluation of E is based on analogous considerations as for the mean power P_d given in (3.20). The δ_n instantaneous step amplitude is computed following a law depending on the particular application.

A schematic representation of the HCDM is shown in Fig. 3.14. An example of hybrid compounding DM suitable for speech signals is reported in Un et al. [29], where the δ_n value was determined by examining the past three pulse signs in the output sequence.

The value of the constant c must be chosen with care: if c is greater than 1, indeed, the decoded signal may be unstable, whilst too small a value of c can give a signal tending to zero, no matter what the input amplitude. A good value reported by Un et al. [29] for the speech processing was $c = 0.8$.

Comparisons among the performance of different DM techniques are quite difficult, due to the sensitivity of these algorithms to the different characteristics of the input signal. However, some considerations can be made which hold in general:

(1) For low values of the slope overloading factor s the signal is, in general, not well followed by the algorithm and the slope overload error is predominant.

(2) For high s values the advantage of a better followed signal is vanished by the increasing granular noise.

Between these two extreme conditions there exists, in general, a range of optimal values for s, which maintain the S/N ratio near a maximum. The LDM is more critical from this viewpoint than adaptive delta modulation

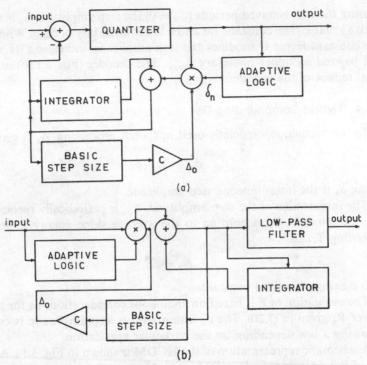

FIG. 3.14. Hybrid compounding delta modulation: (a) encoder and (b) decoder.

algorithms. The latter ones show, in general, longer intervals for the optimal
s [28].

For this particular field of speech compression, experimental results con-
firm the higher performance obtained by syllabic and hybrid compounding
DM, which work better than the instantaneous one.

3.9 Asynchronous Delta Modulation

When adaptivity is achieved by changing the sampling period $T_s = 1/v_s$,
the delta modulation is called *asynchronous*. The basic criteria used to make
decisions on the variation of T_s are mainly the same as for amplitude adaptive
systems.

However, the effects on the reconstructed signal noise are different for the
two algorithms. In this method, the sampling rate is increased during the
periods of high signal activity and it is decreased in the presence of quiescent
behaviour or slow amplitude variations.

The simplest case of asynchronous DM considers only past two sample signs (b_{n-1} and b_{n-2}) to make the decision about the eventual sampling rate variation. A permanence in the signs ($+ +$ or $- -$) is interpreted as a probable slope overload and corresponds to an increment in the sampling rate, which is then multiplied by a constant factor C_1, up to a maximum value v_{max}.

Alternate signs, on the contrary, are considered as indicative of a good signal tracking and the sampling rate will be decreased by a factor C_2, up to a minimum value v_{min}, i.e.,

$$s = b_{n-2}b_{n-1}$$

$$v_n = \begin{cases} v_{n-1}C_1, & \text{if } s \geq 0 \\ v_{n-1}C_2, & \text{if } s < 0 \end{cases} \tag{3.28}$$

In Fig. 3.15 the behaviour of an example of asynchronous DM is reported while processing a step function in two extreme situations. In this case, the frequency variations are made using $C_1 = 1, C_2 = 2$.

This method gives higher signal-to-noise ratios than the classical DM for many types of signals. However, large peak errors can still arise when quick variations occur in the input signal and the algorithm is operating at a low sampling rate; indeed a certain number of pulses is required to have time to reach the v_{max} necessary in such situations.

A further improvement for this type of error can be obtained in the *operational asynchronous* DM (OADM). In this procedure, whenever the difference between the input and the reconstructed signal exceeds a preset tolerance value K the algorithm goes back m samples and inverts the value, adjusting

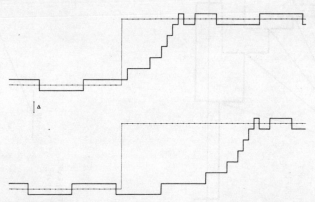

FIG. 3.15. Typical behaviours of asynchronous delta modulation (basic type) applied to a step function. $v_{min} = v_{max}/8$.

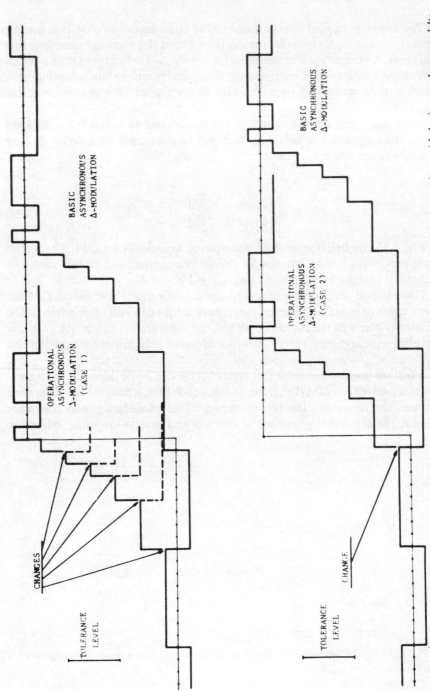

FIG. 3.16. Typical behaviours of operational asynchronous delta modulation (case 1 and 2) in comparison with basic asynchronous delta modulation, applied to a step function.

the sampling period appropriately. In Fig. 3.16 the behaviour of operational DM, with $m = 2$, is shown for comparison with the asynchronous one. Broken lines indicate the cases where the algorithm goes back.

Suitable inhibition controls are necessary in the OADM, to avoid the possibility of closed loops. This requires a little supplementary computational effort, which is, however, well justified by the apparent better performance.

3.10 Use of Transformations

Orthogonal transformations, such as Fourier, Hadamard, Walsh, Haar, slant, Karhunen–Loéve, etc., can be used for source coding or data compression, due to the fact that, in general, they represent a more *compact* representation of source data. This means that the transformed data results extend and exist in a smaller region or *domain* than the original data, which corresponds to have a lower number of *significant* transformed data than original source data [3].

In the following, the definitions of some important transformations with main properties are briefly recalled. The transformations are presented in a *discrete form*, due to the fact that this is the form used in practice. One-dimensional (1-D) and two-dimensional (2-D) forms are described for applications to signal and image compression [30].

3.10.1 General Properties of Discrete Transformations

A discrete linear transformation can be defined through the following relations (1-D and 2-D) [30]:

$$F(k) = \sum_{n=1}^{N} f(n)A(n,k)$$

$$F(k_1, k_2) = \sum_{n_1=1}^{N_1} \sum_{n_2=1}^{N_2} f(n_1, n_2)A(n_1, n_2; k_1, k_2)$$

(3.29)

where $f(n)$ or $f(n_1, n_2)$ are the input data (in general, the samples of the signal or image to be processed) and $A(n, k)$ or $A(n_1, n_2; k_1, k_2)$ is the operator or *forward transform kernel* defining the transformation. If the transformation is invertible, as we suppose, the inverse transformation is expressed by

$$f(n) = \sum_{k=1}^{N} F(k)B(n,k)$$

$$f(n_1, n_2) = \sum_{k_1=1}^{N_1} \sum_{k_2=1}^{N_2} F(k_1, k_2)B(n_1, n_2; k_1, k_2)$$

(3.30)

where $B(n, k)$ or $B(n_1, n_2; k_1, k_2)$ represents the inverse operator or *inverse transform kernel*.

Two-dimensional transformations are called *separable* if $A(n_1, n_2; k_1, k_2)$ and $B(n_1, n_2; k_1, k_2)$ can be decomposed in the following way:

$$A(n_1, n_2; k_1, k_2) = A_c(n_1, k_1)A_r(n_2, k_2)$$
$$B(n_1, n_2; k_1, k_2) = A_c(n_1, k_1)B_r(n_2, k_2) \tag{3.31}$$

where the subscripts r and c indicate row and column 1-D transform operations. A 2-D separable transformation can be performed in two steps. At first, a 1-D transform is performed for any column of the source data matrix

$$F_c(k_1, n_2) = \sum_{n_1=1}^{N_1} f(n_1, n_2)A_c(n_1, k_1) \tag{3.32}$$

Hence, a 1-D transform is performed for any row of $F_c(k_1, n_2)$

$$F(k_1, k_2) = \sum_{n_2=1}^{N_2} F_c(k_1, n_2)A_r(n_2, k_2) \tag{3.33}$$

It is interesting to observe that the preceding transformations can be expressed in vectorial form. If f_M denotes the image matrix and f the corresponding vector (that is the data sequence of the image along the columns) and, correspondingly, F_M and F denote the matrix of the image transform and the related vector, the relation (3.29) becomes

$$F = Af \tag{3.34}$$

where A is the matrix of the direct transformation. The inverse transformation becomes

$$f = BF \tag{3.35}$$

where B is the matrix of the inverse transformation.

Therefore we have

$$B = A^{-1} \tag{3.36}$$

3.10.2 Some Discrete Transformations

The *discrete Fourier transform* (DFT) is defined, in 1-D and 2-D forms, in the following way [30]:

$$F(k) = \sum_{n=0}^{N} f(n)\exp\left(-\frac{2\pi j}{N}kn\right)$$
$$F(k_1, k_2) = \sum_{n_1=0}^{N-1}\sum_{n_2=0}^{N-1} f(n_1, n_2)\exp\left[\left(-\frac{2\pi j}{N}\right)(k_1 n_1 + k_2 n_2)\right] \tag{3.37}$$

while the inverse discrete Fourier transform (IDFT) is expressed by

$$f(n) = \frac{1}{N} \sum_{k=0}^{N} F(k) \exp\left(\frac{2\pi j}{N} kn\right)$$

$$f(n_1, n_2) = \frac{1}{N^2} \sum_{k_1=0}^{N-1} \sum_{k_2=0}^{N-1} F(k_1, k_2) \exp\left[\left(\frac{2\pi j}{N}\right)(k_1 n_1 + k_2 n_2)\right]$$

(3.38)

The k, k_1, and k_2 indices correspond to frequencies ($v = k\,\Delta v$, $v_1 = k_1\,\Delta v$, $v_2 = k_2\,\Delta v$), where Δv is a constant frequency interval or frequency sampling interval.

With suitable symmetry properties in the source data (samples of signal or image), *discrete cosine transforms* and *sine transform* can also be defined. For cosine transform (1-D and 2-D forms) we have

$$F(k) = 2 \sum_{n=0}^{N-1} f(n) \cos\left[\frac{k\pi}{N}\left(n + \frac{1}{2}\right)\right]$$

$$F(k_1, k_2) = 2 \sum_{n_1=0}^{N-1} \sum_{n_2=0}^{N-1} f(n_1, n_2) \cos\left[\frac{k_1\pi}{N}\left(n_1 + \frac{1}{2}\right)\right] \cos\left[\frac{k_2\pi}{N}\left(n_2 + \frac{1}{2}\right)\right]$$

(3.39)

The *Hadamard transform* is based on the properties of the Hadamard matrix (square form with elements equal to ± 1, having orthogonality between the rows and the columns). A normalized Hadamard matrix, of $N \times N$ size, satisfies the relation

$$\mathbf{H}\mathbf{H}^T = 1$$

(3.40)

The orthonormal Hadamard matrix of lowest order is the 2×2 Hadamard matrix

$$\mathbf{H}_2 = \frac{1}{\sqrt{2}} \begin{bmatrix} 1 & 1 \\ 1 & -1 \end{bmatrix}$$

(3.41)

This transform is also known in the literature as the *Walsh transform* [30]. Harmuth (1969) proposed a frequency interpretation of the preceding Hadamard matrix. The number of sign changes along any Hadamard matrix row divided by 2, is called the "*sequence*" of the row. The rows of Hadamard matrix of order N can also be considered to be obtained as samples of rectangular functions having a sub-period equal to $1/N$. These functions are called *Walsh functions*.

The *Haar transform* is based on the Haar matrix, which contains elements equal to ± 1 and 0. The *slant transform* is an orthogonal transform which can be derived from the Hadamard transform.

One of the most efficient transforms is represented by the *Karhunen–Loéve transform*, which can be defined in the following way (1-D, 2-D):

$$F(k) = \sum_{n=0}^{N-1} f(n)A(n,k)$$

$$F(k_1, k_2) = \sum_{n_1=0}^{N-1} \sum_{n_2=0}^{N-1} f(n_1, n_2)A(n_1, n_2; k_1, k_2)$$

(3.42)

where the $A(n,k)$, $A(n_1, n_2; k_1, k_2)$ kernels satisfy the relations

$$\lambda(k)A(n,k) = \sum_{n'=0}^{N-1} K(n, n')A(n', k)$$

$$\lambda(k_1, k_2)A(n_1, n_2; k_1, k_2) = \sum_{n'_1=0}^{N-1} \sum_{n'_2=0}^{N-1} K(n_1, n_2; n'_1, n'_2)A(n'_1, n'_2; k_1, k_2)$$

(3.43)

where $K(n, n')$, $K(n_1, n_2; n'_1, n'_2)$ denote the covariance functions of 1-D or 2-D source data; and $\lambda(k)$ and $\lambda(k_1, k_2)$ are constants (*eigenvalues* of covariance functions) for fixed values of k, k_1 and k_2.

The previously considered discrete transformations can be, in general, evaluated in a *fast form*. The procedures for computing the transformations in a fast way are generally based on the division of the computing operation into a sequence of subsequent computing steps, in such a way that the results of the first computing steps (*partial results*) can be utilized repetitively in subsequent steps. Efficient software packages are available for fast Fourier transform (FFT) and fast Walsh transform (FWT). For instance the number of operations required to evaluate FWT of 2-D data results in $2N^2 \log_2 N$ instead of $2N^3$.

3.10.3 Transformations for Data Compression

As previously indicated, transformations can be used to perform data compression, due essentially to the *high concentration* of transformed data. The most meaningful transformed data are indeed generally concentrated in a relatively small region with respect to the extension of original source data: the number of significant transformed data is appreciably smaller than the number of the original source data. A trivial example is represented by a signal constituted by a sine wave; while in the time domain a large number of samples is required to represent the signal, in the frequency domain (use of Fourier transform) two frequency values (amplitude and phase) specify the signal. Analogously, an image constituted by sudden variations in the gray levels (near rectangular form of gray level variation along the rows and columns) will be represented in the Walsh transformed domain by few transformed data.

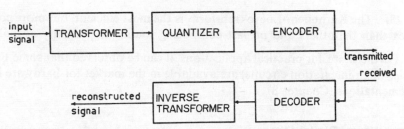

FIG. 3.17. Block diagram of a typical data compression system using transformations.

Furthermore, the transformed data can be compressed in a stronger way by applying simple algorithms such as thresholding (setting to zero the values under a small threshold as, i.e., 1%) or prediction interpolation (Fig. 3.17).

In particular, in image compression variable word-length encoding can be used for different transformed data regions. In practice, the transformed data are divided into several equal squares and a minimum word length (a bit number sufficient to represent the maximum absolute amplitude value in the square plus 1 bit for the sign) is employed for each of them. In the actual storing or transmission of the processed image data, an additional fixed-length word is inserted before each square amplitude data, in order to specify the number of bits used to represent the square coefficients.

For 2-D FWT use, if $N = 2^n$ (with n an integer) is the number of rows and columns of the sampled image and L is the number of gray levels, the maximum value which the transform will assume (corresponding to the co-efficient representing the addition of all the image samples) will be N^2L. If q is the quantization value for the transform coefficients, the number of bits required to specify the word length used in a square will be [3]

$$n_b = \log_2\{\log_2[(N^2L/q) + 1]\} \qquad (3.44)$$

where the logarithms are rounded to the upper integer.

A modification of the preceding method for 2-D data processing by FFT or FWT consists of applying the same procedure of variable word-length encoding of the coefficients in a limited number of transformed image sub-areas (in particular no value can be maintained for those sub-areas where the sum of the absolute values of the coefficients is below a given threshold).

Finally, as a comparison criterion among the different transformations we can observe the following points:

(1)   In general, FFT results are more efficient for signals or images having regular continuous variations (in time or space);

(2)   FWT results are more efficient for rectangular signals or images with sudden variations in the gray level;

(3)   The Karhunen–Loéve transform is the most efficient, but more complex than the others and no fast computing routine is presently available.

Furthermore, for practical applications, it can be observed that some FFT *chips* (high-integration circuits) are available in the market for hardware implementations (Chapter 8).

3.11   Use of Digital Filters

Digital filters can be used in several ways to perform data compression, due to their capability of extracting some frequency bands, or perform spectral estimation. In the following, some general properties of digital filters are presented, and their use for data compression is described.

3.11.1   General Properties of Digital Filters

A linear digital filter can be defined through the following difference equations (1-D and 2-D) [31]

$$y(n) = \sum_{k=0}^{N} a(k)f(n-k) - \sum_{k=1}^{M} b(k)y(n-k)$$

$$y(n_1, n_2) = \sum_{k_1=0}^{N_1} \sum_{k_2=0}^{N_2} a(k_1, k_2)f(n_1 - k_1, n_2 - k_2) \qquad (3.45)$$

$$- \sum_{k_1=0}^{M_1} \sum_{k_2=0}^{M_2} b(k_1, k_2)y(n_1 - k_1, n_2 - k_2), \qquad k_1 + k_2 \neq 0$$

where $f(n)$ or $f(n_1, n_2)$ are the input data (in general, the samples of the signal or image to be processed), $a(k)$ and $b(k)$ or $a(k_1, k_2)$ and $b(k_1, k_2)$ the coefficients of the digital filter, defining its performance and its frequency response, and N and M or N_1, N_2 and M_1, M_2 are suitable positive integers.

If in (3.45) $b(k)$ or $b(k_1, k_2)$ is equal to zero, the digital filter has a finite impulse response (FIR). In this case, the difference equation is a *convolution* between the input data (input matrix) and the coefficients (coefficient matrix), and no *feedback* of previous outputs is present.

Digital filters described by the relations (3.45) with at least one of the coefficients $b(k)$ or $b(k_1, k_2)$ different from zero have an infinite impulse response (IIR), and some previous outputs are again processed (feedback).

Further digital filters can be classified as *non-recursive* or *transversal* filters and *recursive* filters, according to their structures: FIR digital filters have generally non-recursive structures, while IIR digital filters have recursive structures.

By using the z-transform, the transfer function of the digital filters (1-D and 2-D) can be found [31]:

$$H(z) = \sum_{k=0}^{N} a(k)z^{-k} \Bigg/ 1 + \sum_{k=1}^{M} b(k)z^{-k}$$

$$H(z_1, z_2) = \sum_{k_1=0}^{N_1} \sum_{k_2=0}^{N_2} a(k_1, k_2)z_1^{-k_1}z_2^{-k_2} \Bigg/ 1 + \sum_{k_1=0}^{M_1} \sum_{k_2=0}^{M_2} b(k_1, k_2)z_1^{-k_1}z_2^{-k_2}$$

$$k_1 + k_2 \neq 0 \quad (3.46)$$

The z complex variables are connected to the Laplace complex variables and hence to the frequency values through the following relations

$$z = e^{pT} = e^{(\sigma + j\omega)T}$$

$$z_1 = e^{p_1 X} = e^{(\sigma_1 + j\omega_1)X} \quad (3.47)$$

$$z_2 = e^{p_2 X} = e^{(\sigma_2 + j\omega_2)X}$$

where p, p_1 and p_2 are Laplace complex variables, ω, ω_1 and ω_2 the angular frequencies ($\omega = 2\pi v, \omega_1 = 2\pi v_1, \omega_2 = 2\pi v_2, v, v_1$ and v_2 being the frequencies), σ, σ_1 and σ_2 the real parts, T the time sampling interval and X the space sampling interval (both selected according to the sampling theorem) [31].

By setting $\sigma = \sigma_1 = \sigma_2 = 0$ and, as it is generally used, $T = X = 1$ (which corresponds to have normalized frequencies), the frequency transfer functions or frequency responses of the digital filters can be easily obtained.

Many design techniques are known for FIR and IIR digital filters. A synthetic description is given in the following, while for more details the pertinent literature is available [31].

With regard to FIR digital filters (1-D and 2-D), three important design methods are the *window* method, the *frequency sampling* method and the *optimum filter* design. In the window method we start from an impulse response which has to be truncated, thus introducing the minimum error in the frequency response. To this purpose the obtained values of the sampled impulse response, $h(k)$ or $h(k_1, k_2)$, are multiplied by the samples, $w(k)$ or $w(k_1, k_2)$, of a suitable window function having zero value in the region out of the truncation and high concentration in the frequency domain (many window functions are available such as the Lanczos window, the Kaiser window and the Cappellini window [31]). An example of an FIR digital filter designed with this technique of low-pass type is shown in Fig. 3.18. In the frequency sampling method, a suitable number of equispaced values (samples) of the frequency response are chosen, the IDFT of these frequency samples is evaluated and linear programming techniques are used to reduce oscillations in band and out of band. In the optimum filter design methods, optimality

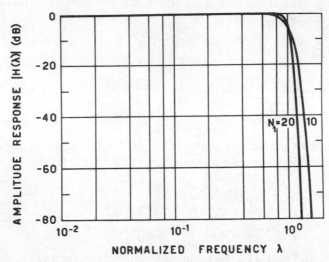

FIG. 3.18. Example of frequency response of an FIR digital filter of low-pass type, designed by means of the window method; $N_1 = (N - 1)/2$ with N odd in the relation (3.45).

criteria are used for designing the desired frequency response, in general, by varying some parameters in such a way so as to minimize an *error function* related to the desired optimal frequency response and to that actually obtained in the designing procedure [31].

Concerning IIR digital filters, a distinction must be made between 1-D and 2-D design methods, In the 1-D case, three important methods are the use of *bilinear transformations, frequency transformations* and *analytic techniques*. By means of the bilinear transformation, the complex variable p in the transfer function $H(p)$ of a continuous filter is replaced by

$$p \to k(1 - z^{-1})/(1 + z^{-1}) \qquad (3.48)$$

where k is a real positive constant, thus obtaining the $H(z)$ transfer function of the IIR digital filter. By means of the frequency transformations, the complex variable z^{-1} is mapped through appropriate function in such a way so as to transform a given digital filter of low-pass type to other digital filters (low-pass, high-pass, and band-pass). Through analytic techniques, the square of the amplitude response of the IIR digital filter is determined by means of different approximation procedures of the ideal required response (amplitude response as close to one as possible in the pass-band and near to zero as possible in the stop-band): in particular, Butterworth, Chebyshev and elliptic filters can be designed. In the 2-D case, the design is rather more difficult, due to the lack of an appropriate *factorization theorem* of algebra [31], and to the connected *stability* problems (which can, in general, be solved in the

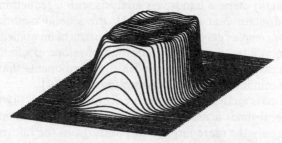

FIG. 3.19. Example of frequency response of a 2-D IIR digital filter of low-pass type, approximating a fourth order Chebyshev low-pass filter.

1-D case in a relatively easy way). Some approaches for designing 2-D IIR digital filters are, however, available as well as some methods to test their stability [31]. A useful design method is based on *transformation of the squared magnitude function* of a 1-D digital filter to a 2-D domain and stabilization procedure. An example of a 2-D IIR digital filter of this type, approximating a fourth-order Chebyshev low-pass filter having a 2% in-band ripple, a normalized cutoff frequency $v_c = 0.25$ and a -20-dB frequency $v_{-20} = 0.35$ is shown in Fig. 3.19. The filter has a numerator and a denominator with 5×5 coefficients with a maximum in-band ripple equal to 0.042 and a transition band (defined as the difference between the normalized frequencies, where the amplitude of the frequency response is, respectively, 90% and 10% of the in-band nominal value) equal to 0.0937 [32].

3.11.2 Data Compression Techniques using Digital Filters

Digital filters perform operations in the frequency domain on the input signals or images, in general, extracting some useful bands. Any digital filtering operation reducing the frequency spectrum extension corresponds to a form of data compression, due to the fact that a lower bandwidth requires a lower sampling frequency and corresponding number of bits.

Due to the preceding consideration, a digital filtering (in particular of low-pass or band-pass type) represents a very useful *pre-processing* before the application of other data compression techniques as described in the previous sections. Smoothed data can be more efficiently compressed by specific compression algorithms.

Some interesting data compression methods use digital filtering and data reduction or "*decimation*". They are based on the extraction of a given frequency band through digital filtering and subsequent reduction of samples toward the minimum value required to represent the remaining limited bandwidth. Two of these methods are described here. The first uses a single low-pass digital filter and a *frequency shift* of the sampled signal spectrum to perform, in many steps, a band-pass analysis with a reduction of the sample number by a factor 2 at each step [33]; the second method (*complex demodulation* or *complex envelope detection*) consists of an algorithm which uses a digital Hilbert filter to extract the complex envelope of a limited bandwidth signal by means of in-phase and quadrature components that approach the theoretically minimum number of sampling data [34].

The band-pass analysis operation, performed through digital filtering, represents several times a useful form of compressed representation , due to the fact that only the more important bands (from the information amount viewpoint) can be maintained or, by using all the bands, the amplitude or power spectrum can be easily obtained (for instance the rms value for any band output can be evaluated).

In particular, for image data compression a pre-processing using a 2-D digital filter (low-pass or band-pass type) is very useful for reducing the large amount of data required to represent the sampled image, before some other eventual data compression technique.

3.12   Timing

All the decoding techniques which reconstruct exactly or with a limited degree of uncertainty the original data stream are based on the hypothesis of a synchronizing reference clock. It gives the *decompressor* the key to recognize the data and start the reconstruction procedure [3].

In some compression methods, time synchronization is always maintained by the intrinsic strategy of the algorithm. For example, in the DM technique the bit output stream contains all the necessary elements to reconstruct the compressed signal.

For other algorithms, like predictors and interpolators, it is necessary to insert into the output signal (i.e., after each transmitted sample) a suitable *identification word* to give the exact time position of each received sample. The most commonly used methods are:

(1)   time information which represents the number of the non-transmitted samples;

(2)   time information which identifies the temporal position of the transmitted samples.

Obviously the overall compression ratio will include the bits necessary to represent or transmit the time information.

In general, method (2) requires a higher number of bits than method (1). Nevertheless, in real transmissions on noisy channels, method (2) is less sensitive to channel errors.

Higher efficiency can be obtained in some cases by using a variable word length for the time identification words or suitable encoding for synchronization.

3.13 The Buffer

The buffer is a memory of suitable capacity, introduced in most parts of data compression systems, to reorganize the remaining data after *bit compression*, adding also the timing or synchronization data (i.e., as already outlined in Fig. 3.2 for prediction-interpolation algorithms).

The role of the buffer is, therefore, very important in the overall data compression system, in particular, for synchronizing the remaining data and obtaining *bandwidth compression* (setting the remaining data at constant time intervals) [3].

The design of the buffer must try to avoid two unfavourable working conditions:

(1)   the *underflow*, which corresponds to a state in which the buffer is too empty (caused by the selection of too high a value of the output data rate);

(2)   the *overflow*, which corresponds to a state in which the buffer is too full (output data rate too low).

The underflow can cause a loss of synchronization (with method (1)) and the overflow, a loss of data. A simple way to avoid these error conditions is when the compression algorithm utilizes a variable aperture or amplitude tolerance, to control the amplitude tolerance, increasing it when the buffer becomes too full and diminishing it in the contrary case. Another approach is to insert an adaptive pre-compression low-pass digital filter (see Section 3.11); the cutoff frequency is decreased when the buffer is going in overflow state and it is increased for the underflow situation.

The schematic structure of an adaptive data compressor using the preceding controls for a single data stream is shown in Fig. 3.20. Here a decision circuit can control, through the buffer *fullness sensor*, both the amplitude tolerance of the main compressor (bit compressor) and the cutoff frequency of the digital filter, depending on the actual state of the buffer.

In a communication system using data compression on many data channels, the design of the buffer can represent a crucial point (see Chapters 7 and 9).

3.14 Efficiency Evaluations and Comparisons

The efficiency of any data compression system depends on the characteristics of the signals, but generally it is impossible to decide theoretically the most suitable compression method. Usually comparisons are made ex-

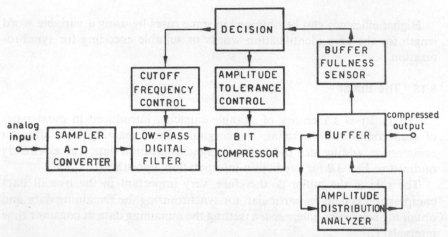

FIG. 3.20. Schematic structure of an adaptive data compressor using a variable amplitude
tolerance and a pre-compression digital filter of low-pass type with variable cutoff frequency.

perimentally for each class of signals. To compare the performance of the
compression algorithms mathematically, the parameters most often used are:
(1) the compression bit ratio C_a, defined as the ratio between the bit number
necessary to represent or transmit the non-compressed data and the bit number necessary for the compressed data, including the time information, (2)
the root mean square (rms) error and (3) the peak error, expressed as a
percentage of the signal dynamics. Subjective testing is also widely used in
practice, but it suffers from the limitation that comparisons are difficult.

The general characteristics of the most interesting compression algorithms
are presented and some typical results are shown and compared, using the
previously described parameters. In order to present it in a satisfactory way,
we first describe some results obtained by analyzing many different telemetry
signals (as typical source data) [3, 4, 35]. These signals were classified,
through time and frequency analysis, in six classes having the following characteristics (Fig. 3.21):

(1)   data with constant or nearly constant value (e.g., data corresponding
to the monitoring of switch positions);

(2)   periodic data, including data constituted by a few sine-wave components (e.g., physical data with nearly constant values obtained through an
interrogation or scanning method);

(3)   slowly varying data (e.g., temperature or battery conditions);

(4)   data resulting from the combination of periodic and slowly varying
components (e.g., data with a periodic component caused by the spinning
movement of the satellite);

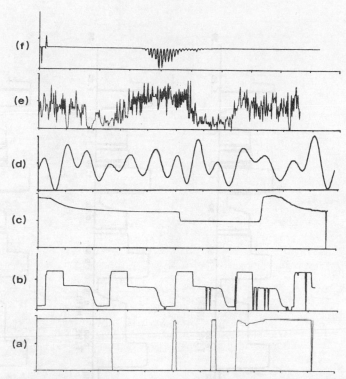

FIG. 3.21. Example of six different typical classes of signals (space telemetry signals–ESRO 1 satellite). (a) Class (1); (b), class (2); (c), class (3); (d), class (4); (e), class (5); and (f), class (6).

(5)   random data;

(6)   data with strong isolated active periods at regular or irregular time intervals (physical data with bursts or spikes).

As an example, we show in detail some results relative to type (2) signals. In Fig. 3.22, from the bottom, the original waveform and the reconstructed signals after a data compression operation are presented. A ZOP floating aperture algorithm was used with different aperture values.

In Fig. 3.23 the results obtained for the same signal using a FOP algorithm are reported. The comparison between Fig. 3.22 and Fig. 3.23 shows that FOP, for this class of signals, presents in many cases a lower efficiency with respect to the ZOP algorithm, especially for high-aperture values. Some oscillations can be noted in the FOP during quiescent periods, due to the approximation of the signal with straight lines. Similar results have been obtained also for ZOI and FOI algorithms.

Figure 3.24 shows the compression ratio C_a (time information has not been taken into account), the rms and peak errors as a function of the nor-

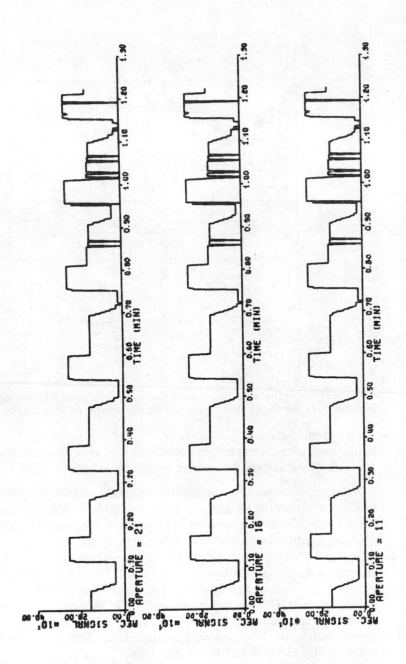

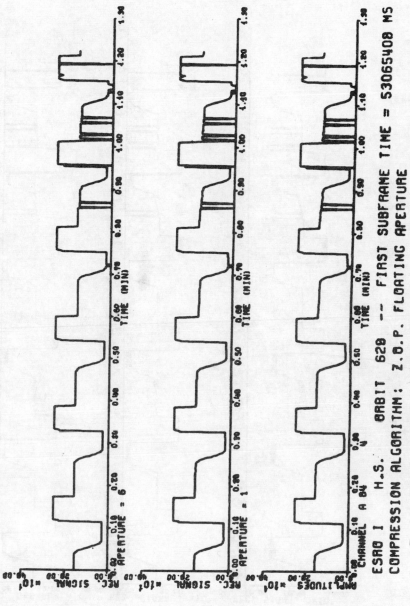

Fig. 3.22. Example of application of ZOP with floating aperture to an ESRO 1 telemetry signal [class (2)].

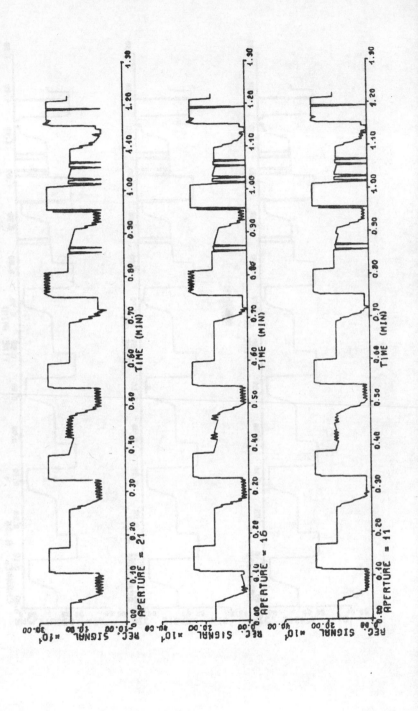

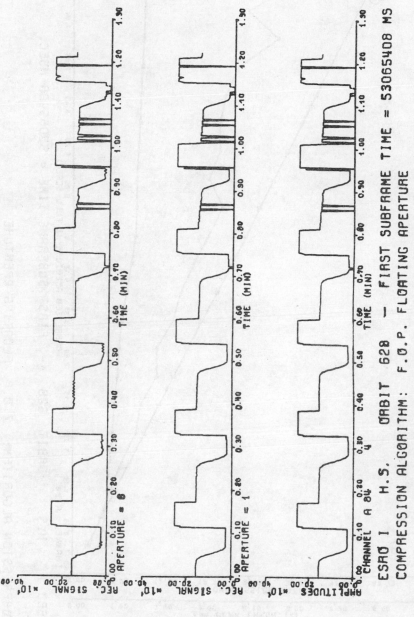

FIG. 3.23. Example of application of FOP algorithm to an ESRO 1 telemetry signal [class (2)].

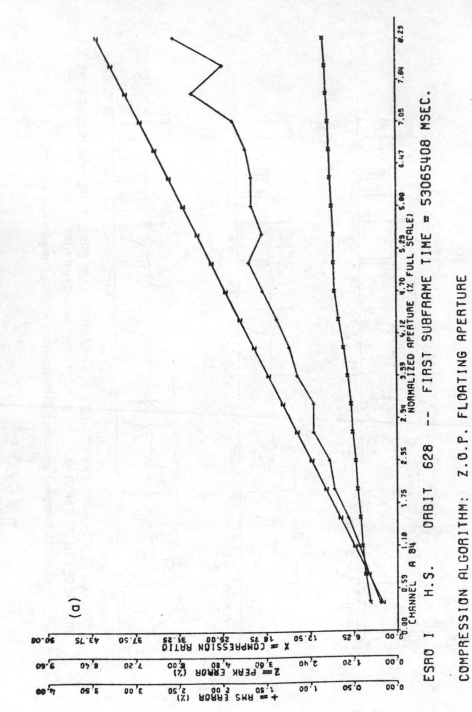

(a)

ESRO I   H.S.   ORBIT 628 -- FIRST SUBFRAME TIME = 53065408 MSEC.

COMPRESSION ALGORITHM: Z.O.P. FLOATING APERTURE

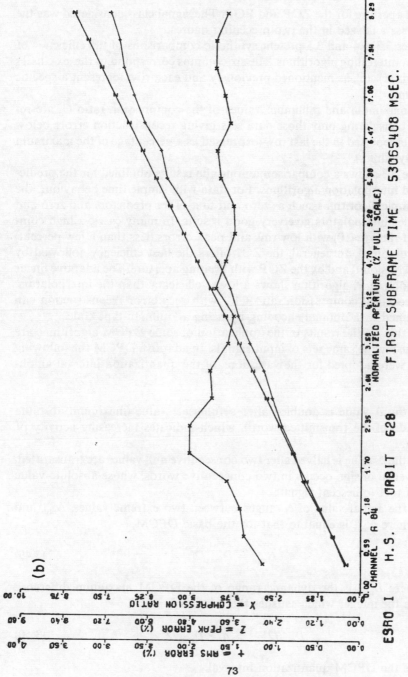

FIG. 3.24. (a) Efficiency curves (C_a, peak and rms errors) for the example in Fig. 3.22. (b) Efficiency curves (C_a, peak and rms errors) for the example in Fig. 3.23.

malized aperture for the ZOP and FOP. The signal class considered was the same class analyzed in the two preceding figures.

Tables 3.3, 3.4 and 3.5 present synthetic comparisons of the efficiency of the most interesting algorithms. The six columns correspond to the six classes of signals (1)–(6), as mentioned previously and each row represent a specific algorithm.

The maximum and minimum values of the compression ratio C_a are reported, considering only those data sets giving reconstruction errors below the limits reported in the last row (expressed as a percentage of the maximum signal dynamics).

Table 3.3 shows a comparison among the results obtained for the prediction and interpolation algorithms. For data with simple time behaviour, the most simple algorithms such as zero and first-order predictors and zero and first-order interpolators give very good results. In many cases, a high compression ratio (>10) with low rms and peak errors (less than a few percent) can be obtained. In general, the ZOI offers the best efficiency, followed by the FOI (disjoint) and by the ZOP with floating aperture. The adaptive linear prediction (ALP) algorithm shows a lower efficiency than the interpolators. The theoretical compression ratio CR_1 with zero error reconstruction can be obtained with optimal encoding by using a Huffman-type code.

In Table 3.4 the results of the application of some DPCM algorithms are shown using the same sets of input signals. In adaptive DPCM the following criteria were adopted for the variations of the quantization interval amplitude Δ:

(1)   the Δ value is doubled after a full-scale value (maximum absolute amplitude of the transmitted word), which indicates increasing activity of the signal;

(2)   the Δ value is halved after two consecutive null values are transmitted, or a reversal of sign occurs in two consecutive words, whose absolute value is equal to 1 (quiescent signal);

(3)   the actual value of Δ ranges between two extreme values, Δ_{min} and Δ_{max}, where Δ_{max} is equal to that for the basic DPCM,

$$\Delta_{min} = D_{max}/2^n \qquad (3.49)$$

and where D_{max} is the dynamic range of the DPCM maximum difference and n is the integer which satisfies the relation

$$D_{max}/2^{n-1} > q \geq D_{max}/2^n \qquad (3.50)$$

and q is the DPCM quantization interval.

TABLE 3.3. Results of prediction and interpolation algorithms applied to six typical space telemetry signals (data channels),[a]

		Channel					
Algorithm		A 25 (1) $CR_1 = 18.9$	A 84 (2) $CR_1 = 6.8$	A 82 (3) $CR_1 = 18.7$	A 74 (4) $CR_1 = 5.2$	D 20 (5) $CR_1 = 2.5$	A 31 (6) $CR_1 = 4.2$
ZOP fixed	C_a	8.3–34.3	2.4–6.6	6.8–40.9	3.6–9.5	—	2.2–7.0
	AP	1–14	1–14	1–10	2–5	—	2–15
ZOP floating	C_a	14.8–39.2	3.9–9.0	15.0–59.1	4.0–9.7	2.8	4.1–9.3
	AP	1–13	1–12	1–9	1–3	3	1–10
ZOP offset	C_a	12.0–37.0	3.4–9.0	15.2–59.1	5.7–11.1	2.6	2.4–8.9
	AP	1–12	1–12	1–10	1–3	3	1–9
FOP floating	C_a	5.8–17.7	2.9–5.1	2.4–10.3	2.5–3.7	—	2.7–6.1
	AP	1–13	1–13	1–8	1–3	—	1–12
ZOI	C_a	18.8–42.1	4.5–10.2	20.1–76.0	6.1–16.4	3.1–5.1	4.9–13.6
	AP	1–11	1–10	1–8	1–3	2–3	1–11
FOI disjoint	C_a	13.4–21.9	3.7–7.5	19.0–59.1	7.1–15.4	4.1	3.3–8.1
	AP	1–13	1–12	1–11	1–4	4	1–12
ALP	C_a	9.8–22.0	2.1–3.2	12.4–44.3	2.0–13.0	2.1–2.9	2.1–7.6
	AP	1–13	1–12	1–9	1–4	2–3	1–12
Maximum error	rms	2%	2%	2%	1%	1%	2%
	Peak	5%	5%	5%	1.5%	1.5%	5%

[a] C_a is the compression ratio (minimum and maximum values); AP the absolute aperture (minimum and maximum values); CR_1 the theoretical lower bound of the compression ratio; input signal range is 0–255.

TABLE 3.4. Results of DPCM applied to the same data as in Table 3.3.[a]

	Channel											
Algorithm	A 25 (1) $CR_1 = 18.9$		A 84 (2) $CR_1 = 6.8$		A 82 (3) $CR_1 = 18.7$		A 74 (4) $CR_1 = 5.2$		D 20 (5) $CR_1 = 2.5$		A 31 (6) $CR_1 = 4.2$	
Basic ZOP C_a	1.60	1.14	1.33	1.14	1.60	1.14	4.00	2.66	2.00	1.60	1.60	1.14
L_w	5	7	6	7	5	7	2	3	4	5	5	7
Basic FOP C_a	1.60	1.14	1.60[b]	1.14[b]	1.60[b]	1.14	4.00	2.67	2.67	1.33	2.00	1.14
L_w	5	7	5[b]	7[b]	5[b]	7	2	3	3	6	4	7
Basic ALP C_a	1.60	1.14	—		1.60	1.14	4.00	2.66	2.00	1.60	1.60	1.14
L_w	5	7	—		5	7	2	3	4	5	5	7
Adaptive ZOP C_a	—		2.96		1.33[b]	1.14[b]	4.00	2.66	2.66	1.60	1.33[b]	1.14[b]
L_w	—				6[b]	7[b]	2	3	3	5	6[b]	7[b]
Adaptive FOP C_a	—				1.33[b]	1.14[b]	4.00	2.66	2.66	1.33	2.66[b]	1.14[b]
L_w	—				6[b]	7[b]	2	3	3	6	3[b]	7[b]
Adaptive ALP C_a	—				1.33[b]	1.14[b]	4.00	2.66	2.00	1.60	2.00[b]	1.14[b]
L_w	—				6[b]	7[b]	2	3	4	5	4[b]	7[b]
VWL ZOP[c] $\bar{C}_a$	5.84		2.96		6.20		4.42		2.00		2.35	
VWL FOP[c] $\bar{C}_a$	5.44		2.73		5.26		4.51		1.69		1.91	
VWL Channel[c] $\bar{C}_a$	3.29		1.70		2.18		1.75		1.96		2.34	
Asynchronous FOP Test 1 C_a	—		—		—		7.11	5.01	7.68	3.31	—	
L_w	—		—		—		2	3	4	6	—	
Asynchronous FOP Test 2 C_a	—		—		—		8.09	5.23	14.23	4.25	—	
L_w	—		—		—		2	3	4	6	—	
Asynchronous FOP Test 3 C_a	—		—		—		8.66	5.23	24.80	4.90	—	
L_w	—		—		—		2	3	4	6	—	
Maximum error rms	2%		2%		2%		1%		1%		2%	
Peak	5%		5%		5%		1.5%		1.5%		5%	

[a] C_a is the compression ratio ($\bar{C}_a$ the mean value); L_w the word length; CR_1 the theoretical lower bound of compression ratio.
[b] Peak error can assume values up to 50% of the PCM full scale.
[c] Zero error.

TABLE 3.5. Results of DM applied to the same data as Table 3.3.[a]

Algorithm	Channel: A 25 (1) $CR_1 = 18.9$			A 84 (2) $CR_1 = 6.8$			A 82 (3) $CR_1 = 18.7$			A 74 (4) $CR_1 = 5.2$			D 20 (5) $CR_1 = 2.5$			A 31 (6) $CR_1 = 4.2$		
	FR	Δ	C_a	FR	Δ	C_a	FR	Δ	C_a	FR	Δ	C_a	FR	Δ	C_a	FR	Δ	C_a
Classical	8	8	1				8	8	1	8	8	1	8	8	1	8	8	1
	8	16	1	8	16	1	8	16	1							8	16	1
										8	4	0.5						
							16	16	1							16	16	1
	16	4	0.5							16	4	0.5	16	4	0.5			
	16	8	0.5	16	8	0.5	16	8	0.5				16	8	0.5			
	16	16	0.5	16	16	0.5	16	16	0.5							16	16	0.5
HIDM							4	8	2							4	8	2
							4	16	2							4	16	2
							4	32	2									
													4	4	1			
	8	4	1	8	4	1	8	4	1	8	4	1				8	4	1
	8	8	1	8	8	1	8	8	1							8	8	1
	8	16	1	8	16	1	8	16	1							8	16	1
							8	32	1									
	16	2	0.5	16	2	0.5	16	2	0.5	16	2	0.5	16	2	0.5	16	2	0.5
	16	4	0.5	16	4	0.5	16	4	0.5	16	4	0.5				16	4	0.5
	16	8	0.5	16	8	0.5	16	8	0.5							16	8	0.5
	16	16	0.5	16	16	0.5										16	16	0.5
							16	32	0.5									
Basic asynchronous Test 1	16	16	2.0	16	16	1.8	8	32	4.0					—		8	32	3.8
	16	8	1.9				16	4	2.0	16	4	2.0				16	4	1.6

(continues)

TABLE 3.5. (*Continued*)

	Channel					
Algorithm	A 25 (1) $CR_1 = 18.9$ FR Δ C_a	A 84 (2) $CR_1 = 6.8$ FR Δ C_a	A 82 (3) $CR_1 = 18.7$ FR Δ C_a	A 74 (4) $CR_1 = 5.2$ FR Δ C_a	D 20 (5) $CR_1 = 2.5$ FR Δ C_a	A 31 (6) $CR_1 = 4.2$ FR Δ C_a
Basic asynchronous Test 2	—	—	8 32 7.8 16 4 3.8	16 4 3.8	—	8 32 7.0 16 4 2.8
Basic asynchronous Test 3	—	—	8 16 15.3	16 4 7.3	—	8 8 14.3 16 4 3.9
Operational asynchronous Test 1	8 16 3.7 16 8 1.9	8 16 3.4 16 8 1.7	8 32 4.0 16 4 2.0	16 4 1.9	16 4 1.8	8 16 3.5 16 4 1.6
Operational asynchronous Test 2	16 16 3.6 16 8 3.4	16 16 3.3 16 8 2.9	8 16 7.8 16 4 3.8	16 4 3.8	16 4 3.4	8 16 5.9 16 4 2.5
Operational asynchronous Test	16 16 6.7	—	8 8 14.7 16 4 7.3	16 4 7.3	—	8 8 7.5 16 4 3.5
Maximum error rms Peak	2% 50%	2% 50%	2% 50%	2% 3%	2% 3%	2% 50%

[a] C_a is the compression ratio; FR is sampling frequency; Δ the step amplitude; CR_1 the theoretical lower bound of compression ratio.

In a manner analogous to those for the asynchronous DPCM, the criteria for the sampling period assignment were the following:

(1)   the maximum sampling frequency v_{max} is set equal to that of PCM;

(2)   the frequency is decreased by a factor 2 ($x = 2$) after two consecutive samples whose amplitude (absolute value) is equal to 1 and opposite in sign;

(3)   the frequency is increased by a factor 2 after a full scale (negative or positive) is transmitted.

Three different tests are shown, using three different ranges for the frequency ratio between the PCM and DPCM sampling frequency. Let

Test 1: $v_{min} = 1,$ $v_{max} = 4,$ $v = 1, 2, 4$

Test 2: $v_{min} = 1,$ $v_{max} = 8,$ $v = 1, 2, 4, 8$

Test 3: $v_{min} = 1,$ $v_{max} = 16,$ $v = 1, 2, 4, 8, 16$

$$(v_{min} \le v < v_{max}).$$

From Table 3.4 it is clear that asynchronous DPCM, followed by FOP, offers the best compression ratio (up to 25), as happens generally with all the asynchronous techniques. The only limitation is that, without special controls, the algorithm does not respond to spikes, especially after a quiescent period, which increases the sampling period.

In basic and adaptive DPCM techniques, the best results are obtained for low dynamic signals. In the adaptive DPCM, large peak errors (more than 50%) appear when processing signals of classes (1) and (2) (Fig. 3.16), mainly due to the sharp amplitude variations on their waveforms.

The VWL DPCM shows good results for many signals, also for highly dynamic signals and permits exact reconstruction of the signal. However, VWL DPCM techniques present, in general, a higher implementation complexity.

In Table 3.5 the results are shown which have been obtained from the application of various delta modulation techniques to the six classes of signals already mentioned. In this case, the C_a value is also the final compression ratio of the transmission chain, any time insertion being unnecessary.

The results presented for basic asynchronous DM are obtained by using the following criteria for the frequency sampling variations:

(1)   the sampling frequency FR is varied between two extreme limits

$$\min \le FR \le \max \tag{3.51}$$

(2)   FR is doubled, if possible, after a change in the sign of the transmitted pulses;

(3)   FR is halved, if possible, after the pulse signs have remained unchanged.

An important problem is the choice of the frequency variations and of the minimum and maximum sampling frequency. Three tests were performed with min = 1. Although related to the analysis of typical space telemetry signals, the preceding considerations and results can be extended to different source signals which behave like the six considered classes of input data.

Other theoretical and experimental comparisons exist in the literature, in particular for the speech signals. We recall the work of Jayant [13] who reported signal-to-noise ratio versus bit rate for: (1) adaptive DPCM using a FOP-like predictor; (2) HIDM using two-bit memory; and (3) log-PCM. The HIDM presents a higher efficiency than the log-PCM at low bit rates, while the log-PCM behaves better at high bit rates.

3.15 Conclusions

In the previous sections, several data compression methods and techniques or more simple or complex types have been presented and some typical examples for their practical application have been reported. Unfortunately, due to the large time–frequency (or space–frequency) variations of the signals (or images) to be processed, it is not very easy to select the best algorithm for a specific application. Simulation methods (some examples have been presented) can, however, greatly help in this selection process by defining the more efficient (and possibly simple) data compression techniques to be actually utilized.

In principle, an *optimum data compression system* for any signal or image to be processed could have the general structure as shown in Fig. 3.25.

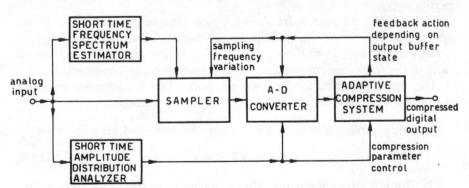

FIG. 3.25. General structure of an "optimum" data compression system of adaptive type.

At first, a suitable sampling frequency is determined through *short-time frequency spectrum estimation* (achieved by means of the FFT algorithm or digital filtering band-pass analysis). Afterwards, the analog-to-digital conversion (by using a lower or higher bit number) can be performed according to short-time amplitude distribution analysis. Finally, an adaptive data compressor (typically with a bit compressor and a buffer) can compress the data in the best way, by using information about the short time amplitude distribution analysis (controlling the compression parameters i.e., as amplitude tolerance). The compressor requires a sensor for the buffer fullness in such a way as to change compression parameters (amplitude tolerance or the sampling frequency).

In practice, according to the specific application and efficiency required, data compression techniques as presented in the previous sections will be utilized with the more useful parts of the system in Fig. 3.25, thus introducing some adaptivity and performance control.

References

1. Kortman, C. M. (1967). Redundancy reduction: a practical method of data compression. *Proc. IEEE* **55**, 253–263.
2. Andrews, C. A., and Schwartz, G. R. (1967). Adaptive data compression. *Proc. IEEE* **55**, 267–277.
3. Benelli, G., Cappellini, V., and Lotti, F. (1980). Data compression techniques and applications. *Radio and Electronic Engineer* **50**, 29–53.
4. Cappellini, V., Lotti, F., Ori, C., Pasquini, G., and Pieralli, F. (1974). A study on data compression techniques. Final Report for the ESTEC/Contract 902/70, ESRO, CR-93.
5. Davisson, L. D. (1966). Theory of adaptive data compression *in* "Advances in Communications," Vol. 2. Academic Press, New York.
6. Davisson, L. D. (1967). An approximate theory of prediction for data compression. *Radio and Electronic Engineer* **43**, 274–278.
7. Davisson, L. D. (1968). The theoretical analysis of data compression systems. *Proc. IEEE* **56**, 176–186.
8. Turner, L. F. (1973). Data compression techniques as a means of reducing the storage requirements for satellite data: a quantitative comparison. *Radio and Electronic Engineer* **43**, 599–608.
9. MacDonald, R. A. (1966). Signal-to-noise and idle channel performance of DPCM systems, particular applications to voice signals. *Bell Syst. Tech. J.* **45**, 1123–1151.
10. O'Neal, J. B., and. Stroh, R. W. (1972). Differential PCM for speech and data signals. *IEEE Trans. Commun. Technol.* **COM-20**, 900–912.
11. O'Neal, J. B. (1966). Predictive quantizing systems (differential pulse code modulation) for the transmission of television signals. *Bell Syst. Tech. J.* **45**, 689–722.
12. Donaldson, R. W., and Chan, D. (1969). Analysis and subjective evaluation of differential pulse-code modulation in voice communication systems. *IEEE Trans. Commun. Technol.* **COM-17**, 10–19.
13. Jayant, N. S. (1974). Digital coding of speech waveforms: PCM, DPCM and DM quantizers. *Proc. IEEE* **62**, 611–632.

14. Xydeas, C. S., and Steele, R. (1978). Dynamic ratio quantizer. *Proc. IEEE* **125**, 25–29.
15. Goyal, S. K., and O'Neal, J. B. (1975). Entropy coded differential pulse-code modulation systems for television. *IEEE Trans. Commun.* **COM-23**, 660–666.
16. Cappellini, V., Lotti, F., Ori, C., Pasquini, G., and Pieralli F. (1974). Application of some data compression methods to ESRO satellite telemetry data. *Alta Freq.* **43**, 673–681.
17. De Jager, F. (1952). Delta modulation; a method of PCM transmission using the 1-unit code. *Philips Res. Rep.* **7**, 442–466.
18. Steele, R. (1975). "Delta Modulation Systems." Pentech Press, London.
19. Schouten, J. F., De Lager, F., and Greefkes, J. A. (1952). Delta modulation, a new modulation system for telecommunication. *Philips Tech. Rev.* **13**, 237–245.
20. Goodman, D. J. (1969). Delta modulation granular quantization noise. *Bell Syst. Tech. J.* **48**, 1197–1218.
21. O'Neal, J. B. (1966). Delta modulation quantizing noise: analytical and computer simulation results for Gaussian and television input signals. *Bell Syst. Tech. J.* **45**, 117–142.
22. Jayant, N. S., and Rovenberg, A. F. (1974). The preference of slope-overload to granularity in the delta modulation of speech. *Bell Syst. Tech. J.* **53**, 3117–3125.
23. Cummiskey, P. (1975). Single-integration, adaptive delta modulation. *Bell Syst. Tech. J.* **54**, 1463–1474.
24. Slepian, D. (1972). On delta modulation. *Bell Syst. Tech. J.* **51**, 2101–2137.
25. Abate, J. E. (1967). Linear and adaptive delta modulation. *Proc. IEEE* **55**, 298–308.
26. Winkler, M. R. (1963). High information delta modulation. *IEEE Int. Conv. Rec.* **11**, 260–265.
27. Jayant, N. S. (1970). Adaptive delta modulation with one-bit memory. *Bell Syst. Tech. J.* **49**, 341–342.
28. Un, C. K., and Lee, H. S. (1980). A study of the comparative performance of adaptive delta modulation systems. *IEEE Trans. Commun.* **COM-28**, 96–101.
29. Un, C. K., Lee, H. S., and Song, J. S. (1981). Hybrid compounding delta modulation. *IEEE Trans. Commun.* **COM-29**, 1337–1344.
30. Pratt, W. K. (1978). "Digital Image Processing." Wiley, New York.
31. Cappellini, V., Constantinides, A. G., and Emiliani, P. (1978). "Digital Filters and Their Applications." Academic Press, London.
32. Cappellini, V., and Emiliani, P. L. (1981). 2-D FIR and IIR digital filters. Invited paper, Proceedings of the ECCTD Conference, The Hague, Holland.
33. Cappellini, V., and Emiliani, P. L. (1970). A special-purpose on-line processor for band-pass analysis. *IEEE Trans. Audio Electroacoust.* **AU-18**, 188–194.
34. Cain, G. D., Cappellini, V., and Del Re, E. (1977). A digital band-pass analysis approach for biomedical signal processing and telemetry. *Proc. EUROCON*, 77 European Conference on Electrotechnics, Venice, Italy.
35. Cappellini, V., Lotti, F., Pasquini, G., and Pieralli, F. (1973). Study on data compression and queuing statistics. Final Report for the ESOC Contract 220/70 AR, University of Florence, Florence, Italy.

Chapter 4

Channel Models and Channel Coding

G. BENELLI

Dipartimento di Ingegneria Elettronica
Università di Firenze
Florence, Italy

C. BIANCIARDI

Ministero Pubblica Istruzione
Siena, Italy
and Dipartimento di Ingegneria Elettronica
Università di Firenze
Florence, Italy

4.1 Introduction

In any real case, the information coming from a source is transmitted to a utilizer through a *medium*, called a *transmission channel*. This channel may be either a space channel, a telephone line, a radio link and so on. From the birth of the Information Theory, a considerable amount of literature has been developed on the so called *channel modeling*.

Channel modeling is defined as the ensemble of mathematical theories related to transmission channels. Nevertheless, it must be pointed out that this theory concerns a mathematical channel model and not a real transmission channel (see Section 1.2). In our case, the aims of the channel modeling theory are:

(1) the mathematical theory establishes the general frame within which particular models of real transmission channels can be introduced;

DATA COMPRESSION AND ERROR CONTROL
TECHNIQUES WITH APPLICATIONS

(2)   the mathematical theory provides an almost precise indication about the construction of the individual blocks in a communication system.

In what follows, we deal with a particular mathematical model, i.e., the *discrete channel* model described in Chapter 1. Further on, some account will be given of the reason for that choice, especially in the particular case of the additive white Gaussian noise (AWGN) channel.

As we have already seen, a discrete channel model is described by a conditional probability assignment, referred to the channel inputs and outputs, when these are letters belonging to two *finite* alphabets. Hence, a probabilistic model is dealt with, by means of which we can take into account the corruption of the transmitted inputs, caused by the noise introduced by the transmission medium and/or by the transmission system itself (such as intersymbol interference). In this context, two classes of discrete channel models will emerge, i.e., the *discrete memoryless channel* (DMC) and the *discrete channel with memory* (DCWM). These two classes of discrete channel models will be examined in some detail, while the general problem of channel coding and the relative reliability function [1] is described in Sections 4.10–4.16.

4.2   Some Discrete Memoryless Channel Models

In this section, some models of particular discrete memoryless channels, such as the Gaussian channel or its special case, the binary-symmetric channel, are presented. The reader is referred to Chapter 1 for the introduction to this topic.

4.2.1   The Additive White Gaussian Noise Channel

In this case, the transmission medium is modeled by a summing function (Fig. 4.1)

$$r(t) = v_m(t) + n(t), \qquad 0 \le t \le T \tag{4.1}$$

By also referring to (1.11), the channel Gaussian noise $n(t)$ must be considered as a stationary random process with a noise power spectral density

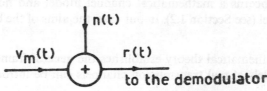

FIG. 4.1. Model for the AWGN channel.

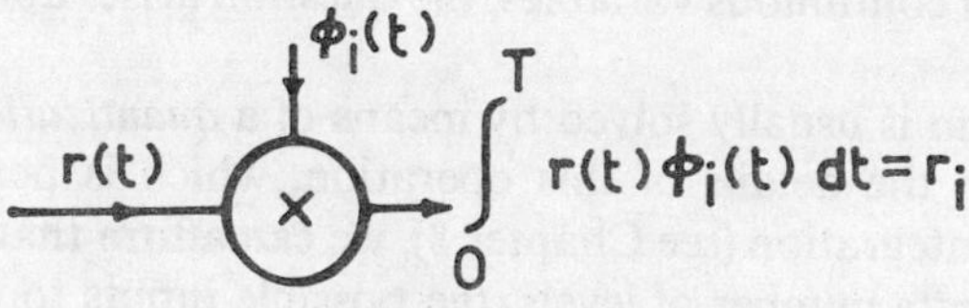

FIG. 4.2. Demodulator function.

N_0 which spreads uniformly over an arbitrarily wide bandwidth. Hence, the input-demodulator received waveform $r(t)$ is also a Gaussian variable [2]. As usual, the demodulator function can be viewed as the dual of that of the modulator. Then, by referring to (1.9), the demodulator consists of a set of multipliers and integrators which map from any received waveform $r(t)$ to a vector $\mathbf{r} = (r_1, r_2, \ldots, r_N)$, as represented in Fig. 4.2 ($i = 1, 2, \ldots, N$). By also referring to (1.11), it is easily seen that

$$r_i = v_{mi} + n_i, \qquad i = 1, 2, \ldots, N \tag{4.2}$$

where

$$n_i = \int_0^T n(t)\Phi_i(t)\,dt$$

In other words, the received components of the vector $\mathbf{r}$ are Gaussian variables (differently from the transmitted components v_{mi}) as the noise components n_i. It is known that the noise components n_i are Gaussian variables with zero mean and a variance $E(n_i^2)$ equal to $\frac{1}{2}N_0$. Also the $\mathbf{r}$-components r_i are Gaussian variables with a mean equal to v_{mi} and the same variance $\frac{1}{2}N_0$.

It is also known that the covariance of r_i ($i = 1, 2, \ldots, N$) is zero or they are uncorrelated Gaussian variables. Then the Gaussian uncorrelated variables r_i are mutually independent from a statistical point of view. From the Gaussian nature of each variable r_i, it also follows that the conditional probability $p(r_i|v_{mi})$ that the output component is r_i, given the input component v_{mi}, is $p(r_i|v_{mi}) = \exp[-(r_i - v_{mi})^2/N_0]/\sqrt{\pi N_0}$. Hence, from the statistical independence of r_i, the conditional probability that the vector $\mathbf{r} = (r_1, r_2, \ldots, r_N)$ is received, when the vector $\mathbf{v}_m$ has been transmitted, is

$$p(\mathbf{r}|\mathbf{v}_m) = \sum_{i=1}^N p(r_i|v_{mi}) = \sum_{i=1}^N \frac{\exp[-(r_i - v_{mi})^2/N_0]}{\sqrt{\pi N_0}} \tag{4.3}$$

Note that each channel output r_i depends only on the corresponding channel input v_{mi} and each received vector $\mathbf{r}$ depends only on the corresponding transmitted vector $\mathbf{v}_m$ (the *memoryless* character of this channel model).

If we give (4.3) for any message $\mathbf{v}_m$, we completely describe this channel model. For this purpose, we need to solve an important problem. Since the

r_i are Gaussian continuous variables, the question arises about their accepted value.

This problem is usually solved by means of a *quantization* process. Without going into the details of this operation, which is performed after the demodulator integration (see Chapter 8), we can affirm that the quantization reduces to a *finite* number of levels, the possible inputs to the final decoder. Hence, the Gaussian transmission medium, together with the modulator and the demodulator–quantizer, are to be considered as a *discrete* channel model because they are characterized by a finite input and a finite (after quantization) output alphabet. In conclusion, an AWGN channel can be modeled as a discrete memoryless channel (DMC) and we note that some practically important channels can be well described in this way (e.g., space channels).

4.2.2   The Binary Symmetric Channel

From the previous argument and from Chapter 1 we note that the input and output alphabets are substantially a matter of choice (also referring to the final quantization). If an AWGN channel model has binary input and binary output alphabets, it is called a *binary symmetric channel* (BSC) and is usually represented as in Fig. 4.3, with the transmitted symbols a_1 and a_2 connected with the received symbols b_1 and b_2 by different probabilities, following the relations:

$$p = \text{prob}(b_2|a_1) = p_{12} = \text{prob}(b_1|a_2) = p_{21}$$

$$1 - p = \text{prob}(b_1|a_1) = p_{11} = \text{prob}(b_2|a_2) = p_{22}$$

According to Sec. 1.4, $A = \{a_1, a_2\}$ is the channel input alphabet and $B = \{b_1, b_2\}$ is the channel output alphabet. Moreover, $P(I) = \{p(a_1) = \alpha, p(a_2) = 1 - \alpha\}$ is the input probability assignment. The BSC is also represented by the channel matrix

$$P = \begin{vmatrix} 1 - p & p \\ p & 1 - p \end{vmatrix} \tag{4.4}$$

according to the scheme of Fig. 4.3.

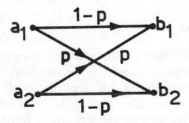

FIG. 4.3. Scheme of a binary symmetric channel.

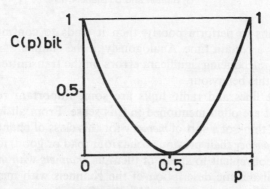

FIG. 4.4. BSC capacity C versus p.

This channel model is symmetric because the transition probability p_{12} from the input a_1 to the output b_2, is equal to the transition probability p_{21} from the input a_2 to the output b_1 $(p_{12} = p_{21} = p < 0.5)$.

By substituting in (1.18) and (1.19), we can derive the *a priori* and the *a posteriori* entropies and, from their difference, the average mutual information $I(I;\theta)$. It can be easily shown that $I(I;\theta)$ is symmetric with respect to the two input probabilities α and $1 - \alpha$ $(0 \leq \alpha \leq 1)$. Hence, it is intuitive that the maximum value of $I(I;\theta)$ with respect to the input probability assignment is reached for $\alpha = 1 - \alpha = \frac{1}{2}$. Then from (1.22) we obtain the BSC *capacity* as

$$C = \max_{P(I)} I(I;\theta) = 1 - H(p) \qquad \text{bits} \qquad (4.5)$$

where $H(p) = -p \log p - (1 - p) \log(1 - p)$ is the channel entropy. The mutual information depends both on the input probability and on the channel transition probability, while the capacity C depends only on the channel itself.

The BSC capacity is usually represented as in Fig. 4.4, that is, the average amount of information we can transmit over the BSC is maximum for $p = 0$ (BSC noiseless channel) or for $p = 1$ (BSC all-noise channel). In any other case, the BSC capacity is less than 1 bit/transmitted symbol. Obviously, no information can be transmitted over a BSC with $p = \frac{1}{2}$, while any $\frac{1}{2} < p < 1$ can be reduced to $0 < p < \frac{1}{2}$ by interchanging the actually received symbols.

4.3 Discrete Channels with Memory

As we emphasized in Section 1.3, the MODEM system together with the transmission medium are to be considered the *discrete* channel to which we refer. It is well known that in many real transmission channels the errors on the transmitted digits tend to cluster or bunch in such a way that if the channel begins to perform poorly, then it tends to continue its poor performance for a certain time. Analogously, if the channel is performing well (i.e., without introducing significant errors on the transmitted digits), it tends to maintain this behaviour.

Telephone lines and radio links are some important real transmission channels that are often mentioned in this sense. From an intuitive point of view, we can think of a sort of *memory* for this class of channels, in the sense that they *remember* their previous behaviour (bad or good) for a certain time. Hence, it is convenient to speak of them as *channels with memory*.

For a probabilistic description of the channels with memory behaviour (see later), it is customary to consider the channel output at a given time as depending both on the current input and on prior inputs and outputs in such a way that the channel memory is reflected on transmitted data. In fact, a certain channel output *remembers* some previous channel inputs and outputs. We recall that memory may arise both from the MODEM system and the transmission-medium noise.

For example, the former may be characterized by an intersymbol interference, which is caused by filtering, and the latter by channel fading, which is slow with respect to the bit rate actually used. Hence, the considered discrete channel will be, on the whole, a *discrete channel with memory*.

After a dicussion on the mathematical connection between memory and capacity, and on error patterns, we outline the past modeling for this class of discrete memory channels.

4.4 Memory and Capacity

Without loss of generality with respect to Section 1.4, let us denote with $A = \{a_1, a_2, \ldots, a_q\}$ the channel input alphabet and with $B = \{b_1, b_2, \ldots, b_q\}$ the channel output alphabet, both belonging to the same Galois field $GF(q)$. Obviously, $q = 2$ will represent the binary communication case. In this digital case the errors introduced by the transmission channel can be denoted by $N = \{n_1, n_2, \ldots, n_q\}$, where $n_i, i = 1, 2, \ldots, q$, belongs to the same field $GF(q)$ and the channel output b_t at an instant t can be expressed as

$$b_t = a_t + n_t \tag{4.6}$$

where a_t is the channel input at the same instant and n_t the mathematical description of the error introduced by the channel, and the addition is over $GF(q)$.

It is obvious that the input sequence $\{a_t\}$ and the error sequence $\{n_t\}$ are statistically independent. Hence, in this description, the error sequence produced by the channel noise is assumed to belong to the same input alphabet and this sequence is simply added to the input one.

Moreover, it is often useful to describe the error sequence $\{n_t\}$ by means of a binary discrete-time stochastic process. In fact, we can consider the mapping M of the error sequence onto $\{0, 1\}$ such that

$$x_t = M(n_t) = \begin{cases} 0, & \text{if } n_t = 0 \\ 1, & \text{otherwise} \end{cases} \tag{4.7}$$

where x_t belongs to the binary random variable X_t for any t.

We now define a transmission channel as having memory m if the probability distribution of the random variable X_t depends only on m past events $X_{t-1}, X_{t-2}, \ldots, X_{t-m}$. It is obvious that $m = 0$ represents a memoryless channel.

In this way, the errors introduced by the transmission channel are viewed as a process (the error process) that is defined by a random variable X_t, with its *uncertainty* and its *memory*.

However, the *uncertainty* of a process is measured by its *entropy* (see Section 1.4.2) and the problem arises if its *uncertainty* (or entropy) is related to the *memory* of the process itself [3].

It is intuitive that the memory *decreases* the uncertainty of the process outcome at the instant t because this outcome remembers some past outcomes. In other words, the memory of the process *decreases* the entropy H of the process itself.

Moreover, the entropy of an error process produced by a channel noise without memory ($m = 0$) will be maximum. It now can be shown that the derivation of an expression for the memory-channel entropy is very difficult even if its upper and lower bounds can be obtained.

It can be useful to compare binary memoryless channels and memory channels. If p is the mean error rate of a channel with memory, we must consider the discrete memoryless channel with the same error rate p. From (4.5), its entropy H_0 and its capacity C_0 are

$$H_0 = -p \log p - (1 - p) \log(1 - p), \qquad C_0 = 1 - H_0 \tag{4.8}$$

From the preceding discussion it follows that the entropy H of a memory channel (with mean error rate p) will be such that

$$H \le H_0 \tag{4.9}$$

It is then possible to measure the influence of the memory on the channel with memory by defining, as the memory itself, the parameter

$$\mu = (H_0 - H)/H_0 \tag{4.10}$$

From (4.9) and (4.10) we have $0 \le \mu \le 1$. For a memoryless channel $\mu = 0$; for a usual memory channel $0 < \mu < 1$ and for a channel noise *without* uncertainty on the error locations $(H = 0)$ $\mu = 1$.

In an analogous way, it is possible to define a capacity C for a memory channel with mean error rate p by letting

$$C = 1 - H \tag{4.11}$$

and obtaining, from (4.8) and (4.10),

$$C = C_0 + \mu H_0 \tag{4.12}$$

In conclusion, for a binary memory channel with mean error rate p and memory μ, we can recognize that its channel capacity C is greater than C_0 (capacity of the binary memoryless channel with the same error rate), while the binary memory channel entropy H is less than H_0 (entropy of the binary memoryless channel with the same error rate). The added capacity μH_0 characterizes the memory of the channel error process and $C_{\text{MAX}} = 1$ bit for a channel without uncertainty on the error locations $(H = 0, \mu = 1)$ [4].

4.5 Error Process Description
for the Discrete Memory Channel

As we have seen in the previous section, the error process can be described in terms of the binary random variable X_t. A typical error sequence in memory channels can be

$$\ldots 0^3 \, 1 \, 0 \, 1^3 \, 0 \, 1 \, 0^3 \ldots \tag{4.13}$$

where the integer numbers, as exponent, indicate the number of consecutive identical symbols (0 as no error, 1 as error).

In a channel with memory, errors tend to cluster and, hence, after an error, the probability of other consecutive errors is high. However, the mean-error probability is obviously less than 0.5. It means that the strings of consecutive zeros are generally numerous and with higher exponents than those of the consecutive ones. Moreover, notice that in the past years two ways were used for a probabilistic description of a memory-channel error process; i.e., a description based on the so-called *gap process* [5] and a second description based on the so-called *burst process*. The former is undoubtedly more rigorous since the definition of *gap* is less ambiguous than that of *burst*.

DEFINITION 4.5.1 *Gap* is a string of consecutive zeros between two ones. The *gap length* is defined as this number of zeros plus one. It is obvious that the sum of all the gap lengths in a sequence equals the length of the sequence itself and that the minimum gap length is one.

Some interesting gap-process statistics emphasize the memory character of a channel, i.e., the probability of an outcome depends on some past outcomes. One piece of statistics is the *error gap probability mass function* (EGPMF) defined as:

$$P_r(\text{Gap length} = l) = P(0^{l-1}1 \,|\, 1) \qquad (4.14)$$

thus giving the probability of a certain gap length in such a way that, obviously, $\sum_{l=1}^{\infty} P(0^{l-1}1 \,|\, 1) = 1$. The expected value $E(\text{Gap length})$ can be calculated and it can be shown that $E(\text{Gap length}) = 1/p$ for an ergodic process of mean error probability p. Another piece of statistics is the *error gap distribution* (EGD) defined as:

$$P_r(\text{Gap length} \geq l + 1) = P(0^l \,|\, 1) \qquad (4.15)$$

thus giving the probability that a gap length is greater than or equal to $(l + 1)$ in such a way that $E(\text{Gap length}) = \sum_{l=1}^{\infty} P(0^l \,|\, 1)$. Moreover, the error process described as a gap process is called *renewal* if successive gap lengths are uncorrelated. Vice versa, it is called *non renewal*, which happens in some cyclic error processes.

The description based on the burst process is more ambiguous because it does not fully explain what a *burst* actually means. A burst is often defined as a string between two ones and its length b as the number of digits in the string, the first and the last ones both included. However, the ambiguity remains for the ones that must be considered the *first* and the *last*.

Only if the memory channel exhibits a *clear* behavior, i.e., good *or* bad in introducing errors, will this ambiguity be resolved. For these reasons, the description of the error process as a burst process is rarely useful.

4.6 Discrete Memory Channel Modeling

We have seen in the previous sections and in Chapter 1 that most results of the Information Theory are related to memoryless channels, as are all considerations about the entropy and capacity. These results are not directly applicable to channels with memory. However, in the past 25 years, a considerable effort was devoted to devise channel mathematical models which would represent the behaviour of a real transmission channel with memory, i.e., a channel in which errors tend to cluster or such that a channel output depends both on its channel input and on some previous inputs and outputs.

This modeling research has followed two ways. In the first way, some structures were proposed (usually Markov chains) that *generate* error sequences analogous to those of real channels with memory. These structures, which would replay the real channel behaviour, are often called *generative models*. In the second way, some statistics were proposed that *describe* the error sequences of real channels with memory. These statistics, which would describe the real channel behaviour, are often called *descriptive models*.

However, we note that, substantially, both ways tend to describe the real memory channel behaviour. In fact, also in the case of the generative models, the aim is the same, i.e., to define an error sequence sufficiently near the real error sequence.

4.7 Generative Gilbert Model and its Extension

A generative model for channels with memory was proposed first by Gilbert in 1960 [6] (see Figure 4.5), with the states G and B defined as:

State G	State B
$\text{prob}(x_t = 0) = 1$	$\text{prob}(x_t = 0) = h$
$\text{prob}(x_t = 1) = 0$	$\text{prob}(x_t = 1) = 1 - h$

$$p + q = P + Q = 1$$

Following this model, the channel is represented by a Markow chain with two states, i.e., G (good state) rigorously error free and B (bad or burst state) where the probability $(1 - h)$ that a transmitted digit is affected by error would be very high (nearly 50%).

The transition probabilities $P = \text{Prob}(G \rightarrow B)$ and $p = \text{Prob}(B \rightarrow G)$ are small with respect to $Q = \text{Prob}(G \rightarrow G)$ and $q = \text{Prob}(B \rightarrow B)$ in such a way that the channel tends to remain in the previous state (it is obvious that a precise state corresponds to a transmitted digit). Note that it is not possible to reconstruct the state sequence from the error sequence $\{x_t\}$. In fact, an error digit $x_t = 0$ would be generated either by G or by B. In his original work, Gilbert derived some interesting statistics according to this model [7].

Gilbert named the EGPMF $v(l)$, defined by (4.14) as the probability of a gap length l, and derived an expression for $v(l)$ in terms of p, P, q, Q, and h. Moreover, he named the EGD $n(l)$, defined by (4.15) as the probability of a gap length greater than or equal to $(l + 1)$, and derived a recurrent formula

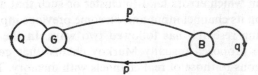

FIG. 4.5. Gilbert's model for a channel with memory.

for $n(l)$ as:

$$n(l) = P(0^l | 1) = (Q + hq)n(l - 1) + h(p - Q)n(l - 2) \qquad (4.16)$$

with $n(0) = 1$ and $n(1) = p + hq$.

In particular, Gilbert derived an expression for $r(b) = \mathrm{Prob}(x_0 = 1, x_b = 1)$, the covariance function, which can be viewed as the probability of a *burst* whose length is $(b + 1)$. Other less interesting probabilities in this model are the probabilities of the two states

$$P(G) = p/(p + P), \qquad P(B) = P/(p + P) \qquad (4.17)$$

and the $\mathrm{Prob}(x_t = 1)$ as

$$P(1) = (1 - h), \qquad P(B) = (1 - h)P/(p + P) \qquad (4.18)$$

Now, it is clear that the Gilbert model *generates* bursts with a certain probability that would be adapted to a real channel behaviour by varying its parameters. However, it is also clear that this model is too *rigid*, for it is *renewal* (successive gap lengths are uncorrelated) or, in other words, the probability that a burst continues is not decreasing even if the burst itself is already long.

The rigidity of the model with respect to real memory channel behaviour suggested a generalization to Elliot in 1963 [8]. Elliot modified the Gilbert model by supposing an error probability $(1 - k)$ also in state G (good or guard-space state). The situation is then the same as in Fig. 4.5, except for the state G, for which we have $\mathrm{prob}(x_t = 0) = k$ and $\mathrm{prob}(x_t = 1) = 1 - k$ with $1 - k \ll 1 - h$.

The probabilities $n(l)$, $v(l)$ and $r(b)$ are also calculated in this Gilbert extended model which is certainly closer to the real channel behaviour than the original Gilbert model, by supposing long periods with small (but nonzero) probability of error followed by long periods with high error probability. Finally, we observe that the preceding pieces of statistics are used in either model (generalized or not) to calculate $P(m, n)$, the probability of m errors in a sequence of length n.

4.8 Successive Generative Models

After the Gilbert model and its extension by Elliot, other sophisticated models were proposed in order to better meet the behaviour of real memory channels and to avoid the limitations of the Gilbert models themselves.

The essential problem was the nonrenewal character of the behaviour in any real channel with memory; i.e., roughly, the probability of a certain state (bad or good) would be decreasing after a certain period in that state. Hence, as a natural consequence, each fundamental state (bad or good) must

G. Benelli and C. Bianciardi

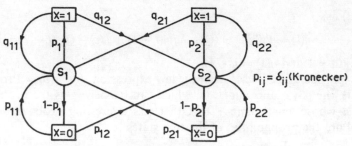

FIG. 4.6. McCullough's model with two states.

be thought of as decomposed in several *substates* with various probabilities, sometimes decreasing, and with suitable transition probabilities between two substates.

This line of research was followed by McCullough, Fritchman and infinite-state model proposers.

McCullough's model [9] is nonrenewal and provides for several error-introducing states with various error probabilities, while the transitions between states are allowed only after an error. For example, in Fig. 4.6 McCullough's model with only two states is represented. Both states can produce errors with probabilities p_1 and p_2 or no error with probabilities $(1 - p_1)$ and $(1 - p_2)$, respectively. After a no error, the model remains in the previous state and, hence, $p_{ij} = \delta_{ij}$ (Kronecker delta). However, it can be noted that for $p_{ij} = q_{ij}$ and $p_2 = 0$, this two-state model becomes the Gilbert renewal model, and that for $p_{ij} = q_{ij}$ and $p_2 \neq 0$ it becomes Elliot's non-renewal model.

Fritchman's model [10] consists of a finite N-state Markov chain, in which k states are error free and $N - k$ states are error states (decomposition of the two fundamental states, bad and good). For $N - k > 1$, this model is nonrenewal, while, for $N - k = 1$, it is renewal (this is intuitive).

Even if this model is very interesting, its results are too complicated to derive some useful statistics such as $P(m, n)$. On the other hand, the case $N - k = 1$ is easier to deal with, but it is too rigid for its single error state.

The infinite-state models are characterized by infinite-state Markov chains of the kind represented in Fig. 4.7. This chain (often called the *slowly spreading chain*) is designed in such a way that $\text{prob}(S_n = s | S_{n-1} = s - 1) = p_s$ and that $\text{prob}(S_n = 0 | S_{n-1} = s) = q_s$, while other transitions are not allowed. The chain can be well adaptable and a *recurrency* can be imposed, i.e., a return to an arbitrarily fixed state.

The study of these Markov chains (finite or infinite) can lead to sophis-ticated descriptions of real memory channels by composing two infinite

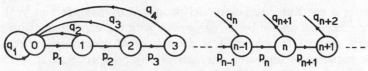

FIG. 4.7. Infinite-state model.

Markov chains (in each of them there are error states and no error states) or by considering high-order Markov chains (in which the transition probabilities between states depend not only on *one* previous state but also on *several* previous states).

However, it must be noted that all these studies on generative models have the recalled aim which lies in calculating $P(m, n)$, the probability of m errors on n transmitted digits, by using the *burst* distribution as we have outlined for the Gilbert model. On the contrary, the descriptive approach is based on the *gap* distribution.

4.9 Descriptive Models

The aim of a *descriptive* model is to devise some statistics that approach as close as possible the behaviour of a real transmission channel with memory. Generally, descriptive models are based on the gap (or multigap) distribution, and this distribution is used in order to estimate $P(m, n)$. As we have outlined earlier, the gap distribution is not only unambiguous from a theoretical point of view, but it is also useful in practice since it is a measurable channel statistic. In this sense, the first important descriptive model was proposed by Berger and Mandelbrot [11]. These authors assumed a *Pareto distribution* for the EGD or they supposed

$$\text{EGD} = P(0^l | 1) = 1/l^\theta \qquad (4.19)$$

where θ is a constant ($\theta > 0$) and $P(0^l | 1)$ represents the probability of a gap length greater than or equal to $(l + 1)$. The model is renewal (i.e., successive gap lengths are uncorrelated) and a comparison between the model and real channels showed that suitable values of θ were such that $0 < \theta < 1$ ($\theta \simeq 0.3$–0.4). Here, θ was recognized as being greater than 1 only if $l > 10^5$ digits.

In 1965, the behaviour of a telephone line (in particular, its measured $P(m, n)$ distribution) suggested to Elliot a descriptive model based on three weighted EGPMF distributions [12]. A trial-and-error search led him to suitably mix the three assumed $P(0^{l-1}1 | 1)$ in such a way that the observed $P(m, n)$ would result from this mixture.

Elliot's model is interesting; however, it can be shown that the method consisting of properly composing three EGPMF is not general, being valid only for a particular n. The model proposed by Munter and Wolf [13] is more successful and in better agreement with the experience (with a tropospheric channel, for example). It consists of M renewal processes and the error sequence is generated alternatively by one process out of the M renewal processes. In other words, for a certain time T, a particular process is chosen that generates the error sequence. After the period T, another process is selected and so on. Any one choice does not depend on previous choices. It can be shown that the overall process is not renewal even if each particular process, chosen for time T, is renewal. The authors derived an expression for $P(m, n)$ by means of the gap distribution and together with other researchers showed its good agreement to the real case of the tropospheric channel.

Finally, we must recall the descriptive models based on multigap distributions [14]. A multigap of order r is defined as r consecutive gaps and the multigap length is the sum of the r gap lengths as defined in Sec. 4.5. The concept of the multigap is very useful because: (1) it is intuitive that the multigap distribution provides for interesting information on the burst structure and (2) it can be shown that $P(m, n)$ and $P(b, n)$, the probability of a burst of length b in a sequence of length n, are easily derived from the multigap distribution.

Moreover, it can be shown that the multigap distributions are correlated with the error rate p in DMC in a simple and elegant form, while these distributions reveal the nonrenewal character of the gap process in DCWM, even if their mathematical expressions are not simple in this case.

4.10 Transmission over Noisy Channels

In the previous sections we emphasized that a transmission over any real channel involves the introduction of errors by the transmission medium or by the MODEMs. The medium together with the MODEM constitutes the *discrete* channel to which we refer. We have seen that this discrete channel can be memoryless or not, with regard to the nature of the introduced error patterns.

In either case, if $A = \{a_1, a_2, \ldots, a_q\}$ is the channel input alphabet and $B = \{b_1, b_2, \ldots, b_q\}$ is the channel output alphabet $(q \geq 2)$, and if a_t is the transmitted digit at time t, the channel is viewed in such a way that we have

$$b_t = a_t + n_t \tag{4.20}$$

where n_t, the error digit introduced by the channel, belongs to the same $GF(q)$ field as a_t and b_t, and the sum is performed on that field [see also Eq. (4.6)].

Now, it is well known that the aim of the utilizer after the transmission medium is to reconstruct the input sequence (which is comprised of input digits as a_t) by means of the output sequence (which is comprised of output digits as b_t) avoiding the effect of the channel-noise digits n_t.

In Section 1.4 we have seen that we gain an average number of bits of information equal to $I(I; \theta)$ by observing a channel output as b_t. However, it is intuitive that it is not possible to reconstruct the input sequence perfectly from the output sequence in such a way as to avoid the error effect completely.

In other words, it remains an *error probability* P_e when we attempt to reconstruct the input sequence from the outputs. In fact, if we consider a memoryless channel, for sake of simplicity, the channel itself can be viewed as its matrix (1.23) formed by input–output symbol probabilities (transition probabilities). When we receive an output digit b_t we must decide what the respective transmitted digit a_t was.

Hence, we must specify a general *decision rule* $d(b_i)$ that establishes a *unique* output symbol for any input symbol. For example, if $A = \{a_1, a_2, a_3\}$ and $B = \{b_1, b_2, b_3\}$, a particular decision rule can be the following:

$$d(b_1) = a_1, \qquad d(b_2) = a_2, \qquad d(b_3) = a_3$$

Generally, if there are q possible inputs and j possible outputs, we have q^j possible *decision rules*. However, it is obvious that all these decision rules are not equally reasonable with respect to the channel matrix (as it would be a decision rule that would *couple* a channel output symbol to an input symbol with a small transition probability to the output itself).

It is then reasonable to adopt a decision rule that *minimizes* the error probability, or the decision rule that couples any output symbol to *the* input symbol with the highest transition probability to that output.

Such a decision rule is called the *maximum likelihood decision rule* (see Section 4.13). It can be shown that for a given channel and given input–output alphabets, the maximum likelihood decision rule cannot be unique. By also adopting a suitable maximum likelihood decision rule, there still exists a nonzero error probability (although minimized).

Hence, the question arises if there are some conditions that allow a further (and if necessary, unlimited) lowering of the error probability P_e. In 1948, Shannon gave a positive answer to this question, establishing the conditions (a proper *channel coding*) under which it would happen [15].

4.11 The Channel-Coding Problem

Let us consider a simple and often used example. If we have transmitted two possible messages, say 0 and 1, over a BSC with a transition probability $p_{12} = p_{21}$ equal to 10^{-3}, we would have an error probability just equal to 10^{-3} if we adopt a maximum likelihood decision rule (Fig. 4.8).

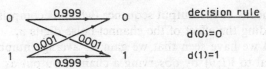

FIG. 4.8. Transmission of two messages over a BSC.

In fact, we *couple* any received symbol to the input symbol with higher transition probability to the received symbol itself. Now, in order to increase the reliability of the transmission or to decrease the error probability, we can first think of the *repetition* of any transmitted message, say three times. Then, the first message is transmitted as 000 and the second as 111. The utilizer, however, can receive for any transmitted message one of the 2^3 possible ternaries considering the effects of the channel noise, i.e., (000, 100, 010, 001, 110, 011, 101, 111). Now, a reasonable decision rule can be the following. The receiver decides that the first message has been transmitted when he receives two or three zeros among the three received symbols; otherwise, the second message has been transmitted. According to this decision rule, the error probability P_e will be the probability of two or three errors on three transmitted symbols, i.e., $P_e = 3p_{12}^2(1 - p_{12}) + p_{12}^3 \simeq 3 \times 10^{-6}$. Hence, we have decreased the error probability from 10^{-3} to 3×10^{-6} by means of repeating any message three times.

It is easy to think that further decreases could be obtained by means of repeating any message, for example, $5, 7, \ldots$ times. In other words, the error probability decreases as the number of the message repetitions increases.

We have also found a method for an unlimited decreasing of error probability (or for an unlimited increasing of the reliability in the transmission). This method is called *channel coding*. The simple message repetition is a *coding method* and all the possible transmitted sequences form *the code*, while each sequence, corresponding to a particular message, is a *code word* (in our example 000 and 111 are the two code words of our code). However, it must be noted that the fundamental character of any coding is also the *price* paid to decrease the error probability. This price is the so-called *redundancy*. In fact, as shown in the above example, we had an error probability equal to 10^{-3} without repetition, i.e., *one* message in one transmitted symbol; while we had a much lower error probability, equal to 3×10^{-6}, with a three-times repetition, i.e., *one* message in three transmitted symbols.

Then, the decreasing error probability was paid for by adding two transmitted symbols for any transmitted message, i.e., by adding *redundancy*. Obviously, any further decreasing in error probability would be paid for by a further increase of redundancy (repeating any message $5, 7, 9, \ldots$ times).

Hence, it would seem that only *channel coding* with the introduction of a *redundancy* on the transmitted messages would allow a practically unlimited decreasing of error probability. Now, the most surprising result of Information Theory ensures us that channel coding is necessary but that it is *not* necessary to have an unlimited increase of redundancy (as in our example) for an unlimited decrease of error probability (see Sec. 4.16).

4.12   Block and Convolutional Encoding

In this section, we recall the most important encoding techniques for the binary case, namely the block coding and the convolutional coding with a tree description. Further details on this topic will be given in Chapter 5 to which we refer.

4.12.1   Block Coding

Referring to Fig. 4.9, let us focus our attention on the channel encoder, supposing that the information data coming from the source encoder are binary digits and that the channel encoder is a *block encoder*. A block encoder divides the incoming binary sequence in equal-length subsequences (blocks) of k binary digits, each one forming a code word of $n \geq k$ binary digits.

This code word of length n, which carries k information digits, is transmitted on the discrete channel. On this line, there are

$$M = 2^k \tag{4.21}$$

possible messages to be transmitted and, hence, 2^k possible code words out of 2^n n-tuples. The way by which any code word is formed is characteristic of a particular block code (and hence, of a particular block encoder). Generally speaking, this way is described by giving a code matrix G that specifies how the $(n - k)$ *redundancy digits* can be formed from the k info-digits and

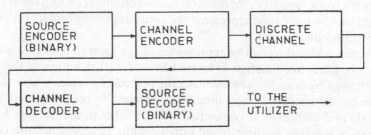

FIG. 4.9. Block diagram for a digital communication system with source coding and channel coding.

added to them to constitute the message to be transmitted. Hence, the so-called code rate

$$R \triangleq \log_2 M/n = k/n \qquad (4.22)$$

will represent the fraction of information carried by any transmitted digit (in the example in the previous section it was $R = 1$ without repetition and $R = \frac{1}{3}, \frac{1}{5}, \ldots$ with a three, five ... times repetition).

If the binary digits are equiprobable, then each of them represents *1 bit* of information (according to Section 1.8). Hence, R can be measured in bits per transmitted digit.

In communication engineering, a temporal description could be useful. If we then transmit one digit each T seconds, R/T represents in bits per second the information transmitted on the channel. It is obvious that the channel capacity C could also be measured in bits per second rather than in bits per transmitted digit as in Chapter 1.

4.12.2 Convolutional Coding and Tree Description

Referring to Fig. 5.5, a convolutional encoder consists of a linear logic circuit with k_0 registers, each of length m (memory or *constraint* length). At any time unit, k_0 digits enter the encoder and $N_0 \geq k_0$ digits leave it and are transmitted through the channel. Each output $j (1 \leq j \leq N_0)$ is connected to each input register $s (1 \leq s \leq k_0)$ by a proper transfer function $G_s^{(j)}(D)$ which is a polynomial of degree m at most. If the convolutional code specified by $G_s^{(j)}(D)$ is *systematic*, then the first k_0 outputs coincide with the k_0 inputs at any time unit.

Each information digit entering the encoder remains m time units in the encoder itself and may *affect* the outputs during all these time units. Then, the quantity $N_A = mN_0$ called the *actual constraint length*, represents the total number of transmitted digits that may be influenced by one input info-digit. In other words, the convolutional coding can be considered as a block coding with block length N_A. Moreover, in convolutional coding the bit rate is defined as $R = k_0/N_0$ and represents the percentage of information carried by each transmitted digit.

Convolutional coding can be represented in the form of a *tree* (as shown in Fig. 5.7). Each tree diagram is formed by *nodes* (that represent the time units) followed by *branches* (representing the possible k_0-tuples which can be taken in by the encoder at any time unit). Hence, 2^{k_0} branches start from each node and each node is connected with 2^{k_0} other nodes. In Fig. 5.7, m_i represents a possible k_0-tuple of info-digits, while c_i represents the corresponding $(N_0 - k_0)$-tuple of parity symbols. In the same figure, only the 0 and 1 instants are considered, while the structure of the tree diagram must be extended to subsequent instants. It can also be noted that the structure becomes repetitive after m time units and that a *particular* transmitted sequence (formed by a *definite* succession of N_0-tuples) will determine a *unique* path in the tree diagram.

4.13 Error Probability on Memoryless Channels

Each transmitted digit, in block or convolutional coding, can be altered by the transmission channel (DMC) with a certain probability. For example, over a BSC this probability is constant and is called the *transition probability*. Now, the aim of the block decoder is to reconstruct the transmitted word from the received one, while the aim of the convolutional decoder is that of reconstructing the *particular path* in the tree diagram.

4.13.1 Block Codes Error Probability

Referring first to block codes, a *decoding error* has occurred when the reconstructed code word does not coincide with the transmitted code word. Any block coding–decoding system connected with a certain transmission channel has a probability of a block decoding error P_e.

If we consider all the possible $M = 2^k$ code words and if $P(\mathbf{c})$ represents the probability that the code word $\mathbf{c}$ is transmitted, then the overall probability of decoding error is given by:

$$P_e = \sum_{c=1}^{M} P(\mathbf{c})P_{e,c} \qquad (4.23)$$

where $P_{e,c}$ is the error probability when the code word $\mathbf{c}$ is transmitted. Note that $P_{e,c}$ also depends on the *decoding rule* actually used. For example, the *maximum likelihood decoding* (MLD) rule is defined in such a way that the decoder, which receives the code word $\mathbf{r}$, chooses the code word $\mathbf{c}'$ as the transmitted one if $P(\mathbf{r}|\mathbf{c}') \geq P(\mathbf{r}|\mathbf{c})$, for any $\mathbf{c} \neq \mathbf{c}'$. In other words, the decoder selects the code word $\mathbf{c}'$ that maximizes the conditional probability that $\mathbf{r}$ is received when $\mathbf{c}$ is transmitted. Now, it can be shown that an upper bound to P_e is found that decays exponentially with the block length n for $R < C$, where C is the channel capacity [1].

This upper bound is obtained by considering the ensemble of all the block codes with certain n and R, that is the ensemble of the (n, R) codes. Each code in the ensemble has its own probability of decoding error, and if we average this error probability over the ensemble, at least one code in the ensemble must have an error probability as small as the average. Then, an upper bound to the ensemble average will give an upper bound to the error probability of this code, or to the error probability $P_e(n, R)$ of the so-called *best code* in the ensemble of the (n, R) codes.

In particular, it has been proved that for the MLD rule, the average probability of decoding error over the ensemble of (n, R) codes is bounded, for any $0 \le \rho \le 1$, by:

$$\bar{P}_{e,c} \le (2^k - 1)^\rho \sum_r \left[\sum_c P(\mathbf{c}) P(\mathbf{r}|\mathbf{c})^{(1/1 + \rho)} \right]^{(1 + \rho)} \tag{4.24}$$

where $P(\mathbf{c})$ is an arbitrary probability assignment that $\mathbf{c}$ is transmitted and $P(\mathbf{r}|\mathbf{c})$ is the conditional probability that $\mathbf{r}$ is received when $\mathbf{c}$ is transmitted. Also, it has been proved that $\bar{P}_{e,c}$ can approach zero exponentially by increasing the block length n for any rate $R < C$ (see Section 4.14).

4.13.2 Convolutional Codes Error Probability

Referring to *convolutional codes* on a DMC, the aim of the decoder is to reconstruct the transmitted sequence (the *particular* path in the tree diagram) from the received sequence. For example, with the Viterbi decoding algorithm the decoder chooses the path in the tree that differs in the minimum number of symbols from the received sequence. At a given node level, this minimum-distance path is referred to as the *survivor*. It is not necessary to consider the entire received sequence at one time, but we can consider the survivor after m time units and then we can proceed step by step through the received sequence. If no decoding error occurs, then the survivor will coincide step by step with the *particular* path in the tree representing the actually transmitted sequence [16].

Hence, the *first-event error probability* P_f is defined as the probability that the *correct path* is excluded for the first time at a certain step, while the *bit error probability* P_b is defined as the expected ratio between the number of bit errors and the total number of transmitted bits up to that step.

As for block codes, the probabilities P_f and P_b can be upperbounded by considering the ensemble of all possible time-varying convolutional codes of memory m. This ensemble could be obtained by randomly varying the transfer functions $G_s^{(j)}(D)$ after each shift in the registers of the encoder. As a consequence, the sequence belonging to each branch of the tree becomes a random binary vector of dimension N_0. This random selection process can be measured by a proper function $f(\mathbf{s})$ of the sequence $\mathbf{s}$ belonging to each branch.

Then, by averaging the P_f of the ensemble, it is possible to derive the following upper bounds:

$$\bar{P}_f < \frac{2^{-m[E_u(R)/R]}}{1 - 2^{-\delta(R)}} (2^{k_0} - 1)$$

$$\bar{P}_b < \frac{2^{-m[E_u(R)/R]}}{[1 - 2^{-\delta(R)}]^2} \frac{(2^{k_0} - 1)}{k_0} \tag{4.25}$$

where

$$E_u(R) = \begin{cases} R_0, & 0 \le R < R_0 \\ E_0(\rho), & R_0 \le R < C, \end{cases} \quad 0 < \rho \le 1$$

$$\delta(R) = \begin{cases} R_0/R - 1, & 0 < R < R_0 \\ E_0(\rho)/R - \rho, & R_0 \le R < C, \end{cases} \quad 0 < \rho < 1$$

with R_0 and $E_0(\rho)$ defined as follows:

$$R_0 \triangleq -\frac{k_0}{N_0} \log_2 \left\{ \sum_r \left[\sum_s f(s)P(r|s)^{1/2} \right]^2 \right\}$$

$$E_0(\rho) \triangleq -\frac{k_0}{N_0} \log_2 \left\{ \sum_r \left[\sum_s f(s)P(r|s)^{1/1+\rho} \right]^{1+\rho} \right\}, \quad 0 < \rho \le 1$$

(4.26)

In these definitions $f(s)$ is the random-process measure; $P(r|s)$ the conditional probability that the sequence r is received when s is transmitted and ρ an arbitrary parameter for minimizing the bound. Also in this case, we remember that at least one code in the ensemble performs as the average and hence (4.25) are to be considered as the upper bounds for the *best* convolutional code of given memory m.

4.14 The Reliability Function E(R)

A development of (4.24) shows that the error probability can asymptotically approach zero by increasing the block length n for any rate $R < C$. This feature is specified and measured by introducing the so-called *reliability function* (or error exponent) $E(R)$. We mention the fundamental conclusions of this topic referring to the binary case and block codes, but they are substantially valid also for any q-ary alphabet and for tree or convolutional codes (Section 4.15).

The *reliability function* is defined as:

$$E(R) \triangleq \lim_{n \to \infty} (1/n)[-\log_2 P_e(n, R)], \qquad R = k/n \qquad (4.27)$$

where $P_e(n, R)$ is the error probability of the *best* code in the ensemble of all the (n, R) codes, or $P_e(n, R)$ is the minimum of the possible error probabilities of the codes belonging to this ensemble.

In other words, we find that, for any rate $R < C$, there exists a finite and positive number $E(R)$ as the exponent with which the error probability vanishes when the block length n goes to infinity or that $P_e(n, R)$ behaves as $2^{-nE(R)}$ for large n. Now, it can be shown [1] that generally $E(R)$ is uniquely known only in a range $R_{cr} \le R \le C$ while, for $0 \le R \le R_{cr}$, $E(R)$ can be only lower and upper bounded respectively by the *random-coding exponent* $E_r(R)$

and by the *sphere-packing exponent* $E_s(R)$. As a consequence, in this range the error probability will be, respectively, upper bounded and lower bounded for large n.

4.14.1   Random-Coding Exponent and Upper Bound on Error Probability

Let us consider the ensemble of (n, R) block codes in the binary case on a DMC with certain transition probabilities. Each digit of each code word is independently selected with a certain probability assignment and any code word belonging to a certain code can be randomly chosen among the 2^{nR} possible code words. Then, it can be shown that for each message the *ensemble average probability* $\bar{P}_{ens}$ of decoding error using maximum likelihood decoding is such that

$$\bar{P}_{ens} \le 2^{-nE_r(R)} = 2^{-(k/R)E_r(R)} \tag{4.28}$$

in the limit of n going to infinity. At least one code of the ensemble must have an error probability as small as the average and hence the bound will be an *upper bound* for the error probability of the best code or of the code with minimum P_e.

4.14.2   Sphere-Packing Exponent and Lower Bound on Error Probability

Let us consider any (n, R) block code on a DMC with certain transition probabilities and let us suppose that all code words are used with the *same* probability. This latter condition is necessary because a nonzero lower bound on P_e would not be possible if, for example, one code word is used with probability 1. Then it can be proved that for *any* (n, R) code the error probability P_e is such that

$$P_e \ge 2^{-nE_s(R)} = 2^{-(k/R)E_s(R)} \tag{4.29}$$

in the limit of n going to infinity.

Now, it is found that generally in any channel there exists a rate R_{cr} such that $E_r(R) = E_s(R) = E(R)$, for $R_{cr} \le R \le C$. In this range, the $P_e(n, R)$ of the best code approaches zero exponentially, with exponent $E(R)$ as n goes to infinity. In the range $0 \le R < R_{cr}$, the exponent $E(R)$ is not uniquely known, being $E_r(R) \le E(R) \le E_s(R)$, and hence the asymptotical behaviour of $P_e(n, R)$ can be only upper bounded and lower bounded, respectively, by assuming $E_r(R)$ or $E_s(R)$ as error exponents. However, we can affirm that the reliability function $E(R)$ is a positive and nonincreasing function of R from $E(0) > 0$ to $E(C) = 0$. A typical behavior of $E(R)$ for block codes in a BSC is plotted in Fig. 4.10.

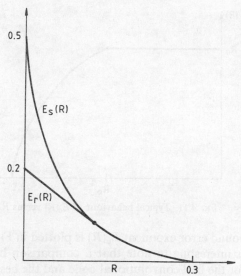

FIG. 4.10. Behaviour of $E(R)$ versus R for a BSC.

4.15   The Computational Cutoff Rate

The asymptotical behaviour of error probabilities in convolutional codes is obtainable in the limit of m going to infinity. As the memory becomes as large as possible, N_A (the actual constraint length, analogous to the block length) also goes to infinity.

It can be shown [16] that there also exists error exponents in the convolutional case. In fact, as m becomes very large, it has been proved that we can choose ρ in (4.25) in such a way that denominators are non zero and numerators are minimized. Then $\bar{P}_f$ and $\bar{P}_b$ are exponentially decreasing to zero as m goes to infinity, for any rate $R < C$, according to:

$$\bar{P}_f < F \, 2^{-(m/R)E_u(R)}$$
$$\bar{P}_b < B \, 2^{-(m/R)E_u(R)} \qquad (4.30)$$

where F and B are constants and $E_u(R)$, the error exponent, is given by (4.25). It is clear that (4.30) is analogous to (4.28) of the previous section for block codes.

Moreover, it can be proved in this case that $\bar{P}_f$ and $\bar{P}_b$ are lower bounded in their asymptotical behaviour for m going to infinity:

$$\bar{P}_b > \bar{P}_f > 2^{-(m/R)E_l(R)} \qquad (4.31)$$

where the error exponent $E_l(R) = E_u(R)$ for $R_0 < R < C$ and $E_l(R) > E_u(R)$ for $R < R_0$. In other words, it is the same situation that happens for $E_s(R)$ and $E_r(R)$ in block codes around R_{cr}.

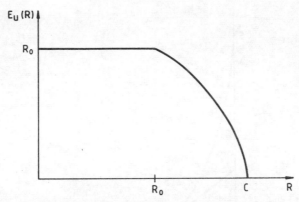

FIG. 4.11. Typical behaviour of $E_u(R)$ versus R.

The upper bound error exponent $E_u(R)$ is plotted in Fig. 4.11 in its typical behaviour. It is interesting to note that a comparison between the asymptotical results for the best convolutional code and the best block code would be favourable to the former (for very noisy channels, in particular); i.e., $E_u(R)$ is generally greater than $E_r(R)$ and the best convolutional code performs better asymptotically.

Now, a discussion on (4.25) emphasizes that the error exponent $E_u(R)$ is constant and equal to R_0 given by (4.26) for $0 \leq R \leq R_0$. Moreover, the error exponent $E_u(R) = E_0(\rho)$, for $R_0 \leq R < C$, decreases to zero as R approaches C and $E_0(\rho) = R_0$ for $\rho = 1$. Notice that R_0 is also important from the viewpoint of the decoding implementation complexity. It has been proved that an MLD decoding system is reasonably feasible only for $m < 10$. Longer memories are necessary at high rates for low error probabilities. However, in these cases, a sequential decoder (see Chapter 5) is more efficient. Moreover, the computation complexity in decoding at high rates and in noisy channels becomes prohibitive. It can be shown that the average number of incorrect paths to be searched in sequential decoding is bounded only for $R < R_0$. For this reason, the rate R_0 given by (4.26) is referred to as the *computational cutoff rate* and it can be shown that in memoryless channels R_0 depends on the random-process measure and on the channel.

4.16 A Discussion on the Noisy-Channel Coding Theorem

The topics of the previous sections lead to the well-known *noisy-channel coding theorem* (the so-called *second theorem of Shannon*) and it is possible to emphasize some important *practical* consequences derived from the communication *principles* which are stated in this theorem. We omit any proof of the theorem, as a well known bibliography exists on this subject. Moreover, we refer the statement of the theorem to block coding without loss of generality.

The noisy channel coding theorem can be stated as follows. Let us consider a channel with input alphabet $A = \{a_1, a_2, \ldots, a_q\}$ and output alphabet $B = \{b_1, b_2, \ldots, b_j\}$, and with a channel capacity C. Let ε be an arbitrary and positive number and $M = q^{n(C-\varepsilon)}$. Then, if n is sufficiently high, it is possible to choose M code words among the possible q^n code words in order to represent M equiprobable messages and in such a way that the error probability in decoding is less than ε.

Referring this statement to the binary block coding of the previous sections and in particular to (4.21) and (4.22), the request that $M = 2^{n(C-\varepsilon)}$ requires that

$$M = 2^k = 2^{nR} < 2^{nC} \qquad (4.32)$$

or that

$$R < C \qquad (4.33)$$

In other words, the code rate must not reach or exceed the capacity of the channel. Under such a condition and *without* an unlimited lowering of R, a proper coding is possible for which the error probability in decoding is arbitrarily small (or less than *any prefixed* ε, as we emphasized in Section 4.14).

The situation can be visualized as in Fig. 4.12 where the stated bound on error probability is plotted versus R. Given an $\varepsilon > 0$, the error probability can be arbitrarily small for $0 < R < C$, i.e., for such an R it can be $P_e < \varepsilon$.

On the contrary, for $R > C$, the error probability P_e is greater than ε and cannot drop down the bound. Hence, it is *not* necessary to have an arbitrarily

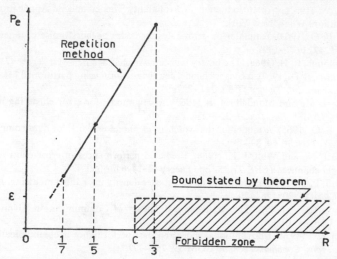

FIG. 4.12. Behaviour of P_e versus R in comparison with the repetition method.

small R for an unlimited lowering of P_e (as in the repetition method), but only that $R < C$. This is the fundamental result of Shannon's Second Theorem. However, it can be noted that in the theorem statement, we have spoken of a *sufficiently* *high* word length n.

We observe that since $M = 2^{nR}$, there is an exponential increase of M for a fixed R (even if $R < C$). Then there is an increase of complexity in the encoding–decoding system. We have recalled this problem as a practical price to be paid to the suggestive principle that an unlimited reliability be possible in transmission without a decrease of the code rate R. However, we must emphasize that the *existence* of a proper code is shown in the proof of the coding theorem and not *how* this code must be.

In this sense, we can affirm that since 1948, all the work of the coders was devoted to better meet this theorem from which, however, a proper code is not derivable.

References

1. Viterbi, A. J., and Omura, J. K. (1979). "Principles of Digital Communications and Coding." McGraw Hill, New York.
2. Gallager, R. G. (1968). "Information Theory and Reliable Communication." Wiley, New York.
3. Wolfowitz, J. (1967). Memory increases capacity, *Information Control* 11, 423–428.
4. Kanal, L. N., and Sastry, A. R. (1978). Models for channels with memory, *Proc. IEEE* 66, 724–744.
5. Haddad, A., Tsai, S., Goldberg, B., and Ranieri G. C. (1975). Markov gap models for real communication channels, *IEEE Trans. Commun.* COM-23 1189–1197.
6. Gilbert, E. N. (1960). Capacity of a burst-noise channel, *Bell Sys. Tech. J.* 39, 1253–1266.
7. Feller, W. (1957). "An Introduction to Probability Theory and its Applications." Vol. 1, 2nd edition. Wiley, New York.
8. Elliot, E. O. (1963). Estimates on error rates for codes on burst-noise channels, *Bell Syst. Tech. J.* 42, 1977–1997.
9. McCullough, R. H. (1968). The binary regenerative channel, *Bell Syst. Tech.* 47, 1713–1735.
10. Fritchman, B. D. (1967). A binary channel characterization using partitioned Markov chains, *IEEE Trans. Inf. Theory* IT-13, 221–227.
11. Berger, J. M., and Mandelbrot, B. (1963). A new model for error clustering in telephone circuits, *IBM J. Res. Dev.* 7, 224–236.
12. Elliot, E. O. (1965). A model for the switched telephone network for data communications, *Bell Syst. Tech. J.* 44, 89–119.
13. Muntuer, N., and Wolf, J. K. (1968). Predicted performances of error control techniques over real channels, *IEEE Trans. Inf. Theory* IT-14, 640–650.
14. Adoul, J. P. A. (1974). Error intervals and cluster density in channel modeling, *IEEE Trans. Inf. Theory* IT-20, 125–129.
15. Shannon C. E. (1949). "The Mathematical Theory of Communication." Univ. of Illinois Press, Urbana, Illinois.
16. Viterbi, A. J. (1971). Convolutional codes and their performance in communication systems, *IEEE Trans. Commun. Technol.* COM-19, 751–772.

Chapter 5

Error Control Coding Techniques

G. BENELLI

Dipartimento di Ingegneria Elettronica
Università di Firenze
Florence, Italy

C. BIANCIARDI

Ministero Pubblica Istruzione
Siena, Italy
and Dipartimento di Ingegneria Elettronica
Università di Firenze
Florence, Italy

V. CAPPELLINI

Dipartimento di Ingegneria Elettronica
Università di Firenze
and Istituto di Ricerca sulle Onde Elettromagnetiche
Consiglio Nazionale delle Ricerche
Florence, Italy

5.1 Introduction

This chapter is devoted to several general considerations concerning the structure and the implementation of *error-correcting and/or error-detecting codes*. Although some of the material has theoretical value only, some of the codes described herein are actually being used in real systems. For many codes, e.g., BCH codes, the highly sophisticated mathematical structure on

109

DATA COMPRESSION AND ERROR CONTROL
TECHNIQUES WITH APPLICATIONS

which they are based sharply contrasts with the relative simplicity of implementation. All of the codes introduced here and later are seen from the viewpoint of channel encoding and not of source encoding. Moreover, the assumption will always be made that the information to be transmitted through the channel is equally important to the information user; as a consequence, all (binary) digits sent to the channel encoder must be protected against noise and all (binary) digits sent through the channel are relevant to the decoder, whose task is to recover the original sequence from the received one. An important parameter, measuring the amount of success obtained by the coder–decoder pair, is the *probability of an error after decoding*.

In what follows, the underlying model to which we refer is the classical communication-system model represented in Fig. 5.1. This model appears oversimplified if compared with any real communication system, but we note that much can be said about a communication system by referring to Fig. 5.1 (see also Chapter 1). Shannon first pointed out the theoretical interrelationships existing among the characteristics of source and channel and the possibility of errorless decoding (Chapter 4).

Although this theory was of fundamental importance from a general and theoretical point of view, it did not indicate how a data transmission system should be designed. In all practical cases, the problem arises of correcting and/or detecting the errors introduced by the channel and of finding the encoding–decoding system that yields the best performance (in the sense of error probability minimization). First of all, it is obvious that the correction of certain error patterns implies their detection, and, hence, error correction techniques are more sophisticated than error detection techniques. However, we observe that there is no sharp distinction between error detecting codes and error correcting codes. Two classes of real channels have tremendously influenced the trends of the research on coding theory in the past, e.g., the space channel in which the noise affects symbols independently, one from another, and the telephone lines, troposcatter channels and HF radio links in which the noise introduces errors in "bursts" (Chapter 4).

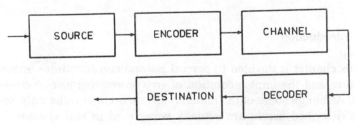

Fig. 5.1. Block diagram of a communication system.

Accordingly some classes of codes have been constructed possessing a certain capability of detecting and correcting random errors and/or burst errors. When a feedback channel is available, it is possible to use these codes in conjunction with retransmission.

In the past 25 years or so, coding theorists devoted great efforts to devise codes and encoding–decoding techniques attractive both from a theoretical and practical point of view. Essentially, two families of codes resulted from this effort, *block codes* and *convolutional codes*, each of them with its own literature and enthusiasts. Moreover, we note that convolutional coding presented a *dichotomy* which was originated by almost independent developments of *sequential decoding* by Wozencraft and *threshold decoding* by Massey (see later in this chapter).

We may assert that all encoding–decoding procedures invented so far are a combination of these basic codes, namely block codes (especially *cyclic codes*) and convolutional codes with sequential and threshold decoding. It is, therefore, reasonable to provide a brief survey of these basic codes without giving too many details. The error detecting and correcting ability of the codes will be considered later on.

5.2 Linear Codes

Linear codes are generally defined in some finite field or Galois field with q elements (Appendix 1). The number q is often chosen to be a power of a prime number; in many cases the transmission is of a binary type and therefore $q = 2$. At the same time, a *metric* or distance must be defined in order to characterize the error-detecting or correcting capability of a linear code. Given a set X of vectors $\mathbf{v}_i$ with n components $(i = 1, 2, \ldots, N)$, a metric is defined over this set if there exists a real-valued function $d(\mathbf{x}_i, \mathbf{x}_j)$ such that:

(1) $d(x_i, x_j) \geq 0$ with the equality if and only if $x_i = x_j$ (positive axiom);
(2) $d(x_i, x_j) = d(x_j, x_i)$ (symmetry axiom);
(3) $d(x_i, x_j) \leq d(x_i, x_k) + d(x_k, x_j)$ (triangle inequality).

The best known and most-used metric [1] in channel coding theory is the *Hamming distance*. Given two vectors $\mathbf{x}_i = (x_{i,1}, x_{i,2}, \ldots, x_{i,n})$ and $\mathbf{x}_j = (x_{j,1}, x_{j,2}, \ldots, x_{j,n})$ with n components, the Hamming distance $d_{\mathrm{H}}(\mathbf{x}_i, \mathbf{x}_j)$ is defined as the number of positions in which they differ, i.e.,

$$d_{\mathrm{H}}(\mathbf{x}_i, \mathbf{x}_j) = \sum_{k=1}^{n} \delta(x_{ik}, x_{jk}) \tag{5.1}$$

where

$$\delta(x_{ik}, x_{jk}) = \begin{cases} 0 & \text{if} \quad x_{i,k} = x_{j,k} \\ 1 & \text{if} \quad x_{i,k} \neq x_{j,k} \end{cases} \tag{5.2}$$

The *Hamming weight* $w(\mathbf{x}_i)$ of the vector $\mathbf{x}_i$ is defined as the number of non-zero components of $\mathbf{x}_i$. The Hamming distance between two vectors $\mathbf{x}_i$ and $\mathbf{x}_j$ is also equal to the Hamming weight of the vector $\mathbf{x}_i - \mathbf{x}_j$, i.e.,

$$d_{\mathrm{H}}(\mathbf{x}_i, \mathbf{x}_j) = w(\mathbf{x}_i - \mathbf{x}_j) \tag{5.3}$$

It can be proved that a code having a Hamming distance d_{H} can detect all the error patterns of $d_{\mathrm{H}} - 1$ or less random errors, and can correct all the error patterns of $(d_{\mathrm{H}} - 1)/2$ or less random errors, where $[x]$ denotes the least integer less than x.

A linear code can be characterized through the following definition

DEFINITION 5.2.1　Given the vector space of n-tuples V, a linear block code C of type (n, k) is a subspace of V with dimension k.

From this definition, any linear block code (n, k) can be defined by any set of k linearly independent vectors of the subspace C. Any code word of C can be written as a combination of these k independent vectors. In order to simplify the notation, a linear code C is defined through a matrix G called the *generator matrix* of C. This matrix has k rows and n columns; its rows are any set of k independent vectors of C.

If $\mathbf{i}$ is a block of k information symbols generated by the source, then the corresponding codeword $\mathbf{c}$ is a vector with n components which can be computed by using

$$\mathbf{c} = \mathbf{i}G = \sum_{l=1}^{k} i_l \mathbf{g}_l \tag{5.4}$$

where i_l is the lth information symbol $(1 \le l \le k)$ and $\mathbf{g}_l$ the lth row of the generator matrix G.

A code can also be defined in an alternative way, through its null subspace. If C is a code (n, k), then C is a subspace of dimension k, its null space C' is a subspace of dimension $n - k$. A vector $\mathbf{c}_1$ is in the subspace C', if and only if

$$\mathbf{c} \cdot \mathbf{c}_1 = 0 \tag{5.5}$$

where $\mathbf{c}$ is any vector of the code C. The subspace C' can be defined by a basis of $n - k$ independent vectors. These vectors are considered as the rows of a matrix H, called the *parity-check matrix* of the code C; the matrix H is formed by $(n - k)$ rows and n columns. If $\mathbf{c}$ is a code word of the code C, then it must result that

$$c \cdot H^{\mathrm{T}} = 0 \tag{5.6}$$

If $\mathbf{c} = (c_0, c_1, \ldots, c_{n-1})$, then (5.6) can be also written as

$$\sum_{i=0}^{n-1} c_i \mathbf{h}_i = 0 \tag{5.7}$$

where $\mathbf{h}_i$ is the ith column of the matrix H. Naturally, each row of the matrix G is *orthogonal* to the rows of the matrix H and, therefore, it results in

$$G \cdot H^{\mathrm{T}} = 0 \qquad (5.8)$$

The parity-check matrix of a linear code is very useful in order to characterize the properties of the code itself.

THEOREM 5.2.1   Let C be a linear block code having the parity-check matrix H. Then for each codeword $\mathbf{c}$ with Hamming weight w, a linear dependence among w columns of H exists. Conversely, for each linear dependence among w columns of H, a code word with Hamming weight w exists.

From this theorem, we arrive at the following corollary, which permits us to establish the Hamming distance of a code.

COROLLARY 5.2.1   A linear block code, having a parity-check matrix H, has a Hamming distance equal to w if and only if every combination of $w - 1$ or fewer columns of H is linearly independent.

A code is called *systematic* if the first k symbols of its code words are equal to the information symbols and the remaining $(n - k)$ symbols are the redundancy symbols. We prove this in the following theorem.

THEOREM 5.2.2   Every linear code can be reduced to a systematic form. For a systematic code the generator matrix and the parity-check matrix can be put in the following form:

$$\begin{aligned} G &= [I_k, P] \\ H &= [-P^{\mathrm{T}}, I_{n-k}] \end{aligned} \qquad (5.9)$$

where I_k and I_{n-k} are the identity matrices with order $k \times k$ and $(n - k) \times (n - k)$ respectively, and P is a $k \times (n - k)$ matrix, which characterizes the particular code.

If we denote with $\mathbf{c}$ the transmitted code word, the received vector $\mathbf{r}$ is

$$\mathbf{r} = \mathbf{c} + \mathbf{e} \qquad (5.10)$$

where $\mathbf{e}$ is a vector, called *error vector*, with n components whose ith component is equal to 0 if the ith component of the vector $\mathbf{r}$ does not contain any error, while it is equal to 1 in the opposite case.

In order to detect or correct the errors introduced by the communication channel, we first compute the *syndrome* vector $\mathbf{s}$ with $n - k$ components at the receiver, defined as

$$\mathbf{s} = \mathbf{r} \cdot H^{\mathrm{T}} = (\mathbf{c} + \mathbf{e}) \cdot H^{\mathrm{T}} = \mathbf{e} \cdot H^{\mathrm{T}} \qquad (5.11)$$

If **s** is equal to zero, the received vector is assumed correct and accepted. In the opposite case, errors are detected in **r**. Therefore, errors are not detected if they transform the transmitted vector **c** in another code word.

Let C be a linear code (n, k) defined in a field with q elements and let $c_1, c_2, \ldots, c_{q^k}$ be its code words. A very useful table in the study of the properties of a code and for its decoding is the *standard array*, [1] which can be formed as in Table 5.1. The standard array has 2^{n-k} rows and 2^k columns in the binary case; each row is called a *coset*, while the first element of a coset is called a *coset leader*.

The standard array is used both for error correction and for characterizing the properties and performance of a linear code. The decoding operation, by using the standard array, is generally performed in the following way. If a vector $\mathbf{r} = \mathbf{c}_j + \mathbf{e}_l$ with $1 \leq j \leq 2^k$ and $0 \leq l \leq (2^{n-k} - 1)$ is received, then this vector is decoded in the code word $\mathbf{c}_j$, which lies in the same column of $\mathbf{r}$; therefore, the received vector is correctly decoded only if the error pattern introduced by the communication channel is $\mathbf{e}_l = \mathbf{r} - \mathbf{c}_j$, i.e., only if the error pattern is a coset leader.

Using this decoding rule, it is convenient to choose the coset leaders as the more probable error patterns introduced by the communication channel. For example, in the case of a binary symmetric channel (BSC), the error patterns with low Hamming weights are the more probable and, therefore, must be chosen as coset leaders in order to minimize the mean error probability. If P is the bit error probability of the BSC, then the probability P_c of correct decoding for a code with code word length n is

$$P_c = \sum_{i=1}^{n} \alpha_i p^i q^{n-i} \tag{5.12}$$

where $q = 1 - p$ and α_i is the number of coset leaders with Hamming weight i.

If a linear code must correct all the configurations of t or less random errors (t being any one integer), then all vectors with Hamming weight t or less must be coset leaders in the standard array. Therefore, in the general case,

TABLE 5.1. Standard array of a linear code $(n - k)$.

		$\longleftarrow$ 2^k columns $\longrightarrow$		
$\uparrow$	$c_1 = 0$	c_2	c_3	$\cdots$	c_{2^k}
2^{n-k}	e_1	$c_2 + e_2$	$c_3 + e_1$	$\cdots$	$c_{2^k} + e_1$
	e_2	$c_2 + e_2$	$c_3 + e_2$	$\cdots$	$c_{2^k} + e_2$
rows	$\vdots$	$\vdots$	$\vdots$	$\cdots$	$\vdots$
$\downarrow$	$e_{2^{n-k}-1}$	$c_2 + e_{2^{n-k}-1}$	$c_3 + e_{2^{n-k}-1}$	$\cdots$	$c_{2^k} + e_{2^{n-k}-1}$

the number of cosets q^{n-k} must be equal to or greater than the number of error patterns with weight t or less; the Hamming upper bound on the redundancy $n - k$, required to construct a block code with length n able to correct t or less random errors, can be obtained as follows [1,2]:

$$n - k \geq \log_q\left[1 + \binom{n}{1}(q - 1) + \binom{n}{2}(q - 1)^2 + \cdots + \binom{n}{t}(q - 1)^t\right] \quad (5.13)$$

The standard array is often impractical because of its high dimensions; nevertheless, it can be related to the syndrome vector **s** defined by (5.11) and in this way can be used for error correction. In fact, the following can be proved.

THEOREM 5.2.3 Two vectors r_1 and r_2 are in the same coset, if and only if their syndromes are equal and vice versa.

Using this theorem, each syndrome pattern is related to a particular coset and the decoding operation is greatly simplified. From the received vector we first compute the syndrome **s** and determine the coset corresponding to this syndrome; then, the error pattern is assumed to be equal to the leader of this coset.

5.3 Hamming Codes

Historically, the first class of linear block codes was proposed by Hamming in 1950 [4]. The binary Hamming code is characterized by a parity matrix H with h rows and $(2^h - 1)$ columns where the column vectors are all the h-tuples except the all-zero h-tuple. Hence, it is not possible to obtain a linear combination of two columns that is zero. As we have seen in Section 5.1, the null space of this matrix has minimum weight 3 and hence, the binary Hamming code is capable of correcting all single errors in a word.

The code vectors are such that $n = (2^h - 1)$ and $k = (2^h - 1 - h)$ for the code length and for the number of information digits in a word, respectively. This code has a standard array in such a way that the all-zero vectors and all single-error pattern vectors are coset leaders. It is possible to generalize the Hamming codes in two ways. First, by reaching any length n different by $2^h - 1$. This is done by considering the smallest h such that $n \leq (2^h - 1)$ and simply by omitting the columns exceeding the nth and second, by extending the code to fields with $q > 2$. It can be shown that in this case $n = (q^h - 1)/(q - 1)$ in order to conserve the linear independence of any two columns. The generalized Hamming codes can be used both for random-error correction in the field of q elements and for burst-error correction by writing any q element in binary form.

5.4 Cyclic Codes

Cyclic codes represent one of the most applied and powerful classes of codes, because they are relatively simple to implement and, at the same time, they include many codes with good error-detecting or correcting capabilities [1, 2, 4].

DEFINITION 5.4.1   A block code C of type (n, k) is a cyclic code if, for each code word c_1 in the code

$$c_1 = (c_0, c_1, \ldots, c_{n-1}) \tag{5.14}$$

all the vectors obtained from c_1 by cyclic shifts, i.e.,

$$c_2 = (c_{n-1}, c_0, c_1, \ldots, c_{n-2})$$

$$c_3 = (c_{n-2}, c_{n-1}, c_0, c_1, \ldots, c_{n-3}) \tag{5.15}$$

$$\vdots$$

$$c_n = (c_1, c_2, \ldots, c_{n-1}, c_0)$$

are code words of C.

To each codeword $c_1 = (c_0, c_1, \ldots, c_{n-1})$ it is useful to associate a polynomial of degree equal to or less than $(n - 1)$:

$$c_1(x) = c_0 + c_1 x + \cdots + c_{n-1} x^{n-1} \tag{5.16}$$

These polynomials are taken modulo $(x^n - 1)$; then the successive cyclic shifts of c_1 are associated with the polynomials $x c_1(x), x^2 c_1(x), \cdots, x^{n-1} c_1(x)$.

Cyclic codes are block codes and, therefore, can be described by the generator matrix G or the parity-check matrix H, as outlined in the previous section. Moreover, their particular structure also permits a different description and a simpler implementation. In particular, a cyclic code (n, k) can be defined through a particular polynomial $g(x)$ of degree $n - k$, called the *generator polynomial*. This polynomial must be a divisor of $(x^n - 1)$ and is the lowest-degree polynomial in the code. The k polynomials $g(x), x g(x),$ $x^2 g(x), \ldots, x^{k-1} g(x)$ are linearly independent and, therefore, can be taken as the basis vectors which define the considered code; the generator matrix G for this code is

$$G = \begin{bmatrix} x^{k-1} g(x) \\ \vdots \\ x^2 g(x) \\ x g(x) \\ g(x) \end{bmatrix} \tag{5.17}$$

If $\mathbf{i} = (i_1, i_2, \ldots, i_k)$ is the information vector, then from (5.4) the corresponding code word $c(x)$ in a cyclic code with a generator matrix G of the form (5.17) is

$$c(x) = i_1 x^{k-1} g(x) + i_2 x^{k-2} g(x) + \cdots + i_k g(x)$$
$$= g(x)[i_1, x^{k-1} + i_2 x^{k-2} + \cdots + i_k] = g(x)a(x) \tag{5.18}$$

where $c(x)$ is the polynomial associated to the code word and

$$a(x) = i_1 x^{k-1} + i_2 x^{k-2} + \cdots + i_k \tag{5.19}$$

Therefore, each code word in a cyclic code is represented by a polynomial which is a multiple of the generator polynomial $g(x)$.

A cyclic code C can be also described through the *parity-check polynomial* defined as

$$h(x) = (x^n - 1)/g(x) \tag{5.20}$$

Such a polynomial has degree k and generates the null space of the code C. Naturally, it results in

$$g(x)h(x) = 0 \bmod(x^n - 1) \tag{5.21}$$

and, therefore, if $c(x) = a(x)g(x)$ is a code word of the code C, then

$$c(x)h(x) = a(x)g(x)h(x) = 0 \bmod(x^n - 1) \tag{5.22}$$

The parity-check polynomial is orthogonal to any code word in the code C.

When a systematic cyclic code is considered, the following convention is generally used. In the code word $c(x)$ the coefficients of $x^{n-1}, x^{n-2}, \ldots, x^{n-k}$ represent the k information symbols to be encoded, while the coefficients of $x^{n-k-1}, x^{n-k-2}, \ldots, x^2, x, 1$ represent the redundancy symbols.

The encoding procedure in a cyclic code can be accomplished in the following way. Let $\mathbf{i}$ be the information vector $\mathbf{i} = (i_1, i_2, \ldots, i_k)$ and $i(x)$ the information polynomial of the form

$$i(x) = i_1 x^{n-1} + i_2 x^{n-2} + \cdots + i_k x^{n-k} \tag{5.23}$$

Then if $i(x)$ is divided for the generator polynomial $g(x)$ of the code, we obtain

$$i(x) = q(x)g(x) + r(x) \tag{5.24}$$

where $q(x)$ and $r(x)$ are the quotient and the remainder, respectively. The remainder $r(x)$ naturally has degree $(n - k - 1)$ or less. Then

$$i(x) - r(x) = q(x)g(x) \tag{5.25}$$

and $i(x) - r(x)$, being a polynomial multiple of $g(x)$, is a code word, in which $i(x)$ is due to the information symbols, while the coefficients of the polynomial $-r(x)$ give the redundancy symbols.

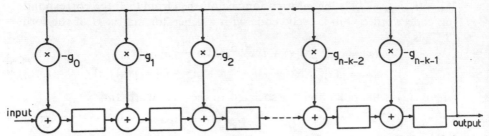

FIG. 5.2. Encoder scheme for a cyclic code; $g_0, g_1, \ldots, g_{n-k-1}$ are the coefficients of the generator polynomial $g(x)$.

The encoding procedure in a cyclic code consists of the computation of the remainder $r(x)$ and can be easily implemented by the circuit shown in Fig. 5.2. The circuit is formed by a shift register with $(n-k)$ stages and performs the division of $i(x)$ by the generator polynomial

$$g(x) = g_0 + g_1 x + \cdots + g_{n-k-1} x^{n-k-1} + x^{n-k} \tag{5.26}$$

The k information symbols followed by $n-k$ symbols equal to zero are entered (one for each shift) in the shift register; after n shifts the symbols contained in the $n-k$ stages of the circuit are the coefficients of the remainder $+r(x)$ and, therefore, are the redundancy symbols.

EXAMPLE 5.4.1   Let us consider the binary cyclic code $(15, 11)$ generated by the polynomial $g(x) = 1 + x + x^4$. The encoder for this code is shown in Fig. 5.3. The number of shifts necessary to compute the redundancy symbols can be reduced to k shifts by using the circuit shown in Fig. 5.4. In this case, after the k information symbols are entered in the shift register, the $n-k$ redundancy symbols are in the stages of the shift register.

A cyclic code can also be described by assigning the roots in some extended Galois field $GF(q^m)$ of the generator polynomial $g(x)$ defined over $GF(q)$. If $\alpha_1, \alpha_2, \ldots, \alpha_r$ are the roots of $g(x)$, then from (5.25) any code word must have the same roots. We define the *minimum function* $p_i(x)$ of the root α_i as the polynomial with lower degree having α_i as the root. Any polynomial

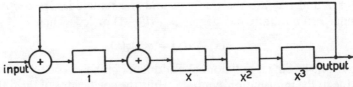

FIG. 5.3. Encoder scheme for the binary cyclic code $(15, 11)$ generated by the polynomial $g(x) = 1 + x + x^4$.

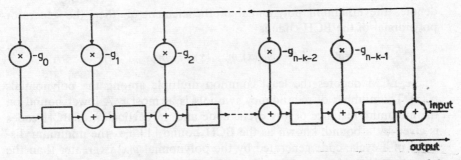

FIG. 5.4. Encoder scheme for a cyclic code; $g_0, g_1, \ldots, g_{n-k-1}$ are the coefficients of the generator polynomial $g(x)$.

$f(x)$, having α_i as the root, is divisible by $p_i(x)$. This is proved in the following theorem.

THEOREM 5.4.1   If $p_i(x)$ is the minimum function of the root α_i, then $\alpha_i^q \alpha_i^{q^2} \cdots \alpha_i^{q^{m-1}}$ are roots of $p_i(x)$ also.

The generator polynomial $g(x)$ of a code can be found once its roots are known. If $\alpha_1, \alpha_2, \ldots, \alpha_r$ are the roots of $g(x)$, then

$$g(x) = \text{LCM}[p_1(x), p_2(x), \ldots, p_r(x)] \qquad (5.27)$$

where LCM denotes the least common multiple. If two roots, for example α_i and α_e, have the same minimum functions, i.e., $p_i(x) = p_e(x)$, then the polynomial $p_i(x)$ is considered only once. The parity-check matrix H of this code is

$$H = \begin{bmatrix} \alpha_1^{n-1} & \alpha_1^{n-2} & \cdots & \alpha_1^2 & \alpha_1 & 1 \\ \alpha_2^{n-1} & \alpha_2^{n-2} & \cdots & \alpha_2^2 & \alpha_2 & 1 \\ \alpha_r^{n-1} & \alpha_r^{n-2} & \cdots & \alpha_r^2 & \alpha_r & 1 \end{bmatrix} \qquad (5.28)$$

5.5   Bose–Chaudhuri–Hocquenghem Codes

Among cyclic codes, the class of random-error correcting codes proposed by Hocquenghem [5] and Bose and Chaudhuri [6, 7], called *BCH codes*, is the most powerful and extensive class of cyclic codes. The BCH codes can be described as follows. Let α be an element of $\text{GF}(q^m)$; given two integers r and d_0, the generator polynomial $g(x)$ of lowest degree over $\text{GF}(q)$ having the elements $\alpha^r, \alpha^{r+1}, \ldots, \alpha^{r+d_0-2}$ as roots, defines a BCH code with minimum distance greater than or equal to d_0. The code-word length n of this code is equal to the least common multiple of the orders of the roots. If $m_i(x)$

denotes the minimum polynomial of the element α^r, then the generator polynomial of the BCH code is

$$g(x) = \text{LCM}(m_r(x), m_{r+1}(x), \ldots, m_{r+d_0-2}(x))$$

where LCM denotes the least common multiple among the polynomials $m_i(x)$. The number of redundancy symbols is at most r. A lower bound on the minimum distance of any cyclic code and, in particular, of BCH codes is given by a bound, known as the BCH bound [1], i.e., the minimum distance of a cyclic code generated by the polynomial $g(x)$ is greater than the largest number of consecutive roots of $g(x)$.

The most important subclass of BCH codes is the subclass of binary BCH codes ($q = 2$), having length $n = 2^m - 1$. These codes are called primitive BCH codes. Within this subclass, the more interesting codes have $r = 1$. By denoting with α a primitive element of GF(2^m) and setting $d_0 = 2t + d_1$, the roots of $g(x)$ are $\alpha, \alpha^2, \ldots, \alpha^{d-2}$; moreover, it can be easily shown that $m_i(x) = m_{2i}(x)$ and, therefore, $g(x)$ is given by

$$g(x) = \text{LCM}(m_1(x), m_3(x), \ldots, m_{2t-1}(x)) \tag{5.30}$$

From the previous definitions, the number of redundancy symbols and the true minimum distance are not exactly determined; we know only that $n - k \leq mt$ and the true minimum Hamming distance d is greater than or equal to $d_0 = 2t + 1$. No general formula has been found to determine exactly these two important parameters. Mann [8] and Berlenkamp [3] have found an algebraic procedure for the computation of the number of redundancy (or information) symbols in a BCH code.

The value d_0 represents a lower bound on the real minimum distance d of a BCH code. For many BCH codes, $d = d_0$; many authors have dealt with the problem of finding the true minimum Hamming distance of BCH codes [3, 9–12] and this distance can be exactly determined theoretically for many BCH codes. For brevity, these results are not reported. We recall only that the true minimum distance of a primitive BCH code defined in GF(q) is bounded by

$$d_0 \leq d \leq qd_0 + q - 2 \tag{5.31}$$

In the binary case, the true distance is less than or equal to $2d_0$. It has also been proved that the real minimum distance is equal to the value of the BCH bound for all the primitive BCH codes. Moreover, many non-primitive codes have been determined to have a distance greater than that given by the BCH bound. Another important and popular subclass of BCH codes is the Reed–Solomon subclass of codes. These codes, which are particularly suitable for burst-error correction, are described in Section 5.23.

The algebraic decoding operation of BCH codes has been extensively studied $[1, 3, 13-15]$; in the following, the most popular decoding algorithm derived first by Peterson $[13]$ is briefly described. Let $c(x)$ be the transmitted code word; the received vector $\mathbf{r}(x)$ is

$$\mathbf{r}(x) = c(x) + e(x) \tag{5.32}$$

where $e(x)$ is the error pattern introduced by the transmission channel. The syndrome $s(x)$ in a binary BCH code has $d - 1 = 2t$ components; the ith component s_i can be written as $[1]$

$$s_i = r(\alpha^i) = c(\alpha^i) + e(\alpha^i) = e(\alpha^i) \tag{5.33}$$

where $c(\alpha^i) = 0$, because α^i is a root of all the code words. If the channel introduces $s \leq t$ errors and their positions are denoted with $p_1, p_2, \ldots, p_s$ ($p_i \neq p_j$ for $i \neq j$ and $1 \leq p_i \leq n + 1 - s$), the error polynomial is

$$e(x) = x^{p_1} + x^{p_2} + \cdots + x^{p_s} \tag{5.34}$$

The ith component of the syndrome is

$$s_i = \sum_{j=1}^{s} (\alpha^{p_j})^i, \qquad \text{for} \quad i = 1, 2, \ldots, n - k \tag{5.35}$$

and, in order to correct the errors, the set of $(n - k)$ equations (5.35) for the variables $\alpha^{p_1}, \alpha^{p_2}, \ldots, \alpha^{p_s}$ must be solved.

In general, these equations have many possible solutions, which correspond to different error patterns. If $s \leq t$, then the error pattern introduced by the channel is the solution with the smallest number of errors.

In the following, we define the ith error-location number $\beta_i = \alpha^{p_i}$ for $1 \leq i \leq s$; the jth component of the syndrome is

$$s_j = \sum_{l=1}^{s} \beta_l^j \tag{5.36}$$

The error-location polynomial $\sigma(x)$ is defined as

$$\sigma(x) = \sigma_0 + \sigma_1 x + \cdots + \sigma_s x^s \tag{5.37}$$

where

$$
\begin{aligned}
\sigma_0 &= 1 \\
\sigma_1 &= \beta_1 + \beta_2 + \cdots + \beta_s \\
\sigma_2 &= \beta_1 \beta_2 + \cdots + \beta_1 \beta_s + \beta_2 \beta_3 + \cdots + \beta_2 \beta_s + \cdots + \beta_{s-1} \beta_s \\
\sigma_s &= \beta_1 \beta_2 \cdots \beta_s
\end{aligned}
\tag{5.38}
$$

The syndrome components s_i and the coefficients of $\sigma(x)$ are related. In fact, by setting

$$
\mathbf{s} = \begin{bmatrix} s_1 \\ s_2 \\ \vdots \\ s_{2s-1} \end{bmatrix}, \qquad \boldsymbol{\sigma} = \begin{bmatrix} \sigma_1 \\ \sigma_2 \\ \vdots \\ \sigma_s \end{bmatrix}
$$

$$
M = \left[\begin{array}{cccccc} 1 & 0 & 0 & 0 & 0 & \cdots & 0 \\ s_2 & s_1 & 1 & 0 & 0 & \cdots & 0 \\ s_4 & s_3 & s_2 & s_1 & 1 & \cdots & 0 \\ \hline s_{2s-2} & s_{2s-3} & s_{2s-4} & s_{2s-5} & s_{2s-6} & & s_{s-1} \end{array} \right] \tag{5.39}
$$

we have

$$
\mathbf{s} = M\boldsymbol{\sigma} \tag{5.40}
$$

In the same way, the polynomial $\sigma(x)$ has as roots $\beta_1^{-1}, \beta_2^{-1}, \ldots, \beta_s^{-1}$, i.e., the inverse of the error location numbers. In this way, from the syndrome components s_i, it is possible to compute $\sigma(x)$ and then, also, the error-location number and the error positions. The decoding algorithm of BCH codes is, therefore, composed of three steps:

(1) computation of the syndrome s_i;
(2) computation of σ_i from s_i;
(3) calculation of the error-location number β_j by finding the roots of $\sigma(x)$.

Step 1 can be easily implemented by using shift registers. Step 2 presents the most difficult task in the decoding of BCH codes. An algorithm is now described which was introduced first by Berlenkamp [3] and then modified by Massey [17].

The decoder must evaluate the coefficients σ_i for $1 \le i \le t$, once the syndrome components s_j for $1 \le j \le 2t$ are known. This computation can be performed in a recurrent way. At the mth step, the decoder analyzes the first m power sums and tries to determine a set of l_m values $\sigma_i^{(m)}$, which satisfy the following $m - l_m$ equations:

$$
\sum_{j=0}^{l_m} s_{m-k-j}\sigma_j^{(m)} = 0 \tag{5.41}
$$

for $k = 0, 1, \ldots, m - l_m - 1$, and setting $\sigma_0^{(m)} = 1$. The number l_m is chosen to be as small as possible. In some cases, it may happen that no equation (5.41) is verified for a given m; in this case, $m = l_m$ and any set of l_m can be considered as a solution. The polynomial $\sigma^{(m)}(x)$ is defined as

$$\sigma^{(m)}(x) = \sum_{j=0}^{l_m} \sigma_j^{(m)} x^j \tag{5.42}$$

and has degree l_m or less.

Once $\sigma^{(m)}(x)$ is known, the decoder tries to determine the polynomial $\sigma^{(m+1)}(x)$. In this respect, the mth discrepancy d_m is defined as

$$d_m = \sum_{j=0}^{l_m} s_{m+1-j}\sigma_j^{(m)} \tag{5.43}$$

which is obtained by using the coefficient $\sigma_j^{(m)}$ evaluated at the previous instant. If the discrepancy is equal to zero, then we assume $\sigma^{(n+1)}(x) = \sigma^{(n)}(x)$ and $\sigma^{(n)}(x)$ is a minimal solution also at the instant $(m+1)$. When $d_m \neq 0$, $\sigma^{(m+1)}(x)$ is different from $\sigma^{(m)}(x)$, and $\sigma^{(m+1)}(x)$ is derived by an iterative process, which is briefly described in the following.

Naturally, $\sigma^{(0)}(x) = 1$, and if no errors are introduced by the channel, this is a solution at each step. If s errors occur (with $1 \leq s \leq t$), then at least one of the components s_j must be nonzero. Then we have

$$\sigma^{(0)}(x) = \sigma^{(1)}(x) = \cdots = \sigma^{(j-1)}(x),$$

$$l_0 = l_1 = \cdots = l_{j-1} = 0, \qquad\qquad l_j \neq 0 \tag{5.44}$$

$$d_{j-1} = s_j \neq 0,$$

and $\sigma^{(j)}(x)$ is a nonzero polynomial of degree l_j or less. Then, it can be shown that [3]

$$\sigma^{(j)}(x) = \sigma^{(j-1)}(x) - d_{j-1}x^j\sigma^{(-1)}(x)$$

$$l_j = j \tag{5.45}$$

where

$$\sigma^{(-1)}(x) = 1, \qquad l_{-1} = 0, \qquad d_{-1} = 1$$

$$\sigma^{(0)}(x) = 1, \qquad l_0 = 0, \qquad d_1 = s_1 \tag{5.46}$$

By considering the procedure for the initial conditions, the polynomial $\sigma^{(m+1)}(x)$ can be computed through the following recursive equation:

$$\sigma^{(m+1)}(x) = \sigma^{(m)}(x), \qquad \text{if } l_{m+1} = l_m$$

$$\sigma^{(m+1)}(x) = \sigma^{(m)}(x) - d_m d_r^{-1} x^{m-r}\sigma^{(r)}(x) \tag{5.47}$$

being $\sigma^{(r)}(x)$, for $1 \leq r \leq m$, one of the previous minimal solutions with $d_r \neq 0$ such that $r - l_r$ has the largest value.

In the last step of decoding BCH codes, the error positions must be determined which are the reciprocals of the roots of $\sigma(x)$. The roots of $\sigma(x)$ can be found by substituting $1, \alpha, \alpha^2, \ldots, \alpha^{n-1}$, being $n = 2^m - 1$, in $\sigma(x)$: if $\sigma(\alpha^i) = 0$, then α^i is a root of $\sigma(x)$ and, therefore, α^{n-1} is the position of one error.

A simpler and faster method to find the roots of $\sigma(x)$, has been proposed by Chien [18]. In this method, the received vector is decoded bit-by-bit; in order to decode the jth bit $(1 \leq j \leq n)$, the decoder forms the sum:

$$\sigma_0 + \sigma_1 \alpha^{n-j} + \sigma_2^{2(n-j)} + \cdots + \sigma_{l_n}^{l_n(n-j)} \tag{5.48}$$

If α^{n-j} is a root of $\sigma(x)$, then the previous sum is zero and the jth bit must be corrected.

5.6 Convolutional Codes

In 1955, Elias suggested *convolutional codes* as an extension of the linear block codes to allow memory to be extended from block to block [19]. In fact, we have seen that the parity checks in a block of linear block codes depend only on the information digits in the same block. In other words, the *memory* of the information digits of a certain block is confined to the block itself.

However, it is possible to extend this concept by allowing the information digits in a block to influence not only the block itself but also a certain number of successive blocks. This is the fundamental character of the so called *convolutional codes*.

It is clear that this extension has not only a theoretical, but also a practical value since, at least in principle, it permits the recovery of the information belonging to a block also from successive blocks. On the contrary, the information of a block in block codes is lost with the block itself.

5.7 Convolutional Encoding

A convolutional encoder can be viewed as in Fig. 5.5. The information digits coming from a source enter the encoder, which consists in a linear logic circuit with K_0 registers, each of length m (memory), for the K_0 inputs and the N_0 outputs.

At any *time unit* (the nth in Fig. 5.5) K_0 digits enter the encoder and $N_0 \geq K_0$ digits leave it and are transmitted through the channel. Each information digit entering the encoder remains m time units in the encoder itself and may *affect* the outputs during all these time units; in other words, the

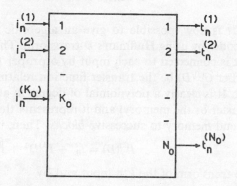

FIG. 5.5. Convolutional encoder.

convolutional encoder is said to be of *memory m*. Hence, the K_0 information digits of an entering block, as the nth of Fig. 5.5 may influence m transmitted blocks, each of N_0 digits. Then, the quantity

$$N_A = mN_0 \tag{5.49}$$

is defined as the *actual constraint length*, which is analogous to the length of a code word in a block-code.[†]

The actual constraint length represents the total number of transmitted digits that may be influenced by one input information digit. In other words, the convolutional coding can be considered as block coding with a block length N_A. In particular, we can extend to convolutional codes the Hamming metric properties just considered for block codes by defining a minimum distance d_{min} among the transmitted blocks of length N_A. Moreover, the error correction and error-detection ability of a general convolutional code can be summarized in the following theorem.

THEOREM 5.7.1   Given a convolutional code of memory m and minimum distance d_{min}, the first block of K_0 input info-digits can be *correctly decoded* if t or fewer channel errors occurred over the first N_A received digits and $(t + 1), (t + 2), \ldots, (t + s)$ errors can be *detected* if and only if

$$(2t + s) \leq d_{min} \tag{5.50}$$

Moreover, note that in convolutional coding the bit rate is defined as

$$R = K_0/N_0 \tag{5.51}$$

and it represents the percentage of information carried out by each transmitted digit.

[†] In fact, it is customary to represent a convolutional code as (mN_0, mK_0).

It is now, possible to give an algebraic description of a convolutional encoder by using Huffman's D-transform. The encoder is such that each output is connected to each input by a proper transfer function.

Let $G_k^{(j)}(D)$ be the transfer function relating the kth input to the jth output. It is clearly a polynomial of degree m at most (the length of each input register or the memory) and it represents the way by which it is possible to extend memory to successive *blocks*. Then, if we indicate by

$$I^{(k)}(D) = i_0^{(k)} + i_1^{(k)}D^1 + i_2^{(k)}D^2 + \cdots \tag{5.52}$$

the transform of the kth input and by

$$T^{(j)}(D) = t_0^{(j)} + t_1^{(j)}D^1 + t_2^{(j)}D^2 + \cdots \tag{5.53}$$

the transform of the jth output[†], there follows the fundamental relationship

$$T^{(j)}(D) = \sum_{k=1}^{K_0} G_{(k)}^{(j)}(D)I^{(k)}(D), \qquad j = 1, 2, \ldots, N_0 \tag{5.54}$$

which connects the jth output to the K_0 inputs at any time unit and which summarizes a suitable algebraic description of a general convolutional code.

Another useful description is presented in Section 5.8 by means of a *tree*. It is now possible to also consider *systematic* codes in the convolutional code case. If we suppose that

$$G_{(k)}^{(j)} = \delta_{jk} \begin{cases} 0 & \text{for } j \neq k, \\ 1 & \text{for } j = k, \end{cases} \qquad j = 1, 2, \ldots, K_0 \tag{5.55}$$

(δ_{jk} of Kronecker) then it follows that

$$T^{(j)}(D) \equiv I^{(j)}(D), \qquad j = 1, 2, \ldots, K_0 \tag{5.56}$$

represents the information sequence transmitted at any instant while $T^{(j)}(D)$, expressed by (5.54) for $K_0 + 1 \leq j \leq N_0$, represents the parity sequence at any instant.

In the same way, the received N_0 sequences can be denoted by

$$R^{(j)}(D) = r_0^{(j)} + r_1^{(j)}D^1 + r_2^{(j)}D^2 + \cdots, \qquad j = 1, 2, \ldots, N_0 \tag{5.57}$$

and the channel-error sequences by

$$E^{(j)}(D) = e_0^{(j)} + e_1^{(j)}D^1 + e_2^{(j)}D^2 + \cdots, \qquad j = 1, 2, \ldots, N_0 \tag{5.58}$$

so that

$$R^{(j)}(D) = T^{(j)}(D) + E^{(j)}(D) \qquad \text{or} \qquad r_n^{(j)} = t_n^{(j)} + e_n^{(j)} \tag{5.59}$$

[†] It is known that the coefficients of polynomials (5.52) and (5.53) are respectively, the input and the transmitted digits at the time units represented by the D-exponents.

if we refer to the jth received digit at the nth unit time. We must remember that memory is m (or memory has order m) means that we agree to decode, for instance, the N_0-tuple transmitted at zero instant or to estimate $e_0^{(j)}$ ($j = 1, 2, \ldots, K_0$) only on the basis of the first m received blocks of N_0 digits [22].

5.8 A Tree Description of Convolutional Encoding

Convolutional coding can also be represented in the form of a tree as in Fig. 5.6 and this further description will be convenient in particular for sequential decoding (see later). For the sake of simplicity when referring to the binary case, first let $K_0 = 1$ and $N_0 = 2$ in the scheme of the convolutional encoder represented in Fig. 5.5 and let $m_0 \in \{0, 1\}$ be the message entering the encoder itself at zero instant. Then the "block" transmitted at this instant will be the pair (m_0, c_0) in systematic form, where $c_0 \in \{0, 1\}$ is the parity formed by the transfer function $G_{(1)}^{(2)}$ at the same instant. Now, the next message m_1 will also be zero or one and its parity c_1^0 or c_1^1, respectively. These two alternatives can be represented by a "node" with two *branches*, the one for $0c_1^0$ and the other for $1c_1^1$.

In an analogous way, the successive message digits and their parities will be placed in one of the two branches which start from any node as represented in Fig. 5.6 (tree structure). In other words, each node corresponds to a transmitted message at a particular time unit and the next message is represented by one of the two following branches.

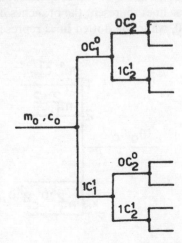

FIG. 5.6. Tree structure of convolutional coding.

It is then clear that a particular transmitted sequence (any sequence being formed by a particular ordering of pairs in this case) will determine *a particular path* in the *tree* represented in Fig. 5.6. A sequence of n information digits entering the encoder will correspond to one of the possible 2^n paths in the tree.

If $K_0 > 1$ and $N_0 > 2$, as in the general case summarized in the scheme of Fig. 5.5, then the encoder takes in K_0 info-digits at a time and gives out N_0 digits at the same time unit. Now, 2^{K_0} branches start from each node (see Fig. 5.7) and any m_i represents a K_0-tuple which can be taken in by the encoder at the ith instant, and c_i the corresponding $(N_0 - K_0)$-tuple of parities formed at the same instant (in Fig. 5.7 the situation is represented at 0 and 1 instants). This is an obvious generalization of the previous case.

In conclusion, any convolutional encoding may be viewed by means of a tree structure in which 2^{K_0} branches start from each node and any *particular* transmitted sequence—comprised of a succession of particular N_0-tuples— determines a *particular* path in the tree. The structure of a tree associated with a convolutional code becomes repetitive after the number of branches equals the memory or constraint length m. As an example, the tree associated with the convolutional code with $K_0 = 1, N_0 = 2$ and $m = 3$ is shown in Fig. 5.8a. In this example, when the ith information symbol enters the encoder, the $(i - 3)$th symbol comes out and no longer influences the encoder output. In this way, two data sequences, which coincide after the $(i - 3)$th information symbol, generate the same code symbols from the ith step.

By taking this into account, a new simplified tree diagram, called a *trellis*, can be drawn. A trellis is composed of $2^{K_0 m}$ states, each state having 2^{K_0} branches emanating from it and 2^{K_0} branches going into it. All paths having $K_0 m$ identical information bits merge together. Figure 5.8b shows the trellis corresponding to the convolutional code depicted in Fig. 5.8a. The continuous lines represent the branches corresponding to an information bit equal to 0, while the dotted lines represent the branches corresponding to 1.

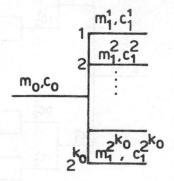

FIG. 5.7. One-node branches for $K_0 > 1$.

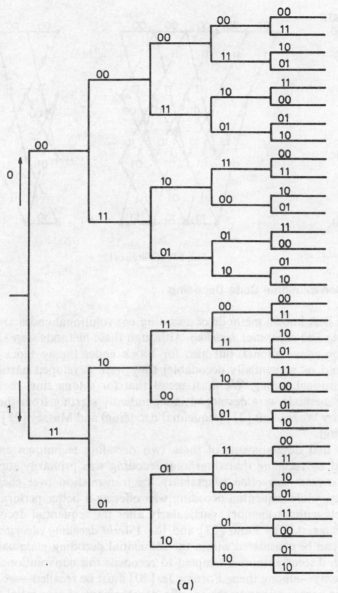

(a)

FIG. 5.8. (a) Tree structure for $K_0 = 1$, $N_0 = 2$, $m = 3$. (b) Trellis for $K_0 = 1$, $N_0 = 2$, $m = 3$.

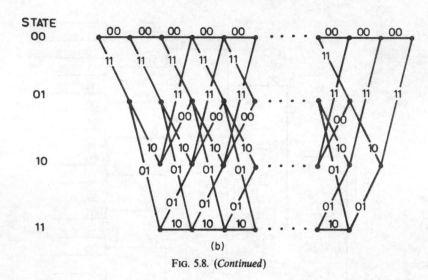

(b)

FIG. 5.8. (*Continued*)

5.9 Convolutional Code Decoding

The best known methods of decoding convolutional codes are *threshold decoding* and *sequential decoding*. Although these methods were devised not only for convolutional, but also for block codes (many block codes are threshold or sequentially decodable) they were developed particularly for convolutional coding. We must recall that for a long time these two decoding methods were developed independently starting from the first proposals by Wozencraft [21] (sequential decoding) and Massey [22] (threshold decoding).

The first developments of these two decoding techniques can be synthetized by recalling that threshold decoding was primarily supported by its *burst-error correction adaptability* for transmission over channels with memory, while sequential decoding was offering a better performance over channels without memory, particularly after the sequential decoding algorithm suggested by Fano [23] and the *Viterbi decoding algorithm* [24, 25] which can be considered within the sequential decoding *philosophy*.

Even if some authors attempted to reconcile this convolutional decoding dichotomy—among them, Forney, Jr. [20] must be recalled—we can affirm that the contributions to the specific development of sequential (or threshold) decoding were more influential, such as the *stack* sequential decoding algorithm proposed independently by Zigangirov [26] and Jelinek [27]. In the next sections, we give only an introduction to threshold decoding, Viterbi decoding and sequential decoding with some simple examples, especially of threshold decoding for its burst-correction performance. Any deepening of these subjects will be allowed only by the specific literature.

5.10   Threshold Decoding

Threshold decoding is a method of decoding based on the concept of *syndrome* and is a method which can be easily implemented. The syndrome sequences depend only on the channel-error sequences and, hence, they provide an evaluation of the error pattern itself. The syndrome sequences are defined as the result obtained by subtracting the received $(N_0 - K_0)$ parity sequences, given by (5.57) for $(K_0 + 1) \leq j \leq N_0$, from the parity sequences formed by *encoding* the received information sequences, given by (5.57) for $1 \leq j \leq K_0$—assuming the convolutional encoding is in systematic form.

In other words, the convolutional decoder for threshold decoding is a *replica* of the encoder, in such a way that $(N_0 - K_0)$ parity digits can be formed at any time unit by *encoding* the *received* info-digits from which the *received* parity digits are subtracted. Hence, the decoder is comprised of a replica of the encoder and of $(N_0 - K_0)$ shift registers storing the syndrome sequences. We then have as the syndrome sequences

$$S^{(j)}(D) = s_0^{(j)} + s_1^{(j)}D + s_2^{(j)}D^2 + \cdots \triangleq \sum_{k=1}^{K_0} G_{(k)}^{(j)}(D)R^{(k)}(D) - R^{(j)}(D)$$
$$j = (K_0 + 1), \ldots, N_0 \qquad (5.60)$$

where the received sequences are given by (5.57) and $G_{(k)}^{(j)}$ is the transfer function between the kth input and the jth output. It follows, however, from (5.56), (5.57) and (5.59) that

$$S^{(j)}(D) = \sum_{k=1}^{K_0} G_{(k)}^{(j)}(D)E^{(k)}(D) - E^{(j)}(D), \qquad j = (K_0 + 1), \ldots, N_0 \qquad (5.61)$$

so that the syndrome sequences are $(N_0 - K_0)$ at any instant and they depend only on the error sequences (5.58). Now, it is obvious that for decoding the *block zero* (or the K_0-tuple that entered the encoder at zero instant) we need the first N_A received digits or the digits received in the first m instants because the block zero could have influenced only these N_A digits.

Moreover, it is known that a set of syndromes, say $\{S_i\}$, can be combined in a set $\{A_i\}$ *orthogonal*[†] on an error sequence, for instance on the error sequence $e_0^{(j)}$ ($j = 1, 2, \ldots, K_0$) related to block zero (the errors on the K_0-tuple entered the encoder at zero instant).

If we consider the set $\{A_i\}$, we can formulate the fundamental *theorem on threshold decoding* in its simplest form (*majority decoding*).

Given a set $\{A_i\}$ of $J = 2T + S$ parity checks orthogonal on e_m, then any pattern of T or fewer errors in the digits checked by the set $\{A_i\}$ will cause

[†] A set for parity checks $\{A_i\}$ is said to be *orthogonal* on e_m if each A_i checks e_m but no other error digit is checked by more than one A_i.

no decoding error and patterns of $(T + 1), (T + 2), \ldots, (T + S)$ errors *will be detected* if e_m is decoded by the rule

$e_m = 1$ if more than $(J + S)/2$ of the A_i have value 1

$e_m = 0$ if $(J - S)/2$ or fewer A_i have value 1

with the detection of $(T + 1), \cdots, (T + S)$ errors otherwise.

In Fig. 5.8 we have outlined the whole coding transmission system, encoder–channel–decoder, with convolutional encoding and threshold (majority) decoding. The encoding, in systematic form, is characterized by the transfer function between the unit input and the second (parity) output

$$G_{(1)}^{(2)}(D) = 1D^0 + 1D^1 + 0D^2 + 0D^3 + 0D^4 + 1D^5 + 1D^6 \qquad (5.62)$$

and by a syndrome set which is chosen to be orthogonal on the digit actually to be decoded (r_0 in Fig. 5.9). Moreover, we have in this case $K_0 = 1, N_0 = 2$, $R = \frac{1}{2}$ and $N_A = 14$ as is evident in Fig. 5.9 itself.

Then, following the decoding rule just examined for $S = 0$, this error e_0 (on r_0) is evaluated as 1 if and only if more than $(J/2) = 2$ of the s_i have value 1 and is evaluated as 0 otherwise. The code is capable of the correction of all two-error patterns on eleven digits and it also corrects many patterns of order greater than two.

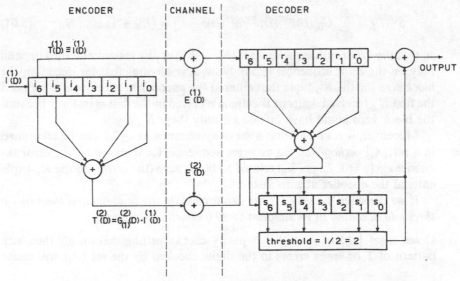

FIG. 5.9. Convolutional coding with threshold decoding ($R = \frac{1}{2}, J = 4, S = 0$).

5.11   Viterbi Decoding Algorithm

The *maximum-likelihood decoding* (see also Chapter 4) permits the achievement, for both block and convolutional codes, of the minimum error probability for equiprobable data symbols. The basic maximum-likelihood decoding algorithm computes the metrics between the received vector and all the possible code words. Hence, for mean or high code-word length n the number of code words is too high and the implementation of a maximum-likelihood decoder can become prohibitively complex.

The Viterbi decoding algorithm [24, 25] is a maximum-likelihood decoding algorithm, which uses the remerging structure of a trellis of a convolutional code to reduce the implementation complexity.

This algorithm is described in the case of a binary symmetric channel, but it can be easily extended to any memoryless channel. In a BSC, the maximum-likelihood decoding reduces to a minimum Hamming distance, which computes the Hamming distance of each code word and the received vector r, and chooses the code word having the lowest distance from r. By considering the trellis of a convolutional code, and recognizing that the branches in the trellis re-emerge continually, it is not necessary to consider the entire received vector r in deciding on the transmitted code word.

We consider a convolutional code (N_0, K_0), with a constraint length m, defined on a binary alphabet. The trellis associated with this code has $2^{K_0 m}$ states and merging in a state occurs in a group of 2^{K_0} branches. At each step, the Viterbi algorithm chooses among the 2^{K_0} branches merging in the same state the branch that has the lowest Hamming distance from the received sequence; this branch is called a *survivor*. At each step, there remains, therefore, $2^{K_0 m}$ survivors, one for each state. In this way, the decoder proceeds through the trellis and, at each step, only a survivor for each state and its Hamming distance from the received sequence are retained and stored. We denote with m_d the number of branches that the decoder can store and define the *decoding constraint length* $n_d = m_d N_0$. In general, n_d is several times larger than the actual encoding constraint length.

At the $(m_d - m + 1)$th step, the decoder has analyzed a vector with length equal to $(m_d - m + 1)N_0$ bits; at this moment, a *tail* of $(m - 1)N_0$ zeros is considered in such a way that each survivor at the $(m_d - m + 1)$th step merges in the state 0. Then, the decoder chooses the survivor with length n_d having the lowest Hamming distance from the received vector.

The Viterbi algorithm can be practically applied to codes having short or moderate code-word lengths; in fact, this algorithm requires a register of $(m_d - m + 1)N_0$ bits for each of the $2^{K_0 m}$ states and, therefore, for high m_d, the implementation cost can be prohibitively high. In these cases, sequential or threshold decoding can be more attractive.

5.12 Sequential Decoding

The *probabilistic sequential decoding*, first introduced by Wozencraft [21], as we have pointed out, appears as the best-performing practical technique for memoryless channels as the space channel. In this introduction to the subject, we refer to the Fano algorithm that greatly outperformed earlier versions of sequential decoders both in theory and practice.

The *philosophy* of sequential decoding can be summarized following Forney, Jr. ". . . a sequential decoder works by generating hypotheses about what information sequence was actually sent until it finds some that are reasonably consistent with what was received" [20]. This may be done by means of a backward and a forward research through the received data. In other words, the decoder starts by going forward generating a proper set of hypotheses. It goes forward as far as it is allowed by the goodness of agreement with these hypotheses. When this agreement becomes poor, it turns back and starts changing the hypotheses until it can go forward successfully again. More precisely, let us consider the tree structure described in Section 5.8 and the nth node in the tree itself.

If M_n is the particular sequence $\{m_1, m_2, \ldots, m_n\}$ belonging to a *particular* path until the nth node in the tree, the decoder computes $P(M_n|R_n)$, where R_n is the corresponding received sequence, and it compares $P(M_n|R_n)$ with a *suitable threshold* (see later) to decide if the $P(M_n|R_n)$ itself is high enough that M_n is very likely the transmitted sequence or the *correct path*. In the binary case and assuming all tree paths equally likely, or $P(M_n) = 2^{-Rn}$, it is easily seen that

$$P(M_n|R_n) = 2^{-Rn} \prod_{i=1}^{n} \frac{p(r_i|m_i)}{p(m_i)} 2^{-N_0} \tag{5.63}$$

if we use Bayes's rule between M_n and R_n.

Equation (5.63) can be written in a more convenient (additive) form by taking logarithms to base two (and introducing a function Φ_i)

$$F_n = \log P(M_n|R_n) = \sum_{i=1}^{n} \left(\log \frac{p(r_i|m_i)}{p(m_i)} - R \right) - N_0 = \sum_{i=1}^{n} \Phi_i - N_0 \tag{5.64}$$

However, $\log[p(r_i|m_i)/p(m_i)]$ is the mutual information between the channel input message m_i and the channel received (output) message r_i, while R is the mean information carried out by each message.

Hence, it follows that, on an average, Φ_i should be positive and F_n should be an increasing function of n if the decoder moves on a *correct* path in the tree and vice versa, if the decoder moves on an *incorrect* path. Then, the aim of the decoder is to choose, for the transmitted sequence, that path for which

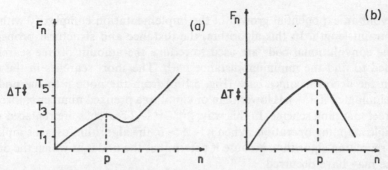

FIG. 5.10. Sequential decoding: (a) a typical correct path and (b) an incorrect path for $n > p$.

F_n is, on an average, an increasing function of n—even if, for a limited period, it may decrease in consequence of some noise events (Fig. 5.10a). In order to compare successive values of F_n, the decoder draws F_n versus n, defining the thresholds T_i where each $T_i = T_{i+1} - \Delta T$ (as in Fig. 5.10). The choice of a particular ΔT is of a certain importance. In fact, if ΔT is too small, then the decoder may very likely mistake an incorrect path for a correct one, but the system is more sensitive and the decoder will remain on the incorrect path for a short time. Conversely, if ΔT is too high, then the decoder will remain on an incorrect path for a longer time, but the path mistake is less likely. In any case, after a proper choice of ΔT, the decoder searches forward and backward through the tree for that path for which F_n is, for n large, an increasing function.

Without entering into the details of this search, we can affirm that the decoder may find itself in two fundamental situations when it is at the nth node. In the first situation, the decoder assumes all the M_n as the correct path (or the sequence M_n as the actually transmitted sequence) and attempts to find an M_{n+1}, belonging to M_n, going forward from the nth node to a suitable $(n+1)$th node. In the second situation, the decoder assumes only the first part of the path M_n as the correct path (for example, until the pth node with $p < n$, see Fig. 5.10) and attempts to find a suitable path starting from the pth node. In this search, it may encounter paths as those outlined in Fig. 5.10b (incorrect paths) and, consequently, must come back to the pth node and continue forward until it finds a path as that outlined in Fig. 5.10a.

The complexity of a sequential decoder does not depend on the constraint length, as for the Viterbi decoder. Moreover, the computational effort of sequential decoders depends on the channel noise, the data rate and the maximum time available for searching in the tree, i.e., the maximum capacity of the buffer.

Ng and Goodman [28] have devised a *maximum-likelihood decoding algorithm*, as for a Viterbi decoder, which uses a sequential decoding strategy to avoid an exponential growth of the implementation complexity with the constraint length. In this algorithm, the distance and structural properties of the convolutional code are used to reduce the amount of tree searching needed to find the minimum-distance path. The short searches in the tree, when the decoder comes back (Fig. 5.10b) from the node n to the node p, are eliminated if $n - p$ is lower than or equal to a prefixed number b, through a direct mapping scheme. In this way, $2^{2(b+1)} - 2$ searches are replaced with a single mapping operation. When $n - p > b$, the algorithm uses a simplified tree-searching algorithm, because it determines the nodes at which the divergence may have occurred.

The decoding error probability obtained from this algorithm is lower than that of sequential strategies.

5.13   Burst-correcting Codes

In order to recall some *burst-error correcting classes of codes*, it is useful to define what is meant by the *burst* and *guard space*, and whether these definitions are somewhat ambiguous, as we underlined in Chapter 4. If e_j is the error introduced by the transmission channel on the jth transmitted symbol and if $e_0, e_1, \ldots, e_n, \ldots$ is the error sequence, then we have the following.

DEFINITION 5.13.1   A sequence of b error symbols $e_i, \ldots, e_{i+b-1}$ is said to be a burst of length b with a *guard space* g if:

(1) $e_i \neq 0$ and $e_{i+b-1} \neq 0$, while the error symbols between e_i and e_{i+b-1} can be nonzero or not;

(2)   the g error symbols preceding e_i and the g error symbols following e_{i+b-1} are zeros,

(3)   there are no g zero-error symbols inside the burst sequence of length b.

Generally speaking, the values of b and g are characteristic of the transmission-channel actually used. Now, it is known that many block or convolutional classes of codes were devised in the past in order to correct such error patterns. In the next sections we shall recall some classes of these burst-error correcting codes.

5.14   The Gallager Bound

Any block or convolutional encoding–decoding technique for burst-error correction must satisfy a general bound which involves the code rate R, g and b or the main characteristics of the code and of the transmission channel.

In fact, it is perceivable that the lengths of b and g would impose only certain values to the transmission rate R.

The first general result concerning the relation among g, b and R was obtained by Gallager in 1968 [29]. However, as we shall see in the next sections, Reiger, Wyner and Ash had obtained analogous results previously, but only for block or convolutional codes.

THEOREM 5.14.1   If a block or convolutional code is capable of correcting *all* bursts of length b or less with a guard space of at least length g, it is necessary that

$$g/b \geq (1 + R)/(1 - R) \qquad \text{(Gallager bound)}$$

or

$$R \geq [(g/b - 1)/(g/b + 1)] \qquad (5.65)$$

Hence, the Gallager bound represents a precise bound on the transmission rate that can be used in a certain transmission channel.

It can be shown that if the receiver knows the actual situation of the channel during the transmission (burst or guard space), the previous bound is less tight and it becomes

$$R \leq [(g/b)/(g/b + 1)] \qquad (5.66)$$

In this case we speak of a *classic-erasure burst channel*; however, it is a practically unreal channel.

5.15 The Reiger Bound

This bound is valid for a block encoding–decoding technique devised in order to correct all bursts, each of a certain length b. It states that it needs at least a minimum redundancy $(n - k)$ for the correction of a burst of length b.

THEOREM 5.15.1   If a block code (n, k) is capable of correcting all bursts, each of length b or less, it is necessary that its redundancy $(n - k)$ satisfy the following inequality:

$$n - k \geq 2b \qquad \text{(Reiger bound)} \qquad (5.67)$$

Moreover, if the code can correct all the bursts, each of length b or less and it can *detect* all the bursts, each of length d or less, $(d \geq b)$, then it is necessary that

$$n - k \geq b + d$$

It can be noted that the bound (5.67) obtained by Reiger in 1960 can be deduced from the general Gallager bound by letting $R = (k/n)$ and $(g + b) = n$ or by adapting the general case provided by Gallager to the block-code case. Hence, we consequently define the burst-error correcting block code *efficiency* as

$$z = 2b/(n - k) \qquad (5.68)$$

where $z \leq 1$ [30].

The burst-correcting codes for which $z = 1$ are said to be optimal for their minimum redundancy related to a certain burst length b. However, we emphasize that for a fixed b the minimum $(n - k)$ (Reiger bound) is stated. It is now desirable, given $(n - k)$, for n to be as large as possible since

$$\lim_{n \to \infty} R = \lim_{n \to \infty} [1 - (n - k)/n] = 1 \qquad (5.69)$$

In this context it is important to note the following theorem that completes the Reiger bound by linking the redundancy $(n - k)$ to the code length n.

THEOREM 5.15.2   A linear block code (n, k) corrects all bursts of length less than or equal to b if its redundancy $(n - k)$ is lower limited as follows:

$$n - k \geq b - 1 + \log_q[(q - 1)(n - b + 1) + 1] \qquad (5.70)$$

where the code symbols belong to $GF(q)$ and n is the code length.

As we shall see later, many classes of codes were devised *optimal* or *asymptotically optimal*. The choice among them is to be done by considering the efficiency of the code rate R, the complexity of encoding–decoding operations, the channel actually used and so on.

5.16   Some Burst-error-correcting Convolutional Codes

It is usual to recall two fundamental burst-correcting types of codes which are called *type B1* and *type B2* [31].

DEFINITION 5.16.1   A convolutional code (N_0, K_0) of actual constraint length $N_A = mN_0$ is said to be of *type B1* with burst correcting capability b, if it is able to correct any error pattern whose nonzero symbols are confined to b *consecutive* symbols within an arbitrary output sequence of length N_A.

From this definition it follows that at least $(N_A - 1)$ correct symbols must be interposed between two consecutive bursts and, hence, the guard space is just $(N_A - 1)$ symbols long for the type B1 codes. Note that a bound can be imposed not only on the number of consecutive symbols affected by a burst, but also on the number of consecutive sub-blocks each of length N_0.

If a certain sub-block is entirely affected by a burst, the burst itself is said to be *phased*.

DEFINITION 5.16.2   A convolutional code (N_0, K_0) of actual constraint length $N_A = mN_0$ is said to be of *type B2* with burst-correcting capability of (rN_0) *phased* bursts, if it is capable of correcting any error pattern whose nonzero symbols are confined to r consecutive sub-blocks, each of length N_0, and there exists at least one incorrigible burst whose length is $(r + 1)N_0$.

From this definition it follows that the burst-correcting capability b must satisfy the following inequality

$$(r - 1)N_0 + 1 \le b \le (r + 1)N_0 - 1 \tag{5.71}$$

Since a burst of length $(r - 1)N_0 + 1$ may affect at most r consecutive sub-blocks, it follows from the first inequality that a type B2 code, with burst correcting capability (rN_0) for phased bursts, can be used as a type B1 code with burst-correcting capability $[(r - 1)N_0 + 1]$.

5.17   The Wyner–Ash Bound

In 1963, Wyner and Ash [32] established a lower bound for redundancy of "phased" burst-correcting convolutional codes.

THEOREM 5.17.1   If a convolutional code (N_0, K_0) of constraint length $N_A = mN_0$, can correct all bursts whose length is less than or equal to b, confined into r consecutive sub-blocks, then its redundancy in any N_A must be at least

$$m(N_0 - K_0) \ge 2b - (r - 1)(N_0 - K_0) \tag{5.72}$$

It can be shown that these type B2 codes must have a memory m such that

$$m \ge [(N_0 + K_0)/(N_0 - K_0)]r + 1 \quad \text{(Wyner–Ash bound)} \tag{5.73}$$

It is easy to see that the Wyner–Ash bound can also be obtained from the Gallager bound (5.65) by letting $R = (K_0/N_0)$, $g = (m - 1)N_0$ and $b = rN_0$. Moreover, note that memory m must increase as the number r of corrupted sub-blocks increases. We can now complete the comparison between type B1 and type B2 convolutional codes by expanding Eqs. (5.71) and (5.73) to type B1 codes deduced for type-B2 codes.

THEOREM 5.17.2   A type B1 convolutional code (N_0, K_0) of constraint length $N_A = mN_0$ can correct any burst whose length is b' if its redundancy in a constraint length is at least

$$m(N_0 - K_0) \ge [(N_0 + K_0)/N_0](b' + 1 - N_0) + N_0 - K_0 \tag{5.74}$$

or if its memory is at least

$$m \geq [(N_0 + K_0)/(N_0 - K_0)][(b' + 1 - N_0)/N_0] + 1 \qquad (5.75)$$

This result extends (5.71), which is valid for the type B2 codes to type B1 codes, where $b' = rN_0$, and it can be shown that the result itself can be obtained from the Gallager bound (5.65) if we let $R = K_0/N_0$, $g = (m-1)N_0$ and $b = b' - N_0 + 1$.

Notice that (5.74) and (5.75) can be violated if we fail to correct *all* bursts of length b' or less. This choice can be done only on the basis of a precise knowledge of the transmission channel actually used.

5.18 Some Burst-correcting Classes of Block Codes

After the preceding theoretical introduction, we can carry out a general survey on the main classes of block codes for burst correction devised by some authors in the past years. The first burst-correcting block code was devised by Abramson [33] and its generalization produced the important class of cyclic burst-correcting codes of Fire [34]. Moreover many cyclic or shortened cyclic codes were proposed by Melas, Kasami and Matoba, or by Stone for more than 1 burst/word.

Successively the research was focused on burst-correcting codes for *phased bursts* (Burton [35]) or for *arbitrary bursts* (Samoylenko [36]) and on codes for random and burst error correction (Hsu, Kasami and Chien). For this brief survey it is important to recall the following.

THEOREM 5.18.1   If $g(x)$ is the generator polynomial of an (n, k) cyclic code that corrects *all* bursts of length less than or equal to b, then the polynomial $g(x^r)$ is the generator polynomial of a cyclic code (rn, rk) that corrects *all* the bursts of length less than or equal to rb.

The so-called *interposition scheme* is based on this theorem and it is possible to devise codes for the correction of bursts with practically arbitrary length.

5.19 Fire Codes

Fire codes represent the first important class of block codes for burst-error detection and correction cited in the literature [34]. These codes are defined by the following theorem.

THEOREM 5.19.1   Let $p(x)$ be an irreducible polynomial of degree m over $GF(p)$ which divides $x^e - 1$, where e is the smallest such possible integer, and let t be an integer prime with e and n the least common multiple between t and e. Then a Fire code exists and is defined by the generator polynomial

$g(x)$ given by

$$g(x) = p(x)(x^t - 1) \tag{5.76}$$

Such a code has a code-word length equal to n and $m + t$ redundancy symbols and is able to correct all the bursts with length $b \le m$ and at the same time detect all the bursts with length $d \ge b$, as long as the following relation is satisfied:

$$b + d - 1 \le t \tag{5.77}$$

When a Fire code is utilized only for burst detection, we can detect any combination of two bursts when the length of the shorter burst is not greater than m and the sum of the length of the two bursts is no more than $t + 1$ or a single burst with length no greater than $t + m$.

When a Fire code is utilized for the correction of bursts with length b or less, we set $t = 2b - 1$ and the generator polynomial can be written

$$g(x) = p(x)(x^{2b-1} - 1) \tag{5.78}$$

The irreducible polynomial $p(x)$ must be of a degree m greater than or equal to b and prime with respect to $x^{2b-1} - 1$. Such a code, therefore, has a code-word length $n = e(2b - 1)$ and $2b + m - 1$ redundancy symbols. Therefore, a Fire code able to correct bursts with length b or less requires at least $(3b - 1)$ redundancy symbols and their efficiency cannot be greater than $2b/(3b - 1)$, i.e., Fire codes do not meet the Reiger bound.

EXAMPLE 5.19.1   Consider the binary Fire code generated by $g(x) = (x^5 + x^2 + 1)(x^9 - 1)$; in this case $t = 2b - 1 = 9$ and $e = 31$, therefore, the code-word length is $n = 279$ and the redundancy is $n - k = 14$. When such a code is utilized for burst-error detection, it can detect either all single bursts with a length no greater than 14 or all the configurations of two bursts, of which the first has a length no greater than 5 and the total length of the two bursts is no greater than 10.

5.20   Burton Codes

Burton codes are similar to Fire codes, but in many cases present better efficiency [35]. These codes can correct phased burst errors; nevertheless, they can be easily modified to correct any other type of burst errors. Burton codes can be defined by the following theorem.

THEOREM 5.20.1   If $p(x)$ is an irreducible polynomial of degree b and with exponent e, and $p(x)$ is prime with respect to $x^b + 1$, then the polynomial $g(x) = (x^b + 1)p(x)$ generates a cyclic code $(n, n - 2b)$ able to correct all the phased bursts with length b.

Through an interleaving operation, it is possible to correct nonphased bursts with Burton codes. To this end, the code word of a Burton code is divided in e subblocks, each of length b symbols. Then an interleaving of degree r between subblocks from r different code words is performed. In this way, an interleaved code $(nr, nr - 2br)$, which is able to correct any burst with length equal or less than $(r - 1)b + 1$, is realized. Therefore, the efficiency of a Burton code, utilized in this way, is

$$z = 1 - (b - 1)/rb \qquad (5.79)$$

When the degree r of the interleaving approaches infinity, z approaches 1. Therefore, Burton codes are asymptotically optimal with respect to the Reiger bound.

5.21 Binoid Codes

The burst-correcting codes, previously described, are cyclic codes and are interesting for their simple implementation, as will be shown in the next section. Nevertheless, when the encoding and decoding operations must be performed through the computer, such codes are complex to implement, particularly for high-order Galois fields.

Samoylenko *binoid codes* are block codes which are particularly simple to implement on general or special computers [36]. This class of binoid codes is particularly wide and includes random or burst-error-correcting codes. We describe only burst-error-correcting codes.

Let A be a set of elements $\{a_i\}$, and M a set of operators $\{m_i\}$; $+$ denotes addition of elements in A and in M, $\cdot$ indicates multiplication between elements in A and M; a binoid is the pair of sets $\langle A, M, +, \cdot \rangle$ if A is a group with respect to the operation $+$ and if $(a \cdot m) \in A$, for $a \in A$ and $m \in M$. The binoid will be termed commutative if the group $\{A, +\}$ is commutative. The binoid will be termed distributive if the operation $\cdot$ is distributive with respect to the addition $+$. The univalence domain A^* of A is the set formed by all the nonzero elements of A, for which

$$am_i \neq am_j \qquad \forall m_i, m_j \in M \qquad \text{and} \qquad m_i \neq m_j \qquad (5.80)$$

Let us consider a commutative and distributive binoid $\langle A, M \rangle$, where M has a zero element 0_M and a unity element 1_M, and define the following matrix:

$$H_b = \begin{bmatrix} I_b & I_b & \cdots & I_b & I_b & 0 \\ m_1 I_b & m_2 I_b & \cdots & m_N I_b & 0 & I_b \end{bmatrix} \qquad (5.81)$$

where I_b is the identity matrix $b \times b$, 0 is the all zero $b \times b$ matrix and

$m_1, m_2, \ldots, m_N$ denote the nonzero elements of set M. Then the following theorem can be proved.

THEOREM 5.21.1   For any integer b, the matrix H_b in (5.81) is the parity-check matrix of a binoid code with a length $n = b(N + 2)$, which is able to correct all bursts with length b or less and some percentage of longer bursts with components from the univalence domain A^* of the binoid.

For example, let A be the additive group $GF(2^{n_0})$ and M the set of the $2^{n_0} - 1$ nonzero n_0-ples. Then the length n of the corresponding binoid code can vary between $3bn_0$ and $(2^{n_0} + 1)b$. The code-word length will be chosen according to the channel error statistics.

The efficiency of a binoid code is $z = 1$ if the transmission is in $GF(2^{n_0})$ and in this case Samoylenko binoid codes are optimum. When a binary alphabet is utilized to operate in $GF(2^{n_0})$, the elements of M are represented by a sequence of n_0 binary symbols and the code can correct binary bursts with length equal or less than $[(b - 1)n_0 + 1]$.

In this case, the code efficiency is

$$z = 2[(b - 1)n_0 + 1]/2bn_0 = 1 - (n_0 - 1)/bn_0 \qquad (5.82)$$

Samoylenko binoid codes are, as Burton codes, asymptotically optimum, i.e., z tends to unity when b is increased.

Binoid burst-error correcting codes can be modified to obtain, in some cases, a higher data rate transmission and a higher code-word length, as shown by Benelli et al. [37].

Some other simple burst-error-correcting codes, which can be easily implemented through a computer, are the generalized Hamming codes [38].

5.22   Decoding of Cyclic-burst-error-correcting Codes

Cyclic codes for burst-error correction can be easily decoded using error-trapping techniques [39]. If we denote the transmitted code word by $c(x)$ and the error polynomial introduced by the transmission channel by $e(x)$, then the received vector $r(x)$ is

$$r(x) = c(x) + e(x) \qquad (5.83)$$

and the syndrome $s(x)$ is a polynomial of degree m given by

$$s(x) = r(x) \bmod g(x) \qquad (5.84)$$

If the transmission channel introduces a burst with length b confined in first low-order positions of the received vector $r(x)$, i.e., $r_0, r_1, \ldots, r_{b-1}$, then the first low-order components of the syndrome $s(x)$ are equal to the error

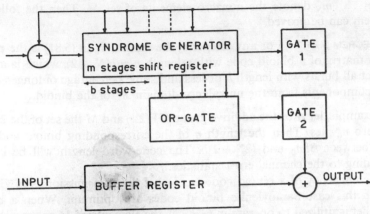

FIG. 5.11. Decoder of a cyclic code for burst-error correction.

introduced by the channel and the other components of $s(x)$ are zero, i.e.,

$$
s_i = 1 \quad \text{for} \quad 0 \le i \le b - 1
$$
$$
s_i = 0 \quad \text{for} \quad b \le i \le m
$$

(5.85)

If the burst spans certain b consecutive positions of $r(x)$, then after some cyclic shifts of $r(x)$, the error will be shifted in the first low-order positions of $r(x)$. Therefore, a situation similar to the previous one is obtained and the burst can be easily corrected.

The decoder of a cyclic code for burst-error correction is shown schematically in Fig. 5.11. The received vector $r(x)$ is sent to a buffer and the syndrome register $s(x)$. The OR gate detects when the burst is contained in the last low-order position and when the other $(m - b)$ components are all zero. In the beginning, gate 1 is open, and gate 2 is turned off. The syndrome $s(x)$ is formed by shifting $r(x)$ in the syndrome register. The received vector is then read out of the buffer, one symbol for each time interval and simultaneously the syndrome register is shifted once with no input. This procedure is stopped when the OR gate detects all zeros, i.e., the last $m - b$ syndrome components are all zeros. In this case, the first b stages of the syndrome register contain the burst-error pattern. Then gate 1 is closed and gate 2 is opened to correct the first b symbols which leave the buffer.

5.23   Multiple-burst-error-correcting Codes

In some channels, the bursts can occur too frequently and single-burst-error-correcting codes cannot be used. This happens, for example, if the bursts appear in *clusters* or if the mean guard space is not well defined. In these cases, it can be convenient to use codes able to correct two or more bursts per code word.

The lower and upper bounds on the redundancy of multiple-burst-error-correcting codes show many interesting and attractive properties of these codes [40, 41]. The lower bound on the redundancy is given by the following theorem [41].

THEOREM 5.23.1   A (n, k) linear block code that corrects up to s bursts per block, each of length b or less and weight $e \leq b$ or less, has a redundancy

$$n - k \geq \log_q \sum_{r=0}^{s} \binom{n - sb + r - 1}{r} \{(q - 1)[1 + (q - 1)]^{b-1, e-1}\}^r$$

$$\times \{[1 + (q - 1)]^{b, e}\}^{s-r} \tag{5.86}$$

where $[1 + x]^{x, t}$ is the incomplete binomial expansion up to the term x_t in the ascending power of x.

Analogously, the upper bound on the redundancy of a multiple-burst-correcting code is defined by the following theorem.

THEOREM 5.23.2   There exists a (n, k) linear block code that corrects s bursts per code word, each with length b or less, and weight e or less, with a redundancy $(n - k)$ such that

$$n - k \leq \log_q \sum_{r=0}^{2s-1} \binom{n - 2sb + r}{r} \{[1 + (q - 1)]^{b-1, e-1}\}^{r+1}$$

$$\times (q - 1)^r \{[1 + (q - 1)]^{b, e}\}^{2s-1-r} \tag{5.87}$$

In Fig. 5.12, the lower and upper redundancy bounds for some different burst-error-correcting codes in the case of dense bursts, i.e., for $e = b$, are shown. A code is *optimum* if its redundancy is equal to the lower bound. As it is shown in Fig. 5.12, an optimum code able to correct s bursts per code word requires a redundancy higher than an optimum code able to correct one burst per code word.

Nevertheless, it can be shown that optimum or near-optimum codes able to correct s bursts per code word can be very useful in the cases where it is possible to use single-burst-error-correcting codes. The code-word length n for single-burst-error-correcting codes is generally chosen according to the channel error statistics and to the mean frequency of the bursts, to have only one burst per code word.

If we denote with C an optimum code (n, k) able to correct one burst per code word $(s = 1)$ and with C_1 an optimum code having a code-word length sn and able to correct s bursts per code word, then code C corrects, in general,

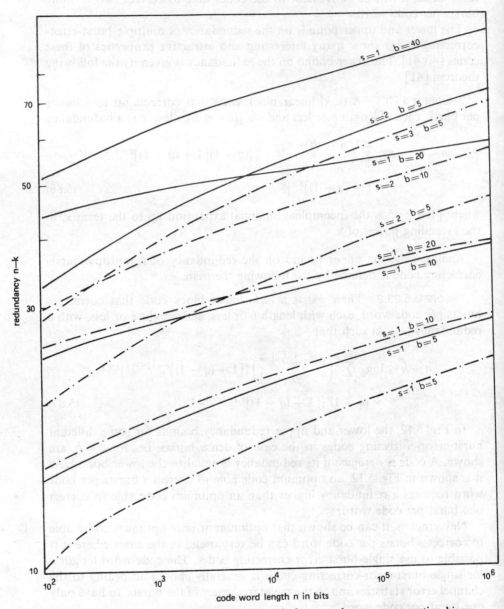

FIG. 5.12. Lower and upper redundancy bounds for some burst-error-correcting binary codes; the lower bounds are represented with dashed curves, while the upper bounds with continuous curves.

s bursts in sn symbols, i.e., s code words if each burst occurs in a different code word and it requires $s(n - k)$ redundancy symbols and code C_1 can correct (besides the error patterns correctable with the code C) many other error patterns, i.e., all the error patterns of s bursts in sn symbols. An optimum code C_1 requires only a few bits more than an optimum code C. For example, if $s = 2$, C is a code able to correct two bursts in $2n$ symbols, and code C_1 often requires only one redundancy bit more than a code C. In Fig. 5.13 the redundancy difference between an optimum binary code C_1 and an optimum binary code C, expressed as a percent of the redundancy of the code C itself, is given as a function of the code-word length n of C for different values of b. Similarly, in the case of $s = 3$, the code C_1 requires only two redundancy bits more than C in many cases.

These results show the great interest in developing multiple-burst-error-correcting codes, having a near-optimum redundancy. However, while many single-burst-error-correcting codes, block and convolutional, are known in the literature, only few results are obtained for multiple-burst-error-correcting codes.

The most popular and efficient class of multiple-burst-error-correcting codes is the Reed–Solomon code [42]. Reed–Solomon codes are cyclic codes and can be considered as a subclass of BCH codes. Let α denote an element of a Galois field $\mathrm{GF}(\alpha)$ of order n. A vector is a code word only if it has as roots the elements $\alpha, \alpha^2, \ldots, \alpha^{d-1}$, d being a prefixed integer. The polynomial generator of this code is then

$$g(x) = (x - \alpha)(x - \alpha^2) \cdots (x - \alpha^{d-1}) \qquad (5.88)$$

This code has $d - 1$ redundancy symbols and a minimum Hamming distance equal to $d = 2t + 1$. The code-word length n of the code is equal to the order of the element α. If α is primitive, then $n = \alpha - 1$.

If $\alpha = p^r$, then each code symbol can be expressed as an r-tuple in $\mathrm{GF}(p)$, and the Reed–Solomon code becomes a code with length $n = r(\alpha^r - 1)$ and $k = r(\alpha^r - 1 - 2t)$ information symbols that are able to correct all error patterns which alter t or less blocks of r symbols.

Therefore, since a burst with length b between $(u - 1)r + 1$ and ur can affect at most u blocks of r symbols, the Reed–Solomon code can correct all the configurations of s bursts with length b or less if $s \leq \lfloor t/u \rfloor$, where $\lfloor x \rfloor$ is the greatest integer less than x.

These codes are the most efficient class of multiple-burst-error-correcting codes, but they present a very complex decoding implementation. Other classes of multiple-burst-error-correcting codes are the Mandelbaum codes [43] and Bahl–Chien codes [44]. These codes often present a simpler implementation with respect to Reed–Solomon codes, but often have a very high redundancy. Some comparisons between Reed–Solomon, Mandelbaum and

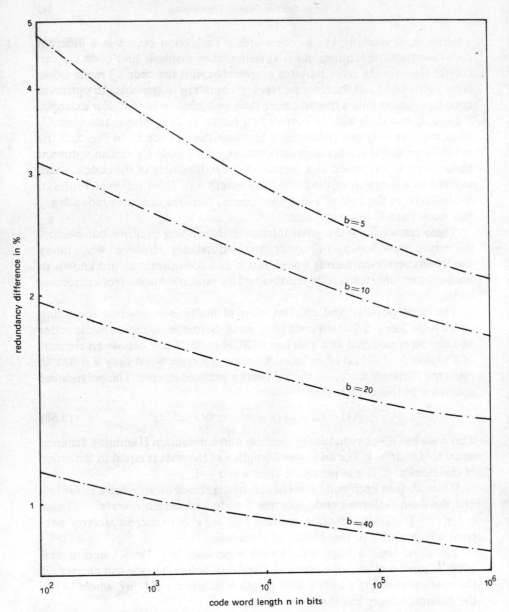

FIG. 5.13. Redundancy difference between an optimum binary code C_l and an optimum binary code C.

TABLE 5.2. Comparison between some binary codes that are
able to correct two bursts per code word.[a]

B–C codes			M codes			R–S codes		
b	n	m	b	n	m	b	n	m
6	231	84	6	405	135	6	155	40
11	572	212	12	242	121	11	155	60
13	780	276	—	—	—	13	378	72
22	1683	403	—	—	—	22	889	112
42	6006	2406	42	2817	939	43	378	192

[a] B–C Codes = Bahl–Chien Codes; M Codes = Mandelbaum Codes;
R–S Codes = Reed–Solomon Codes.

Bahl–Chien codes, show that they are able to correct two bursts per code word, as shown in Table 5.2. Multiple-burst-error-correcting codes can also be constructed using interleaving techniques or with product codes.

5.24 Burst- and Random-error-correcting Codes

In many real communication channels, errors happen both in burst and random ways. Burst errors are often the most important type of errors, because a burst spans many code symbols. Therefore, burst-error-correcting codes are utilized. Nevertheless, these codes can be inefficient and inadequate and in these cases it is necessary to utilize codes able to correct *random and burst errors*.

Many methods for constructing codes for the correction of random and burst errors can be found in the literature. One of the most powerful methods is the utilization of an *interleaving* technique. For example, if the code must be designed to correct bursts with length b and t random errors between two consecutive bursts, then to correct both of these types of errors it is sufficient to interleave b consecutive code words of a code able to correct $(t + 1)$ random errors. In fact, if we perform an interleaving operation between b consecutive code words, then a burst with length b or less alters at most one code symbol of each code word.

Another method for the construction of codes able to correct both random and burst errors in the Galois field $\text{GF}(\alpha)$ is the utilization of a t-random-error-correcting code on the Galois field $\text{GF}(\alpha^m)$. In $\text{GF}(\alpha)$, each code-word symbol can be represented by an m-tuple and, therefore, it can correct all the error configurations in $\text{GF}(\alpha)$ of random and burst errors which alter t or less m-tuple.

Some other methods of deriving random- and burst-error-correcting codes are presented in the literature [45, 46]. The most powerful method is the burst-trapping, which will be described in great detail in the next section.

5.25   Burst-trapping Techniques

Burst-trapping (BT) techniques, proposed by Tong [47], can be considered as a combination of block and convolutional techniques. These techniques offer good efficiency in many real communication channels because of their intrinsic capability to adapt to the channel behaviour. In the BT techniques, each information vector is transmitted twice. The first is encoded through a block code (n, k) and transmitted in its time interval, and the second is superimposed on the parity-check symbols of a subsequent codeword. In this way, if the first version of the information symbols is received without errors, these information symbols are subtracted by the parity-check symbols of the subsequent code word. On the contrary, if a burst alters the first version of the information symbols, then this version is discarded and the information is recovered by the second version. We now give a more detailed description of this technique.

Assume we are block encoding a sequence of information bit blocks I_0, $I_1, \ldots, I_l, \ldots$ where l is an integer. Assume C_l is the code word associated with the information block I_l; to C_l, or more precisely to the parity checks of C_l, the information bits I_0 of the first block are added, so that the channel message at the lth block time is

$$M_l(x) = x^{n-k}I_l(x) + \mathrm{Re}[x^{n-k}I_l(x)]/g(x) + I_0(x) = C_l(x) + I_0(x) \quad (5.89)$$

where $\mathrm{Re}(a(x)/g(x))$ is the remainder of $a(x)$ after division by $g(x)$, and $g(x)$ is the generator polynomial of the cyclic code. Notice that the decoder already knows $I_0(x)$, which is assumed to have been decoded previously, so when $M_l(x)$ (possibly distorted by the channel errors) arrives at the decoder, the latter adds $I_0(x)$ to it so as to convert $M_l(x)$ into $C_l(x)$ (plus possibly the channel errors). Now the decoder estimates the number of errors in $C_l(x)$. If this number is less than a fixed threshold figure, then the decoder corrects them; otherwise the decoder gives up, recognizes that it cannot correct the error pattern and earmarks the information $I_l(x)$ as *erroneous information* $I_l^*(x)$, e.g., by storing a 1 in the error tracer (see Fig. 5.14).

After l block times, the message $M_{2l}(x)$ arrives at the buffer and its syndrome is calculated without the addition of $I_l^*(x)$ (because it is earmarked); therefore if $M_{2l}(x)$ has no error, since

$$M_{2l}(x) = C_{2l}(x) + I_l(x) \quad (5.90)$$

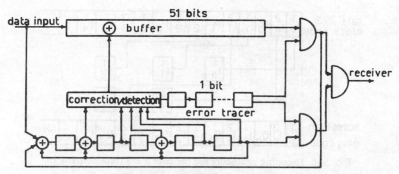

FIG. 5.14. Burst-trapping decoding.

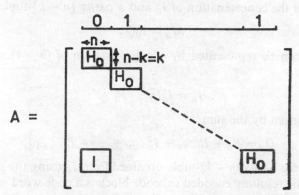

FIG. 5.15. Parity-check matrix of the code.

the syndrome S_{2l} of $M_{2l}(x)$ must be the syndrome of $I_l(x)$. The parity check matrix A of our code is shown in Fig. 5.15, where H_0 is the parity check matrix of a block (cyclic) code, I the $k \times k$ identity matrix, and the *rate* (k/n) is $\frac{1}{2}$[†]. The syndrome of $I_l(x)$ coincides with $I_l(x)$ itself. Thus, if $M_{2l}(x)$ is correctly received, $I_l(x)$ can be sent to the receiver instead of $I_l^*(x)$.

In general, the code used for burst-trapping purposes is a rate $(b-1)/b$ recurrent code whose parity check matrix A is constructed from the parity check matrix H of an (n, k) linear systematic block code $(k/n) = (b-1)/b)$ and the $(n-k)$th order identity matrix I. The *constraint length* of the code is $N = n[(b-1)l + 1]$ where $l \geq 1$ is the *block interleaving constant*. The A matrix completely specifies the encoding. However, it is useful to interpret encoding as the interleaved encoding of l subcodes, in the following way. The first subcode is formed by blocks $0, l, 2l, 3l, \ldots$. The k-tuple of information bits I_{il} of the $[il]$th block $(i = 0, 1, 2, \ldots)$ is encoded into an n-tuple

[†] Except for the shown boxes there is no nonzero element in A.

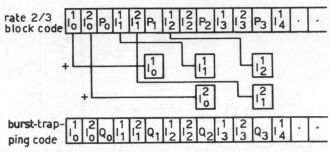

FIG. 5.16. Encoding procedure for the case $b = 3$ (rate 2/3), $l = 1$.

M_{il}, which is the concatenation of I_{il} and a parity $[n - k]$-tuple Q_{il}

$$M_{il} = I_{il}Q_{il} \tag{5.91}$$

In turn, I_{il} can be represented by a concatenation of $(b - 1)$ equal-length segments

$$I_{il} = I_{il}^1 I_{il}^2 \cdots I_{il}^{b-1} \tag{5.92}$$

while Q_{il} is given by the sum

$$Q_{il} = P_{il} + I_{(i-1)l}^1 + I_{(i-2)l}^2 + \cdots + I_{(i-b+1)l}^{b-1} \tag{5.93}$$

where P_{il} is the parity $(n - k)$-tuple obtained from I_{il} using the parity check matrix H. The resulting encoded subcode block is a code word whose parity portion is modified by the addition of an information segment from each of the previous $(b - 1)$ subcode blocks. On the other hand, the $[j]$th information segment of the $[il]$th block is added to the information portion of the $[(i + j)l]$th block $(j = 1, 2, \ldots, b - 1)$. Figure 5.16 illustrates the encoding procedure for the case $b = 3$ (rate 2/3), $l = 1$.

This construction is equivalent to the generation through the (truncated) parity check matrix A which is given in Fig. 5.17 for $l \geq 1$, in Fig. 5.18 for

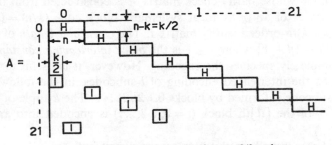

FIG. 5.17. Parity-check matrix of a rate 2/3 code.

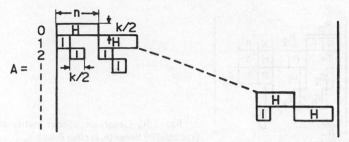

FIG. 5.18. Parity-check matrix of a rate 3/3 code ($l = 1, b = 3$).

interleaving degree $l = 1$, $b = 3$, rate 2/3 and in Fig. 5.19 for interleaving degree $l = 1$ and rate $(b - 1/b)$ for some b. A given block of a subcode is decoded in one of three possible ways, i.e., random error decoding (RED), burst trapping decoding (BTD) and blind faith decoding (BFD). The essential limitation in burst trapping codes is that an error-free interval must follow any occurring burst in order to ensure its correction. If random errors occur in this guard space, burst correction cannot take place any longer. The generalized burst-trapping (GBT) codes described in this section offer an example of a technique enabling correction of some errors in the guard space [48, 49].

In GBT, each information symbol is transmitted twice as in BT:

(1)   the first transmission is encoded with a block code as with the original BT;

(2)   the second transmission is superimposed on check digits of another block, but only after encoding them with a second shortened block code closely related to the first code.

This last coding operation permits the correction of errors in the guard space.

Referring to Fig. 5.20, $G_0(H_0)$ is the generator (check) matrix of a (systematic) linear (n, k) code θ with $d_{\min} = d_0 \cdot G_1$ as the generator matrix

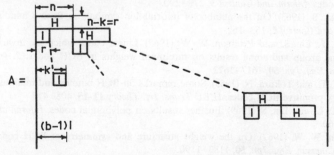

FIG. 5.19. Parity check matrix for a code with interleaving degree $l = 1$ and rate $(b - 1)/b$ for some b.

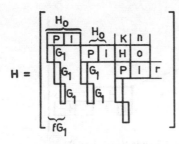

$$H =$$

FIG. 5.20. Generator (check) matrix of a (systematic) linear (n, k) code θ with $d_{\min} = d_0$.

of a code θ_1 obtained by shortening to a length $r = n - k$ a linear code γ having θ_0 as a subcode; this (r, k_1) code θ_1 is used to encode the info-digits for the second time. The parameter $f = [k/k_1]^\dagger$ is the so-called *folding factor*. With the second encoding of the info-digits, it is possible to achieve some error correction which is the main difference between GBTC and BTC. The GBTC decoding procedure is not described herein, but it can be found in the references related to this subject.

References

1. Peterson, W. W., and Weldon, E. J. Jr. (1972). "Error Correcting Codes." MIT Press, Cambridge, Massachusetts.
2. MacWilliams, F., and Sloane, N. J. A. (1978). "The Theory of Error Correcting Codes." North-Holland Publ. Amsterdam.
3. Berlenkamp, E. R. (1968). "Algebraic Coding Theory." McGraw-Hill, New York.
4. Hamming, R. W. (1950). Error detecting and error correcting codes, *Bell Syst. Tech. J.* **29**, 147–160.
5. Hocquenghem, A. (1959). Codes correcteurs d'erreurs, *Chiffres* **2**, 147–156.
6. Bose, R. C., and Ray–Chaudhuri, D. K. (1960). On a class of error-correcting binary group codes, *Inform. and Control* **3**, 68–79.
7. Bose, R. C., and Ray–Chaudhuri, D. K. (1960). Further results on error-correcting binary group codes, *Inform. and Control* **3**, 279–290.
8. Mann, H. B. (1963). On the number of information symbols in Bose–Chaudhuri codes, *Inform. and Control* **5**, 153–162.
9. Kasami, T., Lin, S., and Peterson, W. W. (1967). Linear codes which are invariant under the affine group and some results on minimum weights in BCH codes, *J. Inst. Electr. Commun. Eng. Jpn.* **50**, 1617–1622.
10. Kasami, T., and Tokura, N. (1969). Some remarks on BCH bounds and minimum weights of binary primitive BCH codes, *IEEE Trans. Inf. Theory* **IT-15**, 408–413.
11. Chen, C. L., and Lin, S. (1969). Further results on polynomial codes, *Inform. and Control* **15**, 36–60.
12. Peterson, W. W. (1967). On the weight structure and symmetry of BCH codes, *J. Inst. Electr. Commun. Eng. Jpn.* **50**, 1183–1190.

† $[x]$ denotes the integer part of x.

13. Peterson, W. W. (1960). Encoding and error correction procedures for the Bose–Chaudhuri codes, *IEEE Trans. Inf.* **IT-16**, 459–470.
14. Berlenkamp, E. R. (1965). On decoding binary Bose–Chaudhuri–Hocquenghem codes, *IEEE Trans. Inf. Theory* **IT-11**, 577–580.
15. Chien, R. T. (1964). Cyclic decoding procedure for Bose–Chaudhuri–Hocquenghem codes, *IEEE Trans. Inf. Theory* **IT-10**, 357–363.
16. Forney, G. D., Jr. (1965). On decoding BCH codes, *IEEE Trans. Inf. Theory* **IT-11**, 549–557.
17. Massey, J. L. (1969). Shift register synthesis and BCH decoding, *IEEE Trans. Inf. Theory* **IT-15**, 122–127.
18. Chien, R. T., Cunningham, B. D., and Oldham, I. B. (1969). Hybrid methods for finding roots of a polynomial with application to BCH decoding, *IEEE Trans. Inf. Theory* **IT-15**, 329–334.
19. Elias, P. (1955). Coding for noisy channels, *IRE Nat. Conv. Rec.* **4**, 37–46.
20. Forney, G. D., Jr. (1970). Coding and its application in space communication, *IEEE Spectrum*
21. Wozencraft, J. M. (1957). Sequential decoding for reliable communication, *IRE Nat. Conv. Rec.* **5**, 11–25.
22. Massey, J. L. (1963). "Threshold Decoding." MIT Press, Cambridge, Massachusetts.
23. Fano, R. M. (1963). A heuristic discussion of probabilistic decoding, *IEEE Trans. Inf. Theory* **IT-9**, 64–74.
24. Viterbi, J. (1967). Error bounds for convolutional codes and an asymptotically optimum decoding algorithm, *IEEE Trans. Inf. Theory* **IT-13**, 260–269.
25. Viterbi, J., and Omura, J. K. (1979). "Principles of Digital Communication and Coding." McGraw-Hill, New York.
26. Zigangirov, K. S. (1969). Some sequential decoding procedures, *Probl. Peredachi, Inf.* **2**, 13–25.
27. Jelinek, F. (1969). Fast sequential decoding algorithm using a stack, *IBM J. Res. Dev.* **13**, 673–685.
28. Ng, W. H., and Goodman, R. M. F. (1978). An efficient minimum-distance decoding algorithm for convolutional error-correcting codes, *Proc. IEEE* **2**, 97–103.
29. Gallager, R. A. (1966). Binary codes for burst error correction, *IEEE Trans. Inf. Theory* **IT-12**, 273.
30. Lin, S. (1970). "An Introduction to Error-Correcting Codes." Prentice-Hall, Engelwood Cliffs, New Jersey.
31. Wyner, A. D., and Ash, R. B. (1963). Analysis of recurrent codes, *IEEE Trans. Inf. Theory* **IT-9**, 143–156.
32. Wyner, A. D., and Ash, R. B. (1963). Some results on burst-correction recurrent codes, *IEEE Int. Conv. Rec.*
33. Abramson, N. (1959). A class of systematic codes for nonindependent errors, *IRE Trans. Inf. Theory* **IT-15**, 150–187.
34. Fire, P. (1959). A class of multiple-error-correcting binary codes for nonindependent errors. Sylvania Report, RSL-E-2, Sylvania Rec. System Lab.
35. Burton, H. O. (1969). A class of asymptotically optimal burst correcting block codes, *Proc. Int. Conf. Commun.*, Colorado.
36. Samoylenko, S. I. (1973). Binoid error correcting codes, *IEEE Trans. Inf. Theory* **IT-19**, 95–101.
37. Benelli, G., Bianciardi, C., and Cappellini, V. (1975). Some burst-error-correcting binoid codes, *IEEE Trans. Inf. Theory* **IT-21**, 711–712.
38. Benelli, G., Bianciardi, C., and Cappellini, V. (1975). Generalized Hamming codes for burst–error correction, *Alta Freq.* **44**, 658–661.

39. Meggitt, J. E. (1960). Error correcting codes for correcting bursts of errors, *IBM J. Res. Dev.* **4**, 329–334.
40. Benelli, G., Bianciardi, C., and Cappellini, V. (1977). Redundancy bounds for multiple burst-error-correcting codes, *Electron. Lett.* **13**, 389–390.
41. Benelli, G., Bianciardi, C., and Cappellini, V. (1978). Redundancy bounds for multiple-burst-correcting codes. *Alta Freq.* **47**, 399–403.
42. Reed, J., and Solomon G. (1960). Polynomial codes over certain finite fields, *J. Soc. Ind. Appl. Math.* **8**, 300–304.
43. Mandelbaum, D. (1972). Some classes of multiple-burst-error-correcting codes using threshold decoding, *IEEE Trans. Inf. Theory* **IT-18**, 285–292.
44. Chien, R. T. and Ng, S. W. (1973). Dual product codes for correction of multiple low-density burst errors, *IEEE Trans. Inf. Theory* **IT-19**, 672–677.
45. Kohlenberg, A., and Forney, G. D. (1968). Convolutional coding for channels with memory, *IEEE Trans. Inf. Theory* **IT-14**, 618–626.
46. Ferguson, M. J. (1970). "Diffuse Threshold Decodable Rate 1/2 Convolutional Codes." McGill University, Montreal.
47. Tong, S. Y. (1969). Burst-trapping techniques for a compound channel, *IEEE Trans. Inf. Theory* **IT-15**, 710–715.
48. Burton, H. O., Sulivan, D. D., and Tong, S. Y. (1971). Generalized burst-trapping codes, *IEEE Trans. Inf. Theory* **IT-17**, 736–742.
49. Pehlert, W. K. Jr. (1970). Analysis of burst-trapping error correction procedure, *Bell Syst. Tech. J.* **49**, 493–519.

Chapter 6

Joint Source and Channel Coding

G. BENELLI and E. DEL RE

Dipartimento di Ingegneria Elettronica
Università di Firenze
Florence, Italy

V. CAPPELLINI

Dipartimento di Ingegneria Elettronica
Università di Firenze
and Istituto di Ricerca sulle Onde Elettromagnetiche
Consiglio Nazionale delle Ricerche
Florence, Italy

6.1 Introduction

One of the important results of Shannon's Information Theory [1] was the fundamental separability of the source and channel coding functions; without loss of efficiency in the use of a given channel to transmit a given source with some specified fidelity criterion to a destination, these two coding operations can be designed entirely independently. The very general separability result of Shannon, however, gives little insight as to how complex an efficient communication system may become when the source and channel coding operations are implemented separately. Therefore, a sensible question is to ask whether a single joint source and channel coding couldn't be a more economic (and hopefully even more efficient) alternative to separate source and channel codings.

157

This is actually an open question in the general case. Few results are available and even for the special cases of the binary memoryless source (BMS) and the binary symmetric channel without memory (BSC) the answer is rather complex. Massey [2] has investigated the problem of linear joint source and channel coding applied to the combination of a BMS and a BSC. He found a fundamental difference in the joint coding performance for the distortionless and the nonnegligible distortion cases.

In the distortionless case, where the goal is the reproduction of the source at the destination with an arbitrarily small probability of error, the linear joint source and channel coding can be as *optimal* as the two separate codings. Moreover, the joint coding implementation is, in general, far simpler than the separate implementations of the source and channel encoders. A possible drawback can be represented by a smaller degree of flexibility with respect to changes of the source and/or channel statistics. In the nonnegligible distortion case, where a finite nonzero distortion is accepted in the source reproduction at the destination, the linear joint source and channel coding is, in general, suboptimum with respect to the separate coding operations.

The conclusion of Massey's analysis is that the linear joint source and channel coding can be a highly attractive approach when the goal is the distortionless reproduction of a binary memoryless source through a binary symmetric channel, whereas for a nonzero distortion separate linear source and channel codings achieve a better efficiency. However, in the general case of sources and/or channels with memory, the relative performance of the joint coding with respect to the two separate codings remains an open problem to be investigated.

Source coding (data compression) and channel coding (error control coding) have often been considered in the literature as *independent operations*, each operation being therefore optimized without considering the other one. The performance of data compression algorithms is indeed often considered in the literature with reference to *noiseless channels*. However, in view of a realistic comparison of different algorithms, it is necessary to take into account the effect of the channel noise. Indeed, when a data compression operation is performed, the signal is reconstructed at the receiver by using a small number of data and, therefore, each piece of data has a great importance; many algorithms present an error *propagation* and one error can influence the signal for many sampling instants. Hence, data compression is very vulnerable to channel errors and the channel coding operation appears to be very important in connection with source coding. Moreover, a suitable channel coding operation is to be used for any particular data compression algorithm.

In this chapter, the effect of channel noise on some data compression algorithms such as predictors, interpolators, delta modulation and DPCM is first considered. In particular, the vulnerability of these algorithms with respect to the channel errors and the error propagation phenomenon is outlined. Obviously, the theoretical investigation of these effects is, in some cases, approximate due to analytical difficulties.

In the second part of this chapter, some examples of the integration of the channel coding in the data compression operation are presented, showing that it is often possible to obtain a higher global efficiency with respect to the case in which the two operations are performed in an independent way.

6.2 Effects of Channel Noise on Some Data Compression Algorithms

As outlined earlier, data compression algorithms are often very sensitive to channel noise and distortion, because a signal is reconstructed at the receiver using a smaller number of data and thus, each data has a greater importance. In many algorithms an error propagation for many instants is present [3–5].

In the first part of this chapter we consider the influence of errors on the performance of some data compression algorithms. In particular, predictors and interpolators are considered to be both zero- and first-order. The performance of delta modulation algorithms is also described [6].

6.2.1 Predictors and Interpolators on Noisy Channels

We first consider the influence of noise on the *zero-order predictor* (ZOP) and *zero-order interpolator* (ZOI). In these algorithms the transmitted vector is of the form (see Chapter 3):

$$(y_1, t_1, y_2, t_2, \ldots, y_R, t_R) \tag{6.1}$$

with $y_i = y(t_i)$, t_i the ith time information symbol and R the number of non-predicted samples.

If m_1 and m_2 are the number of bits used to transmit the samples y_i and the time information symbols t_i, and N is the number of the samples before the compression operation, then the compression ratio is

$$C_a = Nm_1/[R(m_1 + m_2)] \tag{6.2}$$

and the mean number of samples predicted after each transmitted sample is $C_b = (N/R) - 1$.

The time information symbol t_i is the number of predicted samples after y_i or the time position of y_i in a frame. The first method permits a higher compression ratio and it is the most used in practical cases, even if it is more sensitive to channel errors.

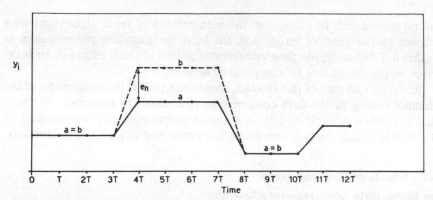

FIG. 6.1. Distortion in the reconstructed signal compressed with a ZOP algorithm for one error on a predicted sample y_i. (a) Reconstructed signal without transmission errors and (b) reconstructed signal with one error on a nonpredicted sample.

We now consider the first time information method and we suppose for simplicity's sake that all the symbols t_i are equal to their mean value C_b. If an error e_i alters the ith transmitted sample y_i, the ith received sample is $r_i = y_i + e_i$ and in the reconstructed signal, t_i samples are set equal to r_i; therefore, an error propagation is present as shown in Fig. 6.1 where an error equal to e_4 is added to the sample y_4.

Analogously, if an error equal to e_i occurs on the ith time information symbol t_i, then in the reconstructed signal we set $t_i + e_i$ samples equal to

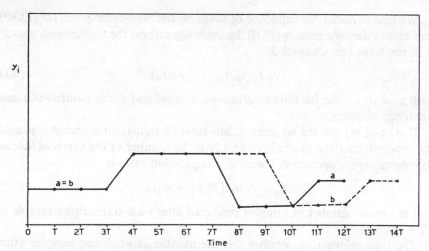

FIG. 6.2. Distortion in the reconstructed signal compressed with a ZOP algorithm for one error on a time-information symbol t_i. (a) Reconstructed signal without transmission errors and (b) reconstructed signal with one error on a time-information symbol.

y_i, while in the original signal only t_i samples are equal to y_i. Therefore, from this instant, a time translation in the reconstructed signal occurs and also in this case an error propagation is present, as it is schematically shown in Fig. 6.2, where an error $e_2 = 2$ is supposed on the second time information number transmitted.

In Fig. 6.3, some examples of the effect of channel errors on zero-order algorithms with the first time information method are presented. In this figure, the original signal shown in Fig. 6.3a is an electrocardiogram (ECG), while the signals compressed with the ZOP and ZOI algorithms are represented in 6.3b and 6.3c, respectively. In Fig. 6.3d an example of a reconstructed signal for a channel error probability equal to 10^{-2} is shown, and in 6.3e and 6.3f, the effect of an error on a sample y_i and on an information symbol t_i, respectively, are shown.

An approximate theoretical expression for the rms error at the receiver can be computed for a binary symmetric channel [4]. If we denote with d_m the mean difference between two signal samples, i.e.,

$$d_m = E\{|y_i - y_j|\} \tag{6.3}$$

and with p the bit error probability in the binary symmetric channel, the rms error as a percentage of the full scale $V_m = 2^{m_1} - 1$ is

$$\varepsilon_{CU} = \frac{1}{2^{m_1} - 1}\left[pa + d_m^2\left(1 - \frac{1}{R-1}\frac{1 - q^{Rm_2}}{1 - q^{m_2}}\right)\right]^{1/2} \tag{6.4}$$

where $a = (2^{2m_1} - 1)/3$.

The approximated rms error, including the distortion ε_d introduced by the compression operation, is

$$\varepsilon''_{CU} = \frac{1}{2^{m_1} - 1}\sqrt{\varepsilon_d^2 + \varepsilon'^2_{CU}} \tag{6.5}$$

where $\varepsilon'_{CU} = (2^{m_1} - 1)\varepsilon_{CU}$.

First-order algorithms, predictors or interpolators are often more sensitive to channel noise than zero-order algorithms [4,7]. In the FOP or FOI algorithms the signal is approximated by straight segments. The first point necessary to identify a segment is the last point of the previous segment, while the second point is a nonpredicted sample. The transmitted vector is then of the form

$$(y_1, y_2, t_2, y_3, t_3, \ldots, y_R, t_R) \tag{6.6}$$

The reconstructed signal is formed by segments. The ith segment starts from the last point of the $(i-1)$th segment and passes through the point $A_{i+1} = \{[(i-1)C_b + i]T, y_{i+1}\}$. If we denote with e_i the error introduced

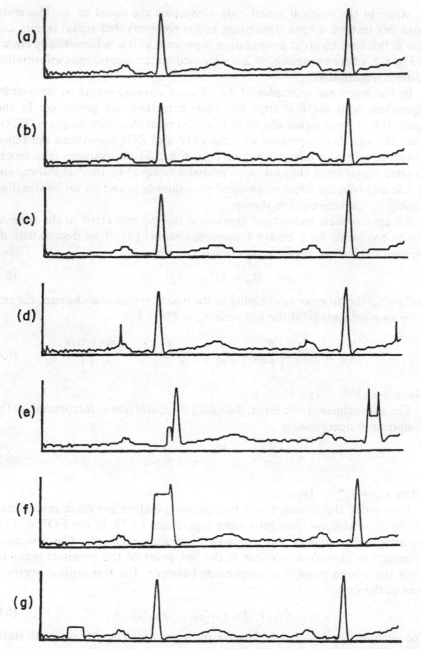

FIG. 6.3. Example of ECG reconstructed signals, compressed by means of a ZOP algorithm, for some different error patterns. See the discussion in the text.

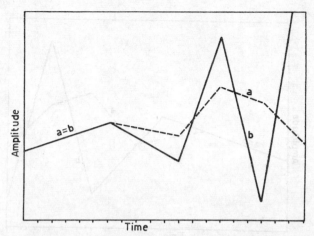

FIG. 6.4. Distortion in the reconstructed signal, compressed by means of an FOP algorithm, for one error on a nonpredicted sample y_i. (a) Reconstructed signal without transmission errors and (b) reconstructed signal with one error on a non predicted sample.

by the channel on the ith transmitted sample y_i, the pth sample in the reconstructed signal is then affected by an error

$$\Delta y = (k + 1)e_i + \sum_{j=1}^{i-2} (-1)^j e_{i-j}(C_b + 1)kC_b^{i-1} + (-1)^{i-1}e_1 C_b^{i-2} \qquad (6.7)$$

The distortion depends on all the errors introduced in the previous samples, each error being amplified by the factor C_b^{i-1}, as shown schematically in Fig. 6.4.

A similar behaviour can be seen in the case of errors on the time information symbols. In zero-order algorithms such errors determine only a time translation in the reconstructed signal. In first-order algorithms the errors on symbols t_i give rise not only to a time translation, but also propagate in an amplified way to the following samples (Fig. 6.5).

If e_j is the error on t_j, the equation of the $(i - 1)$th segment is

$$y = y_i + (y_i - y_i')[x - (i - 2)C_b + (i - 1)T]/T \qquad (6.8)$$

where

$$y_i' = \sum_{j=0}^{i-3} (-1)^j y_{i-j-1}(C_b + 1 + e_{i-j-1}) \prod_{k=2}^{i-j-2} (C_b + e_k)$$

$$+ (-1)^{i-2}y_1 \prod_{k=2}^{i-1} (C_b + e_k) \qquad (6.9)$$

From (6.8) and (6.9) the amplification of errors is evident, because an error on a symbol t_j alters the following segments. Therefore, it is convenient to

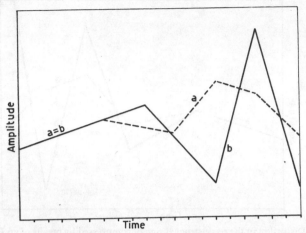

FIG. 6.5. Distortion in the reconstructed signal, compressed by means of an FOP algorithm, for one error on a time-information symbol t_i. (a) Reconstructed signal without transmission errors and (b) reconstructed signal with one error on a time-information symbol.

use these algorithms of first order only in the cases where noise and distortion are absent or negligible.

In Fig. 6.6 some examples of the influence of channel errors on first-order algorithms are shown. In Fig. 6.6a the signal reconstructed at the receiver in the absence of channel errors and after the compression with a FOP algorithm is shown. In Figs. 6.6b–6.6d the reconstructed signals for some error configurations are shown. It is clear from these figures that there is greater sensitivity of such algorithms to channel errors with respect to zero-order algorithms.

As outlined in Chapter 3, by introducing a slight modification in the previous first-order algorithms, a net improvement can be obtained and the performance becomes comparable with that of zero-order algorithms. The modification consists in the transmission of the last sample on the previous segment instead of the nonpredicted sample [4]. Then the transmitted vector is of the form

$$(y_1, t_1, y_2, t_2, \ldots, y_{R-1}, t_{R-1}, y_R) \tag{6.10}$$

The ith segment, which approximates the signal, has as first and last points A_i and A_{i+1} with coordinates

$$A_i = [(i-1)C_b + (i-1)T, y_i] \qquad A_{i+1} = [(iC_b + 1)T, y_{i+1}] \tag{6.11}$$

An error on the sample y_i affects the t_{i-1} samples which precede and the t_i samples which follow y_i, as shown schematically in Fig. 6.7. Therefore, an error on a sample only alters $t_{i-1} + t_i$ samples in the decompressed signal.

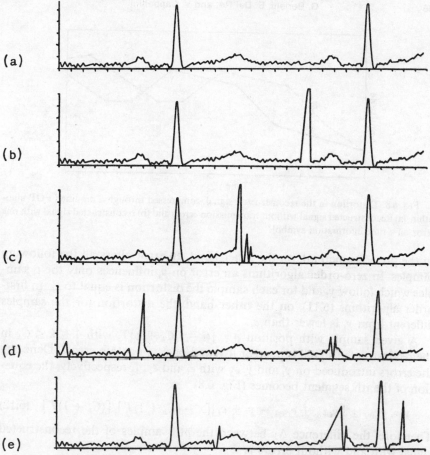

(a)

(b)

(c)

(d)

(e)

FIG. 6.6. Example of ECG reconstructed signals, compressed by means of an FOP algorithm, for some different error patterns. See the discussion in the text.

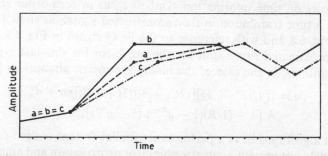

FIG. 6.7. Distortion in the reconstructed signal, compressed through a modified FOP algorithm. (a) Reconstructed signal without transmission errors, (b) reconstructed signal with one error on a nonpredicted sample and (c) reconstructed signal with one error on a time-information symbol.

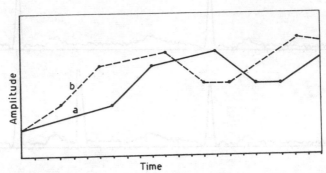

FIG. 6.8. Distortion in the reconstructed signal, compressed through a modified FOP algorithm. (a) Reconstructed signal without transmission errors and (b) reconstructed signal with one error on a time-information symbol.

In the previous method, on the other hand, an error alters all the following samples. In zero-order algorithms an error on y_i influences only the t_i samples which follow y_i and for each sample the distortion is equal to e_i. In first-order algorithms (6.11), on the other hand, the distortion for the samples different from y_i is lower than e_i.

A given sample with position $p = [(i - 1)C_b + k]T$, with $1 \leq k \leq C_b$ in the reconstructed signal is in error if y_i and/or y_{i+1} contain errors. Denoting the errors introduced on y_i and y_{i+1} with e_i and e_{i+1}, respectively, the equation of the ith segment becomes (Fig. 6.8)

$$y = y_{i+1} \pm [y_{i+1} \pm e_{i+1} - y_i \pm e_i][x - (C_b + 1)T]/[(C_b + 1)T] \quad (6.12)$$

Therefore, the difference Δy between the pth samples of the reconstructed signal with and without errors is

$$\Delta y = [\pm ke_{i+1} \pm e_i(k - C_b - 1)]/[C_b + 1] \quad (6.13)$$

The errors on time information symbols t_i, as in zero-order algorithms, determine a time translation in the reconstructed signal, as shown schematically in Fig. 6.8 and with reference to the ECG signal in Fig. 6.9.

An approximated expression for the rms error for this last type of first order algorithms, in the case of the binary symmetric channel, is [4]

$$\varepsilon = \{[1/(2^{m_1} - 1)][(2C_b + 3)/(3C_b + 3)]pa + d_m^2$$
$$\times [1 - (1/R)(1 - q^{Rm_2})/(1 - q^{m_2})]\}^{1/2} \quad (6.14)$$

These last algorithms have a performance similar to that of zero-order algorithms and do not present a catastrophic error propagation and amplification.

In Fig. 6.10 the rms error, utilizing (6.4) for zero-order algorithms and (6.14) for first-order algorithms, in the case of a binary symmetric channel is reported as a function of the signal to noise ratio S/N. Curve a refers to a real

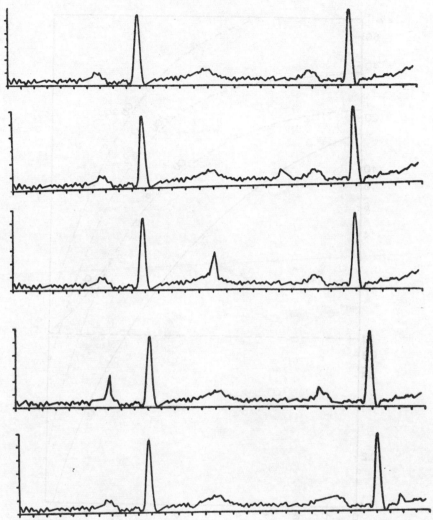

FIG. 6.9. Example of ECG reconstructed signals, compressed through a modified FOP algorithm for some different error patterns.

signal, which is an electrocardiogram (ECG), having $d_m = 15.5\%$ with respect to the full scale, while curve b is a case of independent and equiprobable samples (in this case it can be shown that $d_m = 33.5\%$) [8, 9].

The horizontal dotted line represents the rms error introduced by the compression operation. Obviously, the total rms error (6.5) denoted in Fig. 6.10 with CU_1 cannot go below this line. In the same figure, we have denoted

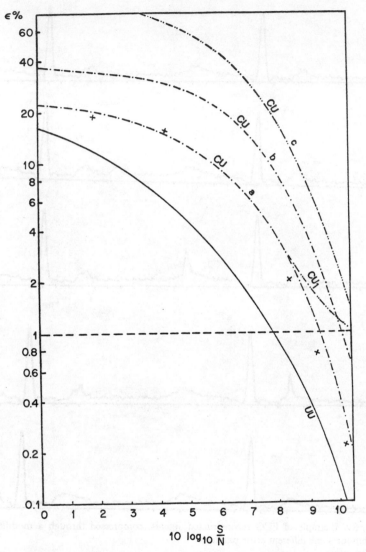

FIG. 6.10. RMS error for CU system: curves *a* and *b* refer to algorithms ZOP, ZOI and modified FOP and FOI; curve *c* refers to the classical algorithms FOP and FOI ($C_a = 3.04$ in all cases with $d_m = 15.6\%$ for *a* and $d_m = 33.5\%$ for *b* and *c*).

with an x some experimental results obtained by computer for the ECG signal. These results are quite similar to those obtained with (6.5).

In Fig. 6.11, the rms error for some compressed-coded (CC) systems is shown. In the following, we denote with (n, k, t) a block code of type (n, k) able to correct t random errors. The compression ratios for all the CU and CC

using single-error correcting codes. For example, Hamming codes and BCH codes with $T = 2$ can be utilized in many cases. For lower S/N, more efficient channel coding methods are required. Nevertheless, in this way, also the introduced redundancy grows and the source compression can be reduced accordingly. Thus, in this case statistical and parametric techniques compete.

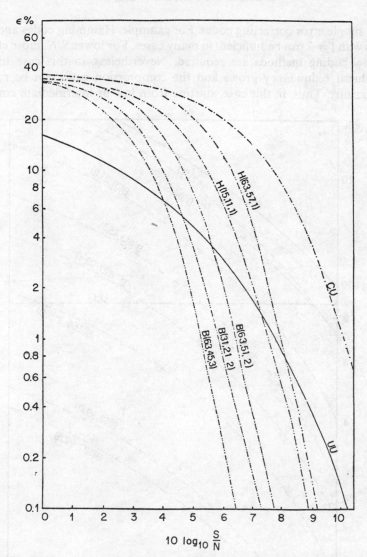

Fig. 6.11. RMS error for some CC systems, utilizing Hamming codes (denoted with H) and BCH codes (denoted with B) for ZOP–ZOI or modified FOP–FOI algorithms ($C_a = 3.04$ and $d_m = 33.5\%$ in all cases).

systems considered are shown in Table 5.1. In this figure, the case of $d_m = 33, 5\%$ is shown. This represents the value for independent samples and can be considered as the worst case [4].

For signal to noise ratios S/N greater than 5–6 dB, CC systems with an rms error lower than in uncompressed-uncoded (UU) systems can be obtained using simple error correcting codes. For example, Hamming codes and BCH codes with $t = 2$ can be sufficient in many cases. For lower S/N, more efficient channel coding methods are required. Nevertheless, in this case too, the introduced redundancy grows and the compression ratio can be reduced significantly. Thus, in this case, starting from low or intermediate compres-

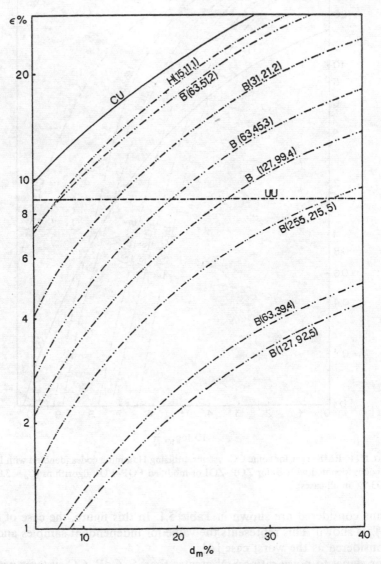

FIG. 6.12. RMS error for UU, CU and CC systems, utilizing Hamming codes (H) and BCH codes (B) for ZOP–ZOI or modified FOP–FOI algorithms ($C_a = 3.04$, $d_m = 33.5\%$ and $S/N = 3$ dB in all cases).

sion ratios for only the data compression operation, CC systems can be less efficient than UU systems because of their higher complexity and limited gain.

In Figs. 6.12, 6.13 and 6.14, the rms error for systems using algorithms of zero order or first order modified as depicted in Section 6.3 is shown as a

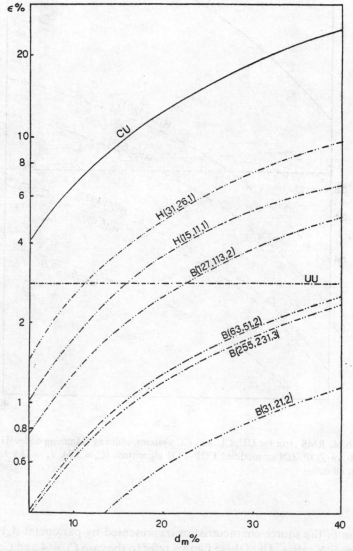

FIG. 6.13. RMS error for UU, CU and CC systems, utilizing Hamming codes (H) or BCH codes (B) for ZOP–ZOI or modified FOP–FOI algorithms ($C_a = 3.04$, $d_m = 33.5\%$ and $S/N = 6$ dB in all cases).

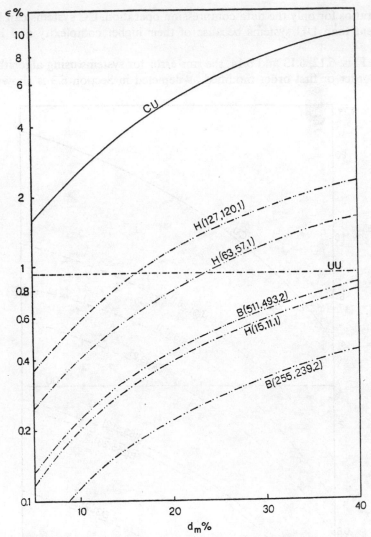

FIG. 6.14. RMS error for UU, CU and CC systems, utilizing Hamming codes (H) or BCH
codes (B) for ZOP–ZOI or modified FOP–FOI algorithms ($C_a = 3.04$, $d_m = 33.5$ and $S/N =$
7.8 dB in all cases).

function of the source characteristics (represented by parameter d_m) and for
different S/N ratios. All of these figures refer to the case $C_b = 4$ and $C_a = 3.07$.
The rms error for the UU system is represented by a horizontal dotted line
and is useful for comparison.

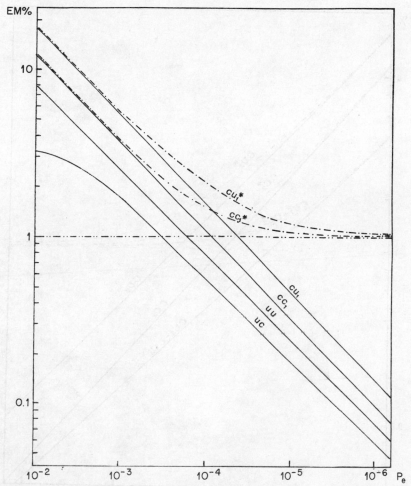

FIG. 6.15. RMS error for UU, UC, CU and CC systems in the case of communication channel with memory.

In Fig. 6.12, $S/N = 3$ dB ($p = 2.27 \times 10^{-2}$). For such a high error probability, Hamming codes are not a good choice. It can be seen from Fig. 6.13, that for $d_m \geq 10\%$ the CC system using the Hamming code $(15, 11, 1)$ always has an rms error greater than the UU system. Obviously, Hamming codes with a code-word length greater than 15 have a higher rms. At the same time, BCH codes that are able to correct two errors give a great improvement, even though the compression ratio can be reduced significantly. For example, with d_m lower than 12% a performance better than in the UU case can be obtained. For a satisfactory performance, codes that correct many errors are necessary [for instance, the codes $(255, 215, 5)$, $(63, 39, 4)$ and $(127, 92, 5)$].

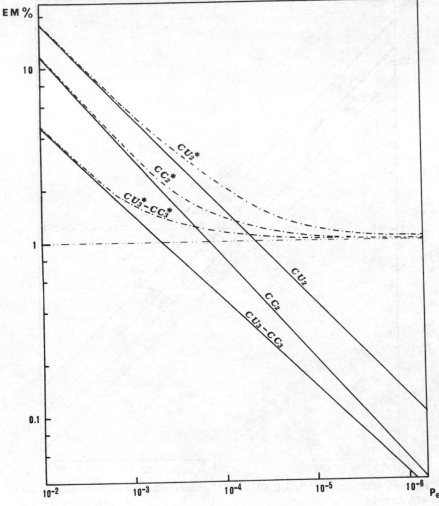

Fɪɢ. 6.16. RMS error for UU, UC and CC systems in the case of communication channel with memory.

For $S/N = 6$ dB many CC systems using BCH codes with $t = 2$ have a good performance. For example, a system with codes $(127, 113, 2)$ has an rms lower than the UU system for $d_m \leq 20\%$, while systems with codes $(31, 21, 2)$ and $(63, 51, 2)$ always perform better.

For higher S/N ratios, CC systems using Hamming codes also give a good performance. For instance, when $S/N = 7.8$ dB (Fig. 6.14), the Hamming code $(15, 11, 1)$ always has an rms error lower than the UU system.

Some results on the performance of predictors and interpolators in the case of channels with memory, obtained through a computer simulation [8,9], are reported in Figs. 6.15 and 6.16. To obtain a more complete comparison, four different structures have been considered: uncompressed-uncoded (UU), compressed-uncoded (CU), uncompressed-coded (UC) and compressed-coded (CC). The transmission channel with memory was simulated by using a Gilbert model (see Chapter 4).

In CU and CC systems, the rms error includes both the distortion introduced by the compression operation and the channel noise. The distortion due only to the channel noise is shown in these cases by dotted lines.

The coded systems (UC and CC) utilize a binoid Samoylenko code (90, 80) defined in the Galois field GF (31) [10]. In the binary transmission, the code is of a type (450, 400) and is able to correct all the bursts having a length of 21 bits or less.

Systems utilizing the first time information method, are denoted with the index 1, while systems utilizing the second time information method are denoted with index 2. For a high channel bit error probability P_e, the rms error is mainly determined by the channel noise, while the influence of the compression distortion is negligible. By reducing P_e, the importance of the compression errors gets higher and higher. Using the second method for time information (CU_2), the improvement is very low compared to the case CU_1. This fact is a consequence of the memory of the transmission channel. In memoryless channels, on the contrary, the second time information method performs very well with respect to the first method. At the same time, the compression ratio can be significantly reduced (in the case of the ECG of Fig. 6.3, the compression ratio is reduced from 3.1 to 2.6).

6.3 Performance of Delta Modulation Algorithms on Noisy Channels

The delta modulation (DM) algorithms are another important class of data compression methods. It is difficult, in general, to describe the effects of channel noise on such algorithms, because they depend strictly on the particular algorithms and on the source statistics. Nevertheless, it is clear that in all DM algorithms, adaptive or not, an error propagation is present [6, 11–13]. This error propagation is schematically illustrated in Fig. 6.17. The staircase function a is the approximation of a hypothetical signal obtained through the DM algorithm. The curves b, c, and d refer to three different error patterns. In the b case, an error is present in the sixth transmitted pulse and such an error propagates up to the signal end and a distortion equal to $2D$ (D being the step size) is present in each interval between the a and b signals. In the c case, two errors in pulses with the same polarities are present

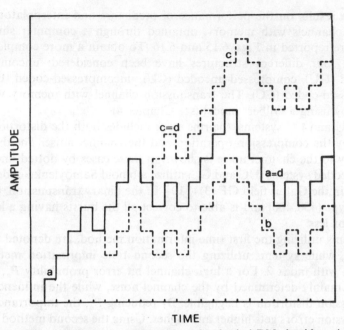

TIME

Fig. 6.17. Effects of different error patterns on the classical DM algorithms. (a) Original signal, (b) reconstructed signal when one transmission error is introduced, (c) reconstructed signal when two errors with the same polarity are introduced and (d) reconstructed signal when two errors with opposite polarity are introduced.

and the errors sum together; while in the *d* case the two errors are present in pulses with opposite signs and therefore compensate. In the last case, the error propagation is limited to the time interval between the first and the second error. From these simple considerations, it is clear that the performance of DM algorithms on noisy channels depends strongly on the source statistics; in particular, if the positive and negative pulses are equiprobable, we have a higher probability of compensation between errors, and therefore the error propagation is less marked, while in the opposite case the error propagation becomes more important.

The influence of channel noise depends on the particular algorithms. For example, the adaptive DM algorithms with compounding are less sensitive to errors than the instantaneous adaptive DM algorithms [12, 13].

Wolf has derived the signal to noise ratio for the classical delta modulation algorithms in the cases of random and burst errors [11]. He has modeled the binary pulses at the output of the DM encoder as a Markov chain with two states (Fig. 6.18), where states 1 and −1 correspond to the transmission of a positive and negative pulse, respectively, and P_t is the probability of the transition between the two states.

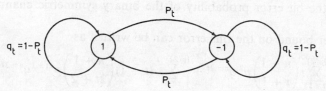

FIG. 6.18. Markov chain with two states, utilized by Wolf to model the output stream of a DM algorithm.

In the case of a binary symmetric channel, Wolf has shown that the signal to noise ratio, due to the channel noise, can be expressed, when the signal is assumed to be of infinite extent, as

$$S/N_0 = (1/4p)\{(1 - P_t)/[P_t + p(1 - 2P_t)]\} \qquad (6.15)$$

where p is the bit error probability of the binary symmetric channel. In this expression, the parameter P_t takes into account the correlation between two consecutive pulses. When the pulses are considered statistically independent, the probability P_t is equal to $\frac{1}{2}$ and the signal to noise ratio is

$$S/N_0 = 1/4p \qquad (6.16)$$

Similar results are presented by Wolf in the case of burst errors, and the channel can be modeled as a Markov chain using the Gilbert model [14]. The Wolf's formulae refer to the classical DM algorithm. They were generalized and applied to a particular HIDN algorithm, i.e., Song's scheme [12].

The upper and lower bounds on the rms error in the case of a classical delta modulation algorithm have also been obtained for a binary symmetric channel [6]. These bounds do not depend on the source statistics and therefore, are, of great practical interest.

The lower bound is obtained by supposing that two consecutive errors always alter two pulses with opposite signs and therefore compensate each other, as in the example in Fig. 6.17. The upper bound, on the contrary, is evaluated by supposing that two consecutive errors always alter two pulses having the same polarity and therefore sum together. The lower bound can then be written as

$$d_S = \frac{1}{nV_m} \left\{ \sum_{n=1}^{n_1} \binom{n+1}{t+1} (2D)^2 \frac{t(t+1)(2t+1)}{6} p^t q^{n-t} \right.$$

$$\left. + V_m^2 \sum_{t=n_1+1}^{n} \binom{n}{t} p^t q^{n-t} \right\}^{1/2} \qquad (6.17)$$

where V_m represents the maximum value of the signal, n is the signal pulse number at the DM encoder output, n_1 the greater integer less than or equal to V_m/D, p the bit error probability of the binary symmetric channel and $q = 1 - p$.

The upper bound on the rms error can be written as

$$d_L = \frac{2D}{nV_m} \left\{ \sum_{t=1}^{\lceil n/2 \rceil} t \binom{n+1}{t+1} p^{2t} q^{n-2t} + \sum_{t=1}^{\lceil n/2 \rceil - 1} (t+1) \binom{n+1}{2t+2} p^{2t+1} q^{n-2t-1} \right\}^{1/2}$$

(6.18)

where $\lceil x \rceil$ represents the greater integer less than x.

The previous results are derived for the classical DM algorithms. Nevertheless, they can be easily extended to the adaptive DM algorithms. In those algorithms where the step amplitude D is varied between a minimum value

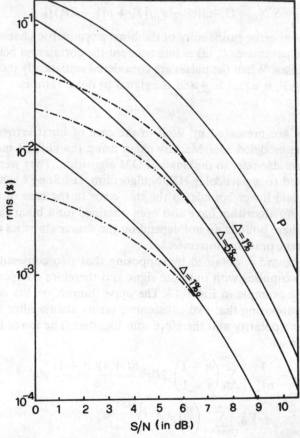

FIG. 6.19. RMS error for a classical DM algorithm (——, upper bound; –·–, average rms error). Curves refer to different values of the step size $\Delta = D$ as percentage of the full scale; curve P refers to a PCM system.

D_1 and a maximum value D_2 according to the signal variations, the upper bound on the rms error is obtained from the previous bound by setting $D = D_2$, while the lower bound is obtained from (6.17) by setting $D = D_1$.

Analogously, in the asynchronous delta modulation algorithms, the sampling rate f_0 is varied between a minimum value f_1 and a maximum value f_2. Therefore, if we define

$$n_s = \lceil f_0 n / f_1 \rceil \qquad n_u = \lceil f_0 n / f_2 \rceil \qquad (6.19)$$

n_s (or n_u) representing the number of pulses which must be transmitted if the sampling rate is equal to the minimum (or maximum) rate during all the transmission rate, then the upper bound on the rms error can be obtained by setting $n = n_u$, while the lower bound can be obtained by setting $n = n_s$.

In Fig. 6.19 the upper bound versus the signal to noise ratio S/N are depicted. For reference, the average rms error is reported when the positive and negative pulses are equiprobable.

The different curves refer to different values of the step size D. The curve P, on the contrary, refers to a PCM system in which the rms error is [14]

$$D = [1/(2^m - 1)][p(2^{2m} - 1)/3]^{1/2} \qquad (6.20)$$

with m being the number of bits used to transmit a sample. In Fig. 6.19 we have assumed $m = 7$; nevertheless, the differences, varying m, are quite small and not perceptible in the figure. We have also assumed that $V_m = 2^m - 1$.

It is clear from these figures that the lower and upper bounds are tight for mean or high S/N values. It is also clear that a PCM system is more sensitive in many cases to channel noise than DM systems. In Fig. 6.20 the gain loss in dB of a PCM system with respect to the upper and lower bounds on the rms error for DM algorithms is reported.

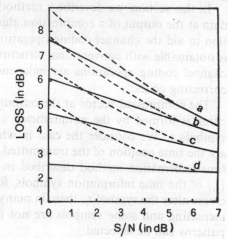

FIG. 6.20. Loss in decibels of a PCM system with respect to a DM system (——, upper bound; ----, lower bound). Curves a, b, c and d correspond to $D = 1, 2, 5$ and 1% of the full scale, respectively.

The different influences of channel noise on PCM and DM follow from the different weights of errors in the reconstructed signal. In a DM system one error on a transmitted pulse produces a distortion equal to $2D$. In a PCM system the distortion varies between 1 and $2^m - 1$. Since $D \ll 2^m - 1$, the distortion in a DM system can be lower than in a PCM system.

Obviously, in DM algorithms a distortion due to the granular and slope-overload noise must be taken into account. Such distortion and that introduced by the channel can be considered independent and therefore, the total rms error is the sum of the two types of error.

6.4   Integration of Data Compression and Channel-coding Operations

As was shown in the previous sections, data compression algorithms are very sensitive to channel noise and therefore, a channel coding operation is necessary to obtain a satisfactory performance.

Although data compression and channel coding are often considered in the literature and in real applications as two *independent operations*, in many cases it is suitable to *integrate* the channel coding operation in the particular structure of the compressed data. In fact, the bits in the compressed vector often have a different importance, i.e., errors in some bits can introduce a higher distortion than the errors in other bits. At the same time, errors on some bits propagate for many instants, while errors on other bits do not propagate. Therefore, it is convenient to protect the transmitted symbols in a different way. In this regard, *asymmetric codes* can be useful. These are codes with different error correcting capabilities for bits in different positions [15, 16].

In this section, we describe a method which exploits the structure of the data at the output of a compression algorithm with prediction or interpolation to aid the channel coding operation. This method is very efficient and is obtainable with conventional structures (i.e., when data compression and channel coding operations are independent) by using very powerful error-correcting codes.

The compressed vector at the output of a predictor or interpolator algorithm is formed by the nonpredicted samples y_i and the time-information symbols t_i. We consider the case in which the time information symbols t_i are the time position of the transmitted sample y_i in a frame (i.e., the second time information method described in Chapter 3). Therefore, the symbols $\{t_i\}$ of the time information symbols, form an increasing sequence. If some errors alter the symbol t_i, then, in many cases, the sequence $\{t_i\}$ is no longer increasing and some symbols are not in sequence. In this way many error patterns can be detected.

Once an error is detected, we can try to correct it. Many methods can be used and we briefly describe one which is very simple. If the ith received time information symbol t_i is not in sequence, i.e.,

$$t_i < t_{i-1} \qquad \text{or} \qquad t_i > t_{i+1} \qquad (6.21)$$

we then substitute t_i for a mean value given by

$$t_i = (t_{i-2} + t_{i+2})/2 \qquad (6.22)$$

This procedure can give some improvement with respect to the systems using the first time information method when the transmission channel can be considered memoryless and the error probability very low. When the channel is with memory or the channel error probability is high, such a method is not suitable because the procedure for the correction of errors on the symbol t_i can fail and introduce new errors. Figure 6.21 shows the performance of this system (denoted with CU_2), which was obtained through a computer simulation and can be compared with that of the first method. A net improvement is obtained. Obviously, the compression ratio is lowered.

We now illustrate a new strategy (denoted in the figures with the symbol CU_3) by using the second time information method which also gives a good performance for burst-type errors. The data compression operation is performed so that a fixed number of samples greater than NMAX is not eliminated consecutively. At the receiver, the t_i succession is examined to see if the sequence of t_i is increasing and obeys the previous restrictions. If this is verified, it is almost certain that no error has occurred and, therefore, nothing is modified. When some consecutive t_i are detected in error following the previous criterion, they are replaced by new t_i equidistant between themselves and with values included between the last exact value which precedes them and the first exact one found after the wrong one. The values of the samples that are relative to the wrong t_i and that immediately follow are modified because they are generally in error; the values that are now assigned to the wrong samples are obtained by making a *weighted mean* of the values of the exact samples which precede them and of those which follow them. The weights given to the exact samples are inversely proportional to the distance between the sample to be replaced and the exact one. The block diagram of this strategy is shown in Fig. 6.21.

Obviously, this procedure can also be used in the presence of memoryless channels, excluding the part relative to the interpolation of samples because errors are uncorrelated. An improvement is obtained in this way, particularly for high-bit-error probability. Nevertheless, errors on samples are not detected. The problem can be solved by using a slight error protection of samples. In the following, for example, we consider each sample y_i encoded through a parity-check code with one redundancy bit and able to detect an

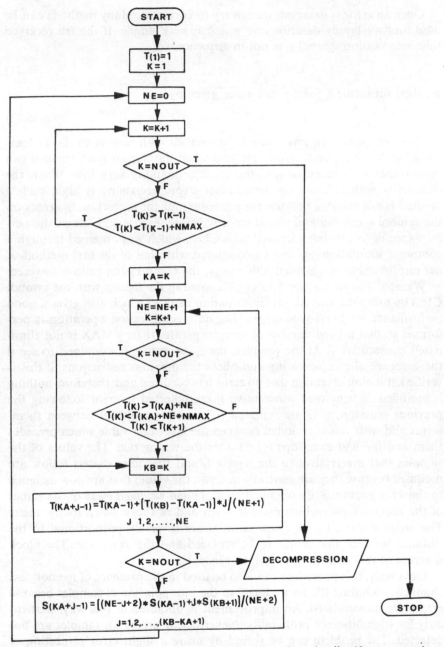

FIG. 6.21. Block diagram of an integrated source coding–channel coding (data compression–error control technique).

odd number of errors. When a sample y_i is detected in error, its received value is replaced with a weighted mean between the adjacent samples which are correctly received. This procedure gives a net improvement in the performance, while the compression ratio is not significantly reduced. In Fig. 6.16 the performance of this method is shown in the case of a channel with memory.

The described method shows a very high efficiency; the rms error, due only to the channel error, is lower than in the UU, UC and other cases. This follows from the possibility of identifying in many circumstances the errors in the time syncronization and thus, of also reducing the influence of the errors in the most important bits of the samples.

The case of CC_3 generally has an efficiency similar to CU_3; when an incorrigible burst occurs, the code can correct some errors in the time information symbols and some information necessary for the identification of the error positions are lost. In this case, a high-error EM can result.

From these results, the great importance of the *time synchronization* in the transmission of compressed data on a noisy channel must be stressed. Few other examples are known in the literature on the integration of channel coding and data compression (or source encoding). Two important examples are given for the transmission of images by Modestino *et al.* [17, 18]. The first method utilizes DPCM for data compression and an error correcting procedure obtained with transform coding. The second method uses a discrete cosine transform (see Chapter 3).

References

1. Shannon, C. E. (1948). A mathematical theory of communications, *Bell Syst. Tech. J.* **27**, 379–423, 623–656.
2. Massey, J. L. (1978). Joint source and channel coding, *In* "Communication Systems and Random Process Theory." (J. K. Skwirzynski, ed.), NATO-ASI series E no. 25, Sijthoff & Noordhoff, Alpen aan den Rijn, The Netherlands.
3. Lynch, T. J. (1967). Performance measures for compressed and coded space telemetry systems, *IEEE Trans. Aerosp. Electron. Syst.* AES-3, 784–795.
4. Benelli, G. (1980). Influence of noise on some data compression algorithms, *Alta Freq.* **49**, 400–405.
5. Benelli, G. (1977). Efficiency comparisons for communication systems using data compression and error correcting codes, *Alta Freq.* **46**, 554–555.
6. Benelli, G. (1982). Performance of delta modulation algorithms on noisy channels, *Alta Freq.* **51**, 313–318.
7. Benelli, G., Cappellini, V., and Lotti, F. (1980). Data compression techniques and applications, *Radio Eng. Electron.* **50**, 29–53.
8. Benelli, G., Cappellini, V., and Del Re, E. (1978). Integrated data communication systems with data compression and error correcting codes, *In* "Communication Systems and Random Process Theory." (J. K. Skwirzynski, ed.), NATO-ASI series E no. 25, Sijthoff & Noordhoff, Alpen aan den Rijn, The Netherlands.

9. Benelli, G., Bianciardi, C., Cappellini, V., and Del Re, E. (1977). High efficiency digital communications using data compression and error correcting codes, *Proc. EUROCON 77*, Venice, Italy.

10. Samoylenko, S. J. (1973). Binoid error correcting codes, *IEEE Trans. Inf. Theory* **IT-19**, 95–101.

11. Wolf, J. K. (1966). Effects of channel errors on delta modulation, *IEEE Trans. Commun.* **COM-14**, 2–7.

12. Figueras-Vidal, A. R., Acebal, J. B. M., and Hernandez, M. A. L. (1980). Comments and extensions of Wolf's signal–to–channel noise formulas for delta-modulated systems, *IEEE Trans. Commun.* **COM-27**, 131–137.

13. Preezas, D. P., and Lo Cicero, J. L. (1981). A study of random channel errors for an ADM system, *IEEE Trans. Commun.* **COM-29**, 117–122.

14. Gilbert, E. N. (1960). Capacity of a burst-noisy channel, *Bell Syst. Tech. J.* **39**, 1253–1265.

15. Masnick, B., and Wolf, J. K. (1967). On linear unequal protection codes, *IEEE Trans. Inf. Theory* **IT-13**, 600–607.

16. Boyarinov, J. M., and Katsman, G. L. (1981). Linear unequal error protection codes, *IEEE Trans. Inf. Theory* **IT-27**, 168–175.

17. Modestino, J. W., and Daut, D. G. (1979). Combined source-channel coding of images, *IEEE Trans. Commun.* **COM-27**, 1644–1659.

18. Modestino, J. W., and Daut, D. G. (1981). Combined source-channel coding of images using the block cosine transform, *IEEE Trans. Commun.* **COM-29**, 1261–1274.

Chapter 7

Software Implementation of Data Compression and Error Control Techniques

G. BENELLI and E. DEL RE

Dipartimento di Ingegneria Elettronica,
Università di Firenze
Florence, Italy

F. LOTTI

Istituto di Ricerca sulle Onde Elettromagnetiche,
Consiglio Nazionale delle Ricerche
Florence, Italy

7.1 Introduction

The organization and implementation of the software for data compression and error control techniques is becoming an important aspect of the general problem of designing an efficient communication system. With the diffusion of microprocessor-based equipment and of VLSI chips, the operations of source and channel encoding/decoding are being performed in a digital way even more. This is done by using software or *firmware*[†] techniques on the numerical data stream. It is, therefore, necessary to develop a considerable number of computer programs to evaluate design parameters, to optimize the available resources and to estimate error bounds and compression ratios.

[†] This term is generally used for implementation techniques where hardware and software approaches are strictly interconnected and integrated.

185

The first step in this approach generally consists of the evaluation of the statistical behaviour of the source output in order to get a general idea of which class of source encoders and which data compression technique will be convenient. As a second step, the particular efficiency of the selected compression method is evaluated to set up all the parameters such as tolerances, word lengths and thresholds. An approximate evaluation of the error range obtained after reconstruction can be very useful in most cases. As a third step, the problems connected with the channel coding are addressed along with simulation algorithms used to estimate the detection/correction capability of the selected code for the particular source statistics and a prefixed model of the channel noise. The overall efficiency of the communication system will result from applying, in sequence, the previously mentioned operations.

In this chapter, several programming procedures will be described for processing digital data, simulating algorithm efficiency and, finally, estimating the overall behaviour of a digital communication link. Appendices 2 and 3 contain the program listings of some of the algorithms considered.

7.2 Software Implementation for Data Compression

Computer programs for data compression have to be separated into two classes: programs which give the efficiency of the particular algorithm in terms of compression ratio and reconstruction errors and programs which really perform data compression and decompression.

Programs of the first class actually perform a *simulation*, for a given input signal, of the behaviour of a particular algorithm for a set of its characteristic parameters. They are largely used in practice to determine the root mean square and peak reconstruction errors, the achievable average compression ratio and to set the criteria for the buffer dimensions. Programs of the second class are further divided into compressors and decompressors.

Software compressors consist of a set of instructions which process an input buffer (vector) of numerical data and, according to the particular compression method, evaluate the compressed stream to be sent to an output buffer including the computations for the time identification of the sequence, when this is required. Decompressors actually perform the opposite operation; taking into account the time information, they compute the reconstructed signal according to the algorithm rules.

The software processing is of particular importance when complicated adaptive compression systems are employed, which perform polynomial evaluation and frequently change the compression coefficients as in the case of adaptive linear prediction. Data compression using transformations usually takes advantage of software *fast transformation* algorithms which have been

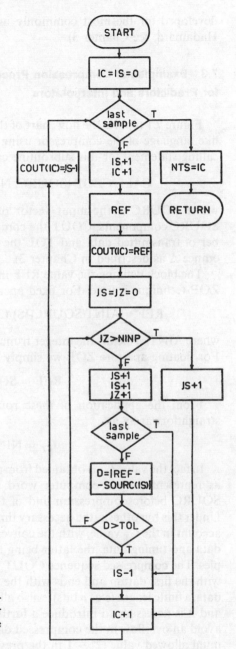

FIG. 7.1. Flowchart of a computer program for data compression using a zero-order predictor. The variables IC, IS, JZ and JS are local counters.

developed for the most commonly used transformations (Fourier, Walsh, Hadamard; see Chapter 3).

7.3 Examples of Compression Procedures
for Predictors and Interpolators

Figure 7.1 reports the flowchart of the computer routine in a FORTRAN-like language of the compressor using the zero-order predictor (ZOP). The calling statement for this subroutine can be of the type:

$$\text{CALL CZOP (SOURC, NINP, TOL, COUT, NTS)} \qquad (7.1)$$

where SOURC is the input vector of source data, NINP the number of SOURC components, COUT the compressed output vector, NTS the number of transmitted data and TOL the aperture value (amplitude of the tolerance Δ as described in Chapter 3).

The block defining the value REF in Fig. 7.1 depends on which particular ZOP technique is used. For fixed aperture we let

$$\text{REF} = \text{AINT(SOURC(IS)}/(2.*\text{TOL}))*\text{TOL}*2. + \text{TOL} \qquad (7.2)$$

where $\text{AINT}(\cdot)$ means the integer truncation of the expression in parenthesis. For floating-aperture ZOP we simply let

$$\text{REF} = \text{SOURC(IS)} \qquad (7.3)$$

From the application of these routines the compression ratio follows straightforwardly as:

$$C_T = \text{NINP/NTS} \qquad (7.4)$$

In fact the value C_T is obtained from (7.4) by considering each single sample as represented by a computer word both as a component of the vector SOURC before compression and of the vector COUT after compression. Under this hypothesis, the necessary time insertion is also correctly taken into account in the C_T value, with the convention of an alternation of information data and timing data, the latter being the count of the nontransmitted samples. The compressed sequence COUT in the previous example always starts with the first datum and ends with the last time count. In the case of integer data, a finite length (e.g., n bits) is also allowed for the time identification words and it is necessary to introduce a further control in the routine, in order to avoid an overflow in the compressed data count when this exceeds the maximum allowed value ($2^n - 1$ in the previous example).

The analogous flowchart for the zero-order interpolator as described in Chapter 3 is shown in Fig. 7.2. It is evident that the complexity is greater with

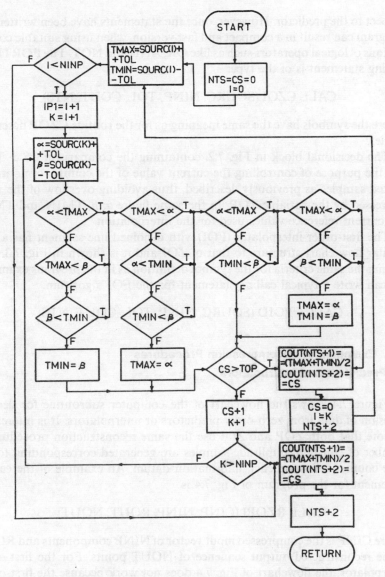

FIG. 7.2. Flowchart of a computer program for data compression using a zero-order interpolator. The variables I, K, IP1 and CS are local counters.

respect to the predictor. However, once the statements have been written, the program can result in a compact and fast version, when using suitable combinations of logical operators such as like OR, AND and NOT. The FORTRAN calling statement is of the type:

$$\text{CALL CZOI (SOURC, NINP, TOL, COUT, NTS)} \qquad (7.5)$$

where the symbols have the same meaning as for the routine CZOP described earlier.

The decisional block in Fig. 7.2, containing the comparison $CS > TOP$, has the purpose of controlling the current value of the counter of nontransmitted samples as previously described, thus avoiding overflow of the value expressed by the variable TOP. In the same figure α, β, TMIN and TMAX are current reference values used for the interpolation.

The first-order interpolator (FOI) with disjoined line segment has a very similar flow chart structure to that of ZOI and it is shown in Fig. 7.3. Following the same criteria for the symbol definition as in the previous examples, we can write a typical calling statement for the FOI algorithm:

$$\text{CALL CFOID (SOURC, NINP, TOL, COUT, NTS)} \qquad (7.6)$$

7.4   Examples of Decompression Procedures
for Predictors and Interpolators

Figure 7.4 shows the flowchart of the computer subroutine for decompression of data from zero-order predictors or interpolators. It is interesting to note that both ZOP and ZOI use the same reconstruction procedure. A number of constant amplitude samples are generated corresponding to the time counter following each information datum. An example of the calling statement for the program of Fig. 7.4 is

$$\text{CALL RZOPI (CINP, NINP, ROUT, NOUT)} \qquad (7.7)$$

where CINP is the compressed input vector of NINP components and ROUT is the reconstructed output sequence of NOUT points. For the first-order interpolator, the flowchart of Fig. 7.4 does not work because the first-order algorithms need a linear interpolation between nonconsecutive transmitted samples. Figure 7.5 shows an example of a reconstruction routine for FOI (disjoined line segment). A typical calling statement is

$$\text{CALL RFOID (CINP, NINP, ROUT, NOUT)} \qquad (7:8)$$

The meaning of the symbols is evident and exactly the same as in (7.7).

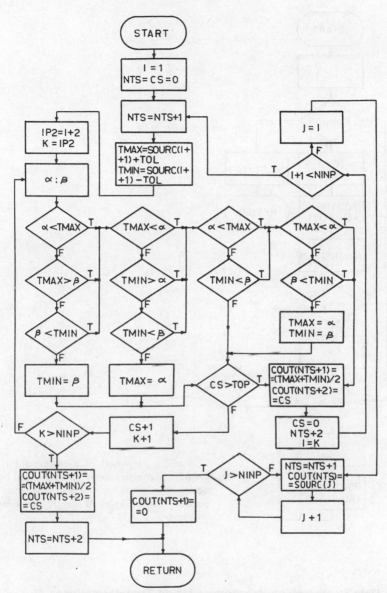

FIG. 7.3. Flowchart of a computer program for data compression using a first-order interpolator, disjoined line segment. The variables I, K, JP2, J and CS are local counters. Here $\alpha = \text{SOURC}(I) + [\text{SOURC}(K) - \text{SOURC}(I) + \text{TOL}]/(K-1)$ and $\beta = \text{SOURC}(I) + [\text{SOURC}(K) - \text{SOURC}(I) - \text{TOL}]/(K-1)$.

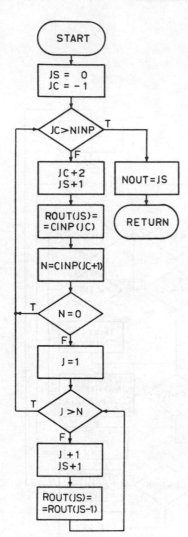

Fig. 7.4. Flowchart of a computer program for decompression of data processed by a zero-order predictor or a zero-order interpolator. The variables JS and JC are local counters.

7.5 Data Compression Procedures Using Transformations

When a discrete Fourier transform (DFT) has to be evaluated to obtain data compression by means of one of the methods described in Chapter 3, it is convenient to use the "fast" algorithm (FFT) first developed by Cooley and Tukey [1]. From the software point of view, there are several different ways

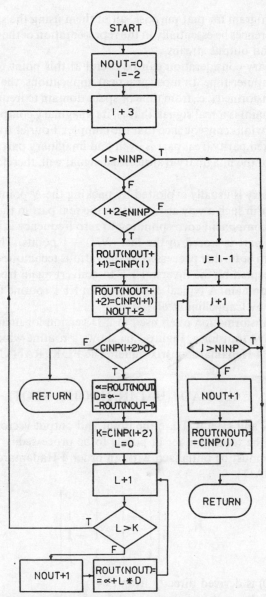

FIG. 7.5. Flowchart of a computer program for decompression of data processed by a first-order interpolator, disjoined line segment. The variables L, I and J are local counters.

of writing a program for that purpose, all of them using the same basic principle. The differences lie essentially in the representation of the complex values of the input and output stream.

An elementary consideration can be useful at this point to save memory space and computer time. In most practical applications, the input signal to be directly transformed (i.e., from time or space domain to frequency or spatial frequency domain) is a real signal, that is, its imaginary components are null. This has the obvious consequence that the complex Fourier transform of such a signal has fixed parity (real part is even and imaginary part is odd) and the middle point of the imaginary transformed signal will, therefore, be equal to zero.

This symmetry is usually exploited by packing the N points of the output complex vector in such a way as to contain the real part in the first $(N/2) + 1$ points (the dc component corresponding to zero frequency is included), while the imaginary part is stored in the last $(N/2) - 1$ points. This is the transformed signal to be further processed by the various techniques and this is also the format accepted by the inverse FFT to convert again from frequency to time or space domain. A typical example of an FFT routine for real samples input is given by Cappellini et $al.$ [2].

Another transformation often used in 2-D version for image compression is the Hadamard transform. Figure 7.6a shows a routine which transforms a signal by a 4×4 Hadamard matrix buffer. The FORTRAN CALL statement could be

$$\text{CALL HAD1 (HADIN, HDOUT, NTOT)} \qquad (7.9)$$

where HADIN and HDOUT are the input and output vectors, respectively, and NTOT is the total number of points to be processed.

The routine must be initialized with an order 4 Hadamard matrix stored in the array HAD

$$H_4 = \frac{1}{4} \begin{bmatrix} 1 & 1 & 1 & 1 \\ 1 & -1 & 1 & -1 \\ 1 & 1 & -1 & -1 \\ 1 & -1 & -1 & 1 \end{bmatrix} \qquad (7.10)$$

Equation (7.10) is derived directly from (3.41).

Figure 7.6b shows the analogous routine for the inverse transform. The calling statement is of the type:

$$\text{CALL HAD2 (HADIN, HDOUT, NTOT)} \qquad (7.11)$$

and the array RHAD must be initialized again with (7.10).

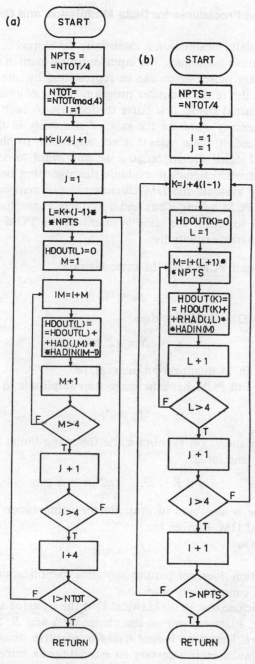

FIG. 7.6. Flowcharts of computer programs to evaluate (a) the direct and (b) the inverse Hadamard transform. The variables I, J, K, L and M are local counters.

7.6 Simulation Procedures for Delta Modulation and DPCM

Software in delta modulation is essentially developed to simulate the behaviour of adaptive techniques. The input/output stream in delta modulation
consists of binary pulses which can be represented by one single bit. However, when the aim of the computer program is that of evaluating the shape
of the reconstructed signal, it is faster to dedicate to each single pulse one
byte or one memory word for the sake of simplicity in the programming
procedure. Indeed, in these cases it is not important to physically generate
the compressed signal stream, because we only want to compare the input
and the reconstructed signals to evaluate the algorithm behaviour.

To correctly evaluate the DM efficiency, a comparison is usually performed with a PCM having n bits and a frequency sampling f_s. In order for
the DM signal to follow the same gradient as the PCM samples, we can
have the two extreme situations:

(1)   if DM and PCM have the same bit rate:

$$f_d = nf_s \tag{7.12}$$

where f_d is the DM frequency, then

$$\Delta = q2^n/n \tag{7.13}$$

where q is the PCM quantization interval; or
(2)   if DM and PCM have the same step amplitude ($\Delta = q$), then

$$f_d = 2^n f_s \tag{7.14}$$

From (7.12) and (7.14) we obtain the following limits for the frequency
ratio $R = f_d/f_s$ and for Δ:

$$n \le R \le 2^n, \qquad q2^n/n \ge \Delta \ge q \tag{7.15}$$

The R value is also used to evaluate the compression ratio, C_a, which,
for the classical DM, is given by:

$$C_a = n/R \tag{7.16}$$

Delta modulation does not require any time identification, therefore (7.16)
gives the total compression ratio.

We can conclude that in the classical DM the C_a value and the theoretical
peak error are a consequence of the choice of Δ and R, therefore they are
known *a priori*. This is no longer true for adaptive or asynchronous DM
for which a simulation is necessary to estimate peak errors, rms errors and
the average compression ratio.

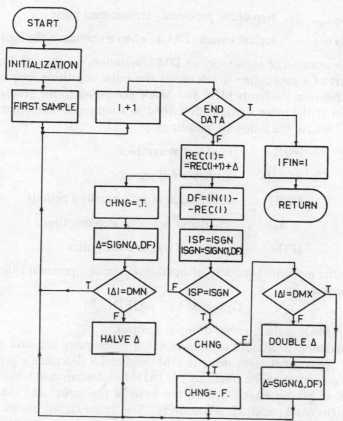

FIG. 7.7. Flowchart of a program to simulate the high information delta modulation (HIDM). The step amplitude Δ ranges between the values DMN and DMX.

Figure 7.7 shows the flowchart of a computer routine to simulate the behaviour of an HIDM algorithm by generating the reconstructed signal. A maximum limit to the step amplitude Δ is given to avoid too large overshoots. Of course, its value must be known by the two communicating partners. The symbols in Fig. 7.7 have the following meanings:

IN(*I*)   input signal samples

REC(*I*)   reconstructed signal

Δ   actual step amplitude

DMN, DMX   minimum and maximum of Δ

IFIN   number of transmitted pulses

ISP   sign of the previously transmitted pulse

CHNG   logical switch (TRUE when a change in the sign occurs)

As an example of asynchronous DM simulation, we show in Fig. 7.8 the
flowchart of a subroutine which varies the pulse repetition frequency (prf)
NPRF between the limits MIN and MAX according to the permanence or
variation of the pulse signs, as described in Chapter 3. The other symbols
in Fig. 7.8 have the following meanings:

IN(I)   input signal samples

REC(I)   reconstructed signal

NPRF   actual value of prf (sampling period)

$\Delta, \Delta 1$ actual and previous step amplitude

JFIN   number of transmitted pulses

Due to the asynchronous way of operation, the compression ratio (7.16) is
now modified by

$$C_a = \text{NMAX} \cdot n/(\text{JFIN} \cdot R) \qquad (7.17)$$

where NMAX is the number of input samples.

An example of a more complicated but much more sensitive method is
that of operational asynchronous DM. Figure 7.9 describes a general program for computing the efficiency of OADM as described in Chapter 3. The
changes in prf are established on the basis of the actual and the past two
pulse signs (Δ, $\Delta 1$ and $\Delta 2$, respectively). The figure clearly shows three different paths. Path 1 corresponds to the classical asynchronous, path 2 to
operational case 1 and path 3 to operational case 2 (see Fig. 3.16). The
sampling period (NPRF) ranges between the two values MIN and MAX.
When the variable INH is greater than 1, case 1 and case 2 are inhibited (to
avoid closed loops), while the logical variable CHNG is TRUE when the
current sample has been inverted. The other variables in the flowchart have
the same meaning as those of Fig. 7.8.

As a final example of adaptivity in prf, let us consider Fig. 7.10, which
reports a typical computer program simulating an asynchronous DPCM. In
this algorithm the sampling frequency changes according to the following
criteria:

(1) maximum sampling frequency equal to that of PCM
(2) the frequency is halved after two consecutive null samples or after
two consecutive samples having an absolute value of 1 and opposite sign
(3) the frequency is doubled after a full scale (negative or positive) is
transmitted.

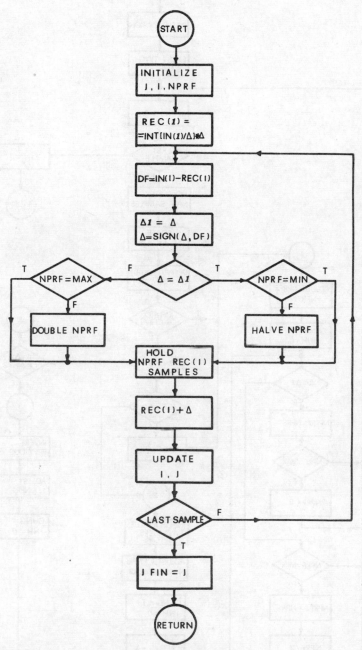

FIG. 7.8. Flowchart of a program to simulate the behaviour of asynchronous delta modulation. The pulse repetition frequency NPRF ranges between the limits MIN and MAX.

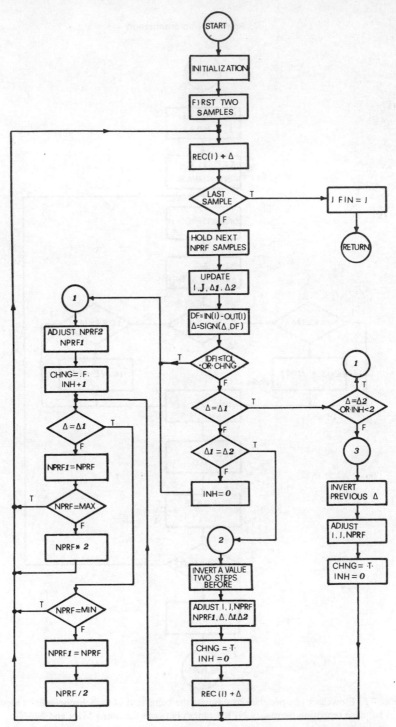

FIG. 7.9. Flowchart for simulation of operational asynchronous delta modulation.

200

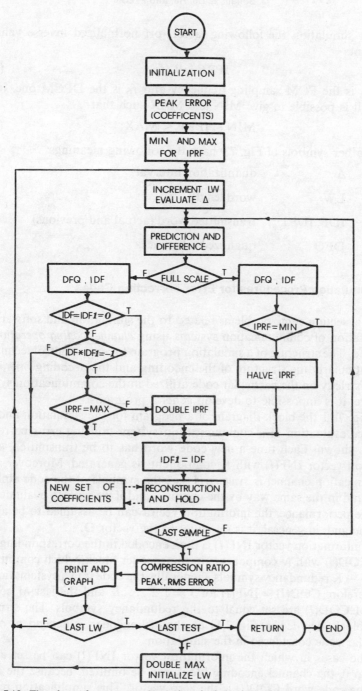

FIG. 7.10. Flowchart of a program simulating the behaviour of asynchronous DPCM. The prf normalized inverse value (IPRF) ranges between MIN and MAX.

For this simulation the following factor (prf normalized inverse value) is important:

$$IRPF = f_s/f_D \tag{7.18}$$

where f_s is the PCM sampling frequency and f_D is the DPCM one. In the routine it is possible to give MIN and MAX such that

$$MIN \leq IPRF \leq MAX \tag{7.19}$$

The other symbols of Fig. 7.9 have the following meanings:

Δ	quantization interval
LW	word length
IDF, IDF1	transmitted word (actual and previous)
DFQ	quantized difference.

7.7   Simulation Procedures for Error-correcting Codes

In this section some problems related to the simulation and software implementation of communication systems using *channel coding operation* are described. The structure of a simulation program for error control techniques and particularly the structure of the encoding and the decoding operations depend strictly on the particular code utilized in the communication system; therefore, it is impossible to develop general programs.

In Fig. 7.11 the block diagram of a program for the simulation and performance evaluation of a communication system utilizing error correcting codes is shown. Each time a new code word has to be transmitted, an information vector INF(I) with K components is generated. Moreover, if the communication channel is *symmetric* (i.e., the symbols of the code alphabet are altered in the same way by the channel) and if we wish to evaluate only the code performance, the information vector can be assumed to be always the same and, in general, it is set equal to the vector **O**.

The information vector INF(I) is then encoded in the corresponding code word COD(I) with N components in the encoder block, which compute the $M = N - K$ redundancy symbols. Generally, the code is in a systematic form and therefore COD(I) = INF(I) for $I = 1, 2, \ldots, K$ and the last M components of COD(I) are set equal to the redundancy symbols. The structure of the block, denoted in Fig. 7.11 as channel encoder, is dependent on the particular code considered in the simulation.

In the cases in which the information vector INF(I) can be set always equal to 0, the channel encoding block can be omitted, because the corresponding code word COD(I) is the zero vector. This simplification reduces in many cases the simulation time by a significant amount.

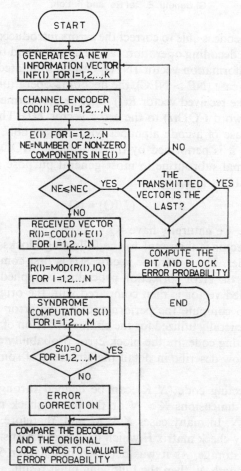

FIG. 7.11. Block diagram of a program for the simulation of a communication system with error correcting codes.

The successive block simulates the behaviour of the communication channel; at its output an integer vector $E(I)$ for $I = 1, 2, \ldots, N$ is given, which represents the errors introduced in the transmitted vector, i.e., if $E(I)$ is equal to zero, then the Ith component of the code word $COD(I)$ is correctly received, while if $E(I)$ is equal to one, then the Ith component of $COD(I)$ is altered by an error. The number of errors introduced by the communication channel is denoted with NE.

In order to reduce the computation time, it is convenient, in the case of error correcting codes, to compare the number NE of errors introduced by the channel with the number NEC of errors which the code is able to correct.

If NE $\leq$ NEC, the code is able to correct the errors introduced by the channel and, therefore, the decoding operation can be avoided and the transmission of the following information vector INF(I) can be simulated.

In the opposite case (NE $>$ NEC), the decoding operation must be simulated. Therefore, the received vector $R(I)$ must be first formed by adding the transmitted code word COD(I) to the error vector $E(I)$. This sum must be executed, in the case of a code alphabet with IQ symbols, with a modulo IQ operation and it is performed by the subroutine MOD(J, IQ), which is generally an internal subroutine in most general purpose computers. The integer J modulo IQ is given by

$$J = J - (J/\text{IQ}) * \text{IQ} \tag{7.20}$$

In the binary case, we naturally have $\text{IQ} = 2$.

The received vector is then sent to the following blocks, which simulate the channel decoder. The syndrome vector $S(I)$ is first computed and then, if $S(I)$ is non-zero, the error correction procedure is applied on the received vector. The decoded vector is then compared with the original transmitted vector in order to compute the performance of the error correcting code. The parameters generally utilized for the characterization of the performance of an error-correcting code are the block-error probability and the bit-error probability. We now describe in detail the structure of some blocks in Fig. 7.11.

An error correcting code (N, K) can be defined through the generator matrix G having dimensions $K \times N$ or the parity-check matrix H having dimensions $M \times N$. In many cases $K \gg M$ and, therefore, it is convenient to utilize the parity-check matrix H which has lower dimensions and requires a lower memory storage. As it was depicted in Chapter 5, if COD(I) is a code word with length N, then the following must result:

$$\sum_{I=1}^{N} \text{COD}(I) * H(J, I) = 0 \qquad \text{for} \quad J = 1, 2, \ldots, M \tag{7.21}$$

$H(J, I)$ being the element of the Jth row and Ith column in the parity-check matrix. In order to detect and to correct the errors introduced by the communication channel, the syndrome vector $S(J)$ is generally computed. This is defined as:

$$S(J) = \sum_{I=1}^{N} R(I) * H(J, I) \tag{7.22}$$

where $R(I)$ is the received vector and $J = 1, 2, \ldots, M$.

In Fig. 7.12 the block diagram of a subroutine is shown which can be utilized for the simulation both of the encoding operation (7.21) and of the syndrome computation (7.22). The subroutine can be utilized for any error

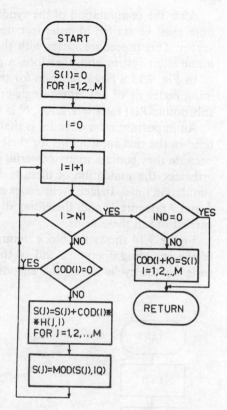

FIG. 7.12. Flowchart of a program for the encoding or syndrome computation of a linear code defined through its parity-check matrix.

control coding technique, once its parity-check matrix is known. The calling statement of this subroutine is:

$$\text{CALL CODEC (COD, } S, N1, M, K, \text{IQ, IND)} \qquad (7.23)$$

The index IND is set equal to 0 to perform the encoding operation, while it is set equal to 1 to simulate the syndrome computation. When the encoding operation is simulated, the parameter $N1$ is set equal to K and the vector $\text{COD}(I)$ has the first K components equal to the information symbols and $S(I)$ is the vector which contains the redundancy symbols. Therefore, after the encoding operation, the last M symbols of the code word are set equal to the components of the vector $S(I)$, i.e.,

$$\text{COD}(K + I) = S(I) \qquad \text{for} \quad I = 1, 2, \dots, M \qquad (7.24)$$

When this subroutine is utilized at the receiver side for the computation of the syndrome vector, then $N1$ is set equal to N and $S(I)$ represents the syndrome.

After the computation of the syndrome $S(I)$, the error correction procedure must be started in order to correct the errors detected in the received vector. This procedure varies with the particular code utilized in the communication system and, therefore, a general program cannot be presented.

In Fig. 7.13 a block diagram for the error-correction operation of Hamming codes or of any other single-error correcting code is shown. In this subroutine $R(I)$ for $I = 1, 2, \ldots, N$ is the received vector.

An important class of codes is that of cyclic codes, which are largely utilized in the real applications for their simple hardware implementation and because they contain many powerful error correcting classes of codes. Nevertheless, the simulation of these codes is often difficult and requires long simulation times. In fact, cyclic codes are defined on Galois fields (see Chapter 5 and Appendix 1) and, therefore, all the operations on the vector must be carried out in these fields.

Figure 7.14 shows the block diagram of a subroutine for the simulation of the encoding operation and of the syndrome computation for a cyclic code. In the cyclic codes, the encoding and decoding operations are per-

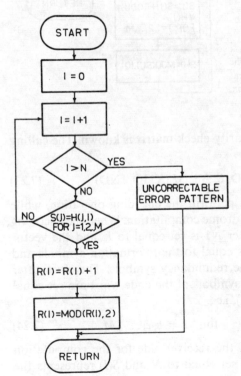

FIG. 7.13. Flowchart of the error correction procedure in a single-error-correcting code defined through its parity-check matrix.

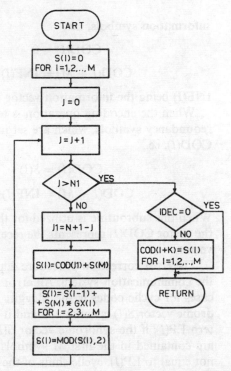

FIG. 7.14. Flowchart of a program for the encoding or syndrome computation of a cyclic code defined through its generator polynomial.

formed by using the generator polynomial $g(x)$ with degree equal to the number m of redundancy symbols. If the generator polynomial $g(x)$ is

$$g(x) = g_0 + g_1 x + \cdots + g_{m-1} x^{m-1} + x^m \qquad (7.25)$$

we consider the vector $GX(I)$, defined as:

$$GX(I) = (g_0, g_1, \ldots, g_{m-1}) \qquad (7.26)$$

The encoding operation in a cyclic code is performed by dividing the information polynomial by the generator polynomial; the remainder of this division gives the redundancy symbols. Analogously, at the receiver the syndrome is computed by dividing the received vector by the generator polynomial. Therefore, also in this case, the two operations, encoding and syndrome computation, are quite similar and can be simulated by using the same subroutine as shown in Fig. 7.14.

When the encoding operation is simulated, the vector $COD(I)$ has the first M components equal to 0 and the last K components equal to the information symbols, i.e.,

$$COD(I) = 0 \qquad \text{for} \quad I = 1, 2, \ldots, M$$
$$COD(I + M) = INF(I) \qquad \text{for} \quad I = 1, 2, \ldots, K \tag{7.27}$$

$INF(I)$ being the information vector defined as in Fig. 7.11.

When the encoding operation is terminated, the vector $S(J)$ contains the redundancy symbols, which are set in the first M components of the vector $COD(I)$, i.e.,

$$COD(I) = S(I) \qquad \text{for} \quad I = 1, 2, \ldots, M$$
$$COD(I + M) = INF(I) \qquad \text{for} \quad I = 1, 2, \ldots, K \tag{7.28}$$

When this subroutine is utilized for the syndrome computation (IDEC = 1), the vector $COD(I)$ represents the received vector $R(I)$ and $S(J)$ the syndrome vector.

The error correction procedure depends on the particular code utilized in the communication system. An error correction procedure utilized in many cases for cyclic codes is the Meggitt scheme [3, 4]. In this scheme the syndrome vector $S(I)$ is computed and it is compared with a prefixed error pattern $EP(I)$; if the syndrome vector $S(I)$ is equal to $EP(I)$, then all the errors are contained in the first M symbols of the received vector, while if $S(I)$ is not equal to $EP(I)$, cyclic shifts of the syndrome $S(I)$ are performed until the vector $S(I)$ is equal to $EP(I)$. If, after N shifts, the syndrome $S(I)$ is never equal to $EP(I)$, then an uncorrectable error pattern is detected. This decoding algorithm is simulated by the subroutine (Fig. 7.15):

$$\text{SUBROUTINE MEGGIT } (S, COD, R, EP, IC, N) \tag{7.29}$$

IC being a parameter which is set equal to 0 if an error correction operation is performed, and equal to 1 if an uncorrectable error pattern is detected. The index NSHF is a local counter of the shift number.

A Meggitt scheme can be utilized for error correction in many cases. For example, we consider the case in which the code is a single-error-correcting code (as Hamming codes). If an error is introduced in the first component of the code word, then the vector $EP(I)$ is equal to a vector with M components given by $(1, 0, 0, \ldots, 0)$.

If $S(I)$ is not equal to $EP(I)$, then some cyclic shifts are performed on the vector $S(I)$ until the previous error pattern configuration is obtained; then the error lies in the first position and can be easily corrected.

The cyclic shifts of the vector $S(I)$ are simulated through a suitable subroutine, having the following calling statement:

$$\text{CALL SHIFT } (S, GX, M) \tag{7.30}$$

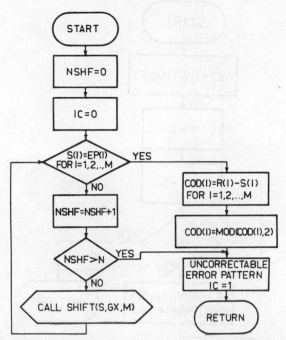

FIG. 7.15. Flowchart for the simulation of a Meggit error correcting procedure in a cyclic code.

The general block diagram of this subroutine is shown in Fig. 7.16 (the symbols in the flowchart are defined next). This subroutine is quite useful in the simulation of cyclic codes and can be utilized in many other subroutines.

The decoding subroutine of Fig. 7.15 can also be utilized, for example, to simulate the correction of burst errors. We consider a cyclic code that is able to correct bursts with length b or less. If a burst with length b alters the first symbols of the transmitted code word, then the error pattern $EP(I)$ is equal to

$$\overset{\longleftarrow b \longrightarrow}{} \overset{\longleftarrow M-b \longrightarrow}{}$$
$$(1, x, x, \ldots, x, 1, 0, 0, \ldots, 0) \tag{7.31}$$

where the symbols x can be 0 or 1. The decoder analyzes the last $M - b$ components of the syndrome vector $S(I)$; if these components are all equal to zero and some components between the first b are non-zero, then a burst is recognized in the first b components of the received vector $R(I)$ and the correction is performed. In the opposite case, some cyclic shifts of the syndrome vector $S(I)$ are performed through the subroutine SHIFT until the

G. Benelli, E. Del Re, and F. Lotti

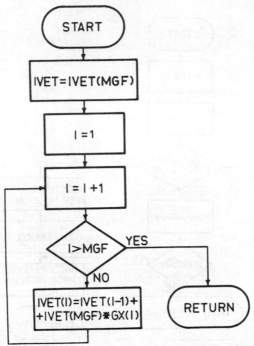

FIG. 7.16. Flowchart for the simulation of a cyclic shift in a shift register.

previous error pattern is obtained. This decoding scheme is also described in Chapter 5 for burst-error-correcting codes.

For some multiple-error-correcting codes, as, for example, BCH or Reed–Solomon codes, the error correction procedure must be carried out by simulating the operations in a Galois field (Appendix 1) having NGF elements, such that

$$NGF = 2^{MGF} \qquad (7.32)$$

In these cases, it is convenient, in order to simulate a Galois field, to compile a table $GF(I, J)$ with $I = 1, 2, \ldots, MGF$ and $J = 1, 2, \ldots, NGF$, having as Jth column the binary representation of the Jth element of the Galois field. This table can be compiled by the subroutine shown in Fig. 7.17, having the calling statement:

$$CALL\ GALOIS\ (GF,\ GX,\ MGF,\ NGF) \qquad (7.33)$$

where $GX(I)$ for $I = 1, 2, \ldots, MGF$ is a vector whose Ith component represents the Ith coefficient of the generator polynomial of the Galois field (see Appendix 1).

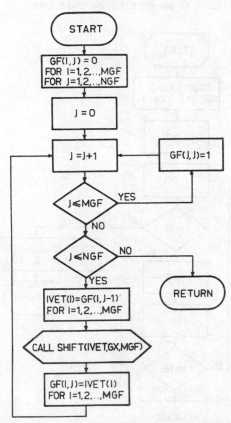

FIG. 7.17. Creation of a table $GF(I, J)$ giving the binary representation of the elements of a Galois field with $NGF = 2^{MGF}$ symbols.

As we have previously outlined, the simulation of cyclic codes often requires high computation time, because it is necessary to simulate the operations on Galois fields having heavy structures for the simulation in FORTRAN or similar higher level languages.

Codes defined on a field of the integers modulo a prime number GF are often simpler and less expensive in the simulation time. Typical examples of these codes are the binoid codes [5] and the generalized Hamming codes [6].

As an example of the implementation of these codes we consider the single-burst-correcting binoid codes, defined by the parity-check matrix H of the form:

$$H = \begin{bmatrix} I_b & I_b & \cdots & I_b & I_b & 0 \\ n_b I_b & (n_b - 1)I_b & \cdots & I_b & 0 & I_b \end{bmatrix} \tag{7.34}$$

n_b being an integer equal or less than $(GF - 1)$ and I_b the $b \times b$ identity matrix.

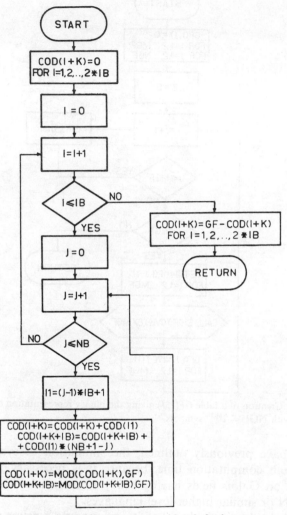

FIG. 7.18. Flowchart of the encoder of a binoid code for burst-error correction.

In Fig. 7.18 the block diagram of the encoding operation of such a binoid code is shown. In this figure IB denotes the length of the bursts which can be corrected by the code (IB = b) and NB = n_b. As shown in the figure, for these codes it is not necessary to store the parity-check matrix, which is automatically constructed during the encoding operation.

In Fig. 7.19 the block diagram of the decoder (syndrome computation and error correction) is shown. These codes are able to correct bursts with

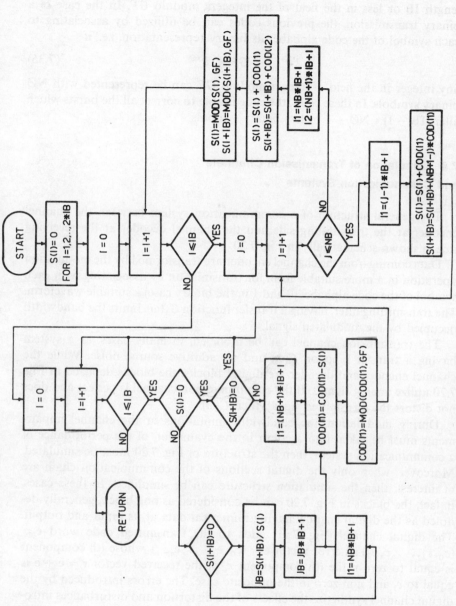

FIG. 7.19. Flowchart of the syndrome computation and error correction procedure for a burst-error-correcting binoid code.

length IB or less in the field of the integers modulo GF. In the case of a binary transmission, the previous codes can be utilized by associating to each symbol of the code alphabet its binary representation, i.e., if

$$2^{N\emptyset - 1} \leq GF < 2^{N\emptyset} \tag{7.35}$$

any integer in the field of integer modulo GF can be represented with $N\emptyset$ binary symbols. In these cases, the code is able to correct all the bursts which alter $(IB - 1) * N\emptyset + 1$ or less binary symbols.

7.8 Simulation of Transmission Channels and Communication Systems

The general structure of a communication system between the channel encoder at the transmitting side and the channel decoder at the receiving side is shown schematically in Fig. 7.20.

Data coming from the channel encoder are transformed by the modulation operation in a more suitable form for transmission by associating with each symbol of the code alphabet (0 and 1 in the binary case) a suitable waveform. The transmitting filter, having a transfer function $G_T(\omega)$, limits the bandwidth occupied by the modulated signal.

The transmission channel can be modeled, in many cases, as a system having a transfer function $C(\omega)$ and an additive source noise. While the channel encoder and decoder are digital blocks, the blocks depicted in Fig. 7.20 utilize analog signals. If the communication channel is perfect and does not distort the transmitted signal, then $C(\omega) = 1$.

During modulation, the bandwidth limitations or the channel impairments must be taken into account in the evaluation of the performance of a communication system, then the structure of Fig. 7.20 must be simulated. Moreover, when only the digital sections of the communication chain are of interest, then the simulation structure can be simplified. In these cases, in fact, the blocks in Fig. 7.20 can be considered as one block, generally denoted as the digital channel having numerical data at its input and output. The digital channel (Fig. 7.21) adds to the transmitted code word $\mathbf{c} = (c_0, c_1, \ldots, c_{n-1})$ an error vector $\mathbf{e} = (e_0, e_1, \ldots, e_{n-1})$, whose ith component is equal to zero if the ith component r_i of the received vector $\mathbf{r} = \mathbf{c} + \mathbf{e}$ is equal to c_i and non-zero in the opposite case. The errors introduced by the digital channel synthetize the effects of the distortion and disturbances introduced by the blocks in Fig. 7.20.

For the simulation of the digital channel, theoretical models or experimental data must be utilized. In this section we briefly describe two subroutines for the simulation of binary channels; the first subroutine simulates

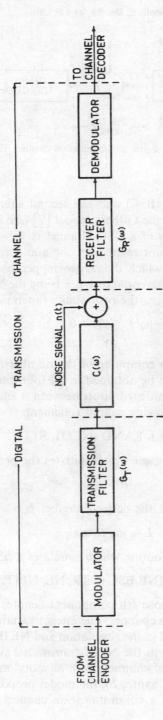

Fig. 7.20. Block diagram of a communication system.

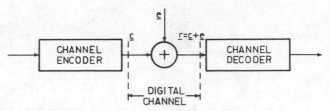

FIG. 7.21. Schematic model of a digital communication channel. The vectors $\mathbf{r}$, $\mathbf{c}$ and $\mathbf{e}$ are underscored in the figure.

a binary symmetric channel (BSC) and the second subroutine simulates a channel with memory, using the Gilbert model [7] (see Chapter 5).

In Fig. 7.22 the flowchart of a BSC channel is shown. In this channel model, the error events are not related to one another and, therefore, the time instants or positions in which the errors happen have a geometric distribution [8, 9] with mean value equal to $1/p$, p being the bit error probability in the transmission channel, i.e., the probability function is:

$$f(L) = pq^L, \qquad L = 0, 1, 2, \ldots \tag{7.36}$$

where $q = 1 - p$.

The generation through a computer of the number n, which represents the position of the errors, can be obtained in the following way [10]. A random number R with uniform distribution between 0 and 1 is generated by a subroutine, having the following calling statement:

CALL RAND (NCO1, R)

where NCO1 is a positive integer which initiates the process. Then

$$R = q^L \tag{7.37}$$

can be written and, therefore, the desired number L is

$$L = \log R/\log q \tag{7.38}$$

The statement of the subroutine which simulates a BSC channel is

SUBROUTINE BSC (ERR, NE, NBIT, P)

where ERR(I) is a vector whose Ith component denotes the position of the Ith error introduced from the channel. The integer variable NBIT represents the number of bits considered in the simulation and NE the number of errors introduced from the channel in the NBIT transmitted symbols.

For the characterization of channels with memory, many models can be found in the literature (see Chapter 5); the model proposed by Gilbert permits a simple simulation of a communication channel with memory and

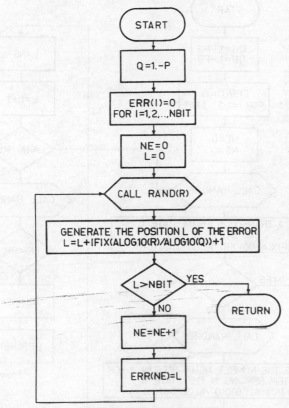

FIG. 7.22. Flowchart of a subroutine which simulates binary symmetric channel.

describes approximately the behaviour of many real channels. The channel is described by a *Markov chain* with two states: state G (good) represents the condition of no-errors, while state B (bad) represents the burst condition, in which errors can occur. We denote with PG the probability of a transition from state G to state B, with PB the probability of a transition from state B to state G and QG = 1 − PG, QB = 1 − PB the probabilities of remaining in states G and B, respectively. In order to describe burst noise, states G and B tend to persist and therefore QG and QB often assume large values.

In the simulation of this channel model, the time in which the channel remains in the states G or B has a mean geometric distribution of 1/PG or 1/PB, respectively [7]. In state B the error probability is PH.

The flowchart of a subroutine which simulates this model is shown in Fig. 7.23 and its statement is

SUBROUTINE GILBER (ERR, NE, NBIT, PG, PB, PH)

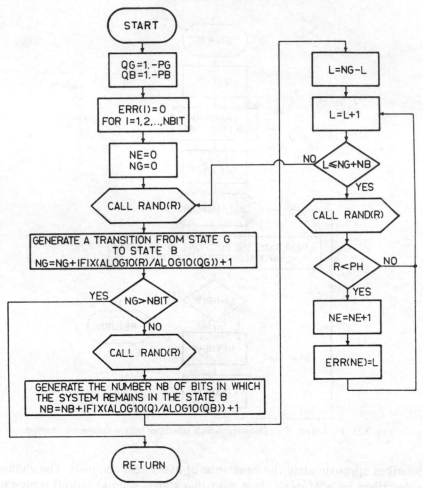

FIG. 7.23. Flowchart of a subroutine which simulates the Gilbert model for channels with memory.

where ERR(*I*), NE and NBIT have the same meaning as the parameters in the subroutine BSC.

Now we consider briefly the case in which it is also necessary to simulate the analog part of the transmission chain shown in Fig. 7.20. A possible structure for the simulation of the analog section is shown in Fig. 7.24.

In the simulation of modulated signals, it is often convenient to deal with an equivalent baseband model in order to reduce computation time and sample number [9]. The filtering of the modulated signal, at both the transmitter and receiver sides can be performed either in the time or frequency

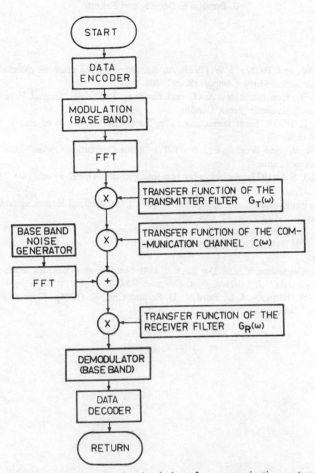

FIG. 7.24. Flowchart for the simulation of a communication system.

domain; generally, this last method is the most suitable, because in many cases the transfer functions of the filters are known. Therefore, the modulated signal is first transformed in frequency by an FFT algorithm and multiplied for the transfer function of the filters $G_T(\omega)$, $G_R(\omega)$ and the transfer function of the channel $C(\omega)$. Analogously, the noise is generated in the time domain and transformed in the frequency domain. At the receiver side, before the demodulation operation, the signal is transformed from the frequency into the time domain by the inverse FFT algorithm (FFT^{-1}).

Greater details on this simulation structure and other particular aspects are given in Benelli *et al.* [9].

References

1. Cooley, J. W., and Tuckey, J. W. (1975). An algorithm for the machine calculation of complex Fourier series. *Math. Comput.* **19**, 297–301.
2. Cappellini, V., Constantinides, A. G., and Emiliani, P. (1978). "Digital Filters and Their Applications." Academic Press, London.
3. Meggitt, J. E. (1960). Error correcting codes for correcting bursts of errors. *IBM J. Res. Dev.* **4**, 329–334.
4. Peterson, W. W., and Weldon, E. J., Jr. (1972). "Error Correcting Codes." MIT Press, Cambridge, Massuchusetts.
5. Samoylenko, S. I. (1973). Binoid error correcting codes. *IEEE Trans. Inf. Theory* **IT-19**, 95–101.
6. Benelli, G., Bianciardi, C., and Cappellini, V. (1975). Generalized Hamming codes for burst-error correction. *Alta Freq.* **44**, 658–661.
7. Gilbert, E. N. (1960). Capacity of a burst-noisy channel. *Bell Syst. Tech. J.* **39**, 1253–1265.
8. Feller, W. (1967). "An Introduction to Probability Theory and Its Applications." Wiley, New York.
9. Benelli, G., Cappellini, V., and Del Re, E. (1984). Simulation system for analog and digital transmissions. *IEEE J. Selected Areas Commun.* **SAC-2**, 77–88.
10. Naylor, T. H., Balintfly, J. L., Burdick, D. S., and Chu, K. (1966). "Computer Simulation Techniques." Wiley, New York.

Chapter 8

Hardware Implementation of Data Compression and Error Control Techniques

V. CAPPELLINI

Dipartimento di Ingegneria Elettronica
Università di Firenze
and Istituto di Ricerca sulle Onde Elettromagnetiche
Consiglio Nazionale delle Ricerche
Florence, Italy

E. DEL RE

Dipartimento di Ingegneria Elettronica
Università di Firenze
Florence, Italy

8.1 Introduction

In many applications, as in the case of information transmission, a necessary requirement for a data compression and/or error control system is the real-time operation. This is generally achieved by a specialized hardware implementation of the involved compression-coding algorithms. The hardware solution is indeed becoming more and more attractive due to the increased processing rate and performance of the integrated digital circuits and their continuously decreasing cost. It can also benefit from the use of high-density large-scale integration (LSI) and very large-scale integration (VLSI) of digital circuits, which allows even complex data compression and error control algorithms to be implemented by a few chips and, in perspective, even by only

221

one VLSI chip. Moreover, the introduction and development of microprocessors can offer a programmable, highly flexible and low-cost dedicated approach to the hardware implementation.

According to the preceding considerations, an increased use of specific hardware implementation of data compression and error control algorithms is emerging in applications such as the digital communications of voice, data and images through satellite systems and the new integrated-service digital network (ISDN).

This chapter, after a brief review of binary arithmetic and digital binary circuits, presents some possible hardware implementations of the data compression and error control algorithms considered in the previous chapters.

8.2 Review of Binary Arithmetics

Binary numbers are generally represented in the fixed point form or in the floating point form. The fixed point representation has several variations, each differing in the binary point position (right or left justified numbers) and in the negative number representation [1].

If the right justified fixed point form is used, each number is represented by a sequence of positive powers of two. To clarify what we mean let us consider an arithmetic operation with 16 bits (15 for the magnitude and 1 for the sign), which is common, for example, in many minicomputers. Any of the possible 32,768 ($= 2^{15}$) sequences of 15 bits, having positive sign (sign bit 0), represents a number whose magnitude can be expressed by means of the relation

$$N = \sum_{i=0}^{M-1} d_i 2^i \qquad (8.1)$$

where d_i is a binary variable assuming only the values 0, 1 and $M = 15$.

On the other hand in the left justified fixed point case, when the binary point is assumed at the left of the most significant bit, any of the previously considered sequences represents a number whose value is given by

$$N = \sum_{i=1}^{M} d_i 2^{-i} \qquad (8.2)$$

that is, a number in the range $(1 - 2^{-M}, 0)$.

These definitions can be expressed by saying that the right justified fixed point numbers represent integers, while the left justified fixed point numbers represent fractions.

The main difference between the two representations is in the multiplication operation. The multiplication of two fractions is a fraction and, therefore, it cannot exceed the length of the registers if the least significant bits are eliminated during the operation.

Obviously overflow in the addition operation can occur with either of the two forms. Hence, particular care must be given to the overflow problems in the implementation of fixed point binary operations.

In the floating point representation the sequence of binary digits, which represents the number, is divided into two sub-sequences. The first, called the *mantissa m*, is normally a left justified, signed, fixed point number which represents the normalized magnitude of the number. The second, known as the *exponent e*, represents the signed exponent of the power of two by which the mantissa has to be multiplied to obtain the value of the number. Accordingly the number is given by the relationship

$$N = \pm m 2^{\pm e} \qquad (8.3)$$

It is evident that the floating point representation is more convenient when a great dynamic range of numbers has to be represented, because a few extra bits in the exponent can be used to accommodate a great range of representable numbers.

Another item to consider is the representation of negative numbers. The simpler representation is that of sign magnitude representation. In this case one of the bits is reserved for the sign (normally 0 positive, 1 negative), while the rest of the digits constitute the positive magnitude of the number. The second representation examined here is the one based on complements. Two types of complements are possible in the binary base, the 1-complement and the 2-complement. Of these two we consider the 2-complement which is the most commonly used representation. In this case, positive numbers are represented as in the sign magnitude case (sign 0), whilst negative numbers are represented in the integer case as

$$N_{neg} = 2^M - \sum_{i=0}^{M-1} d_i 2^i \qquad (8.4)$$

or in the fractional case as

$$N_{neg} = 1 - \sum_{i=1}^{M} d_i 2^{-i} \qquad (8.5)$$

where M is the number of binary digits of the systems.

Thus, for example, in the 16 bit system considered before, the number 1 is represented as 0 000 0000 0000 0001 whereas the number -1 is represented by $2^M - 1$, that is 1 111 1111 1111 1111. It can be noted that in this case too, negative numbers are identified by the sign bit 1, but the representation of the rest of the number is completely different from that in the sign magnitude representation. Some comments on the 2-complement representation are in order.

First, the representation is circular, that is, if we start from zero and keep adding 1 to the preceding number, we obtain all the positive numbers from 0 to $2^M - 1$. Then adding again 1 we obtain a negative number because the sign bit becomes equal to 1 and its magnitude corresponds to 2^M. Continuing on with the unity increment we obtain all the negative numbers to -1, then 0, that is the number from which the operation was started.

A consequence of this is a very important feature of this number system, namely that if the result of an addition of more than two positive and negative numbers is such as to be representable with the available number of binary digits, then the result is exact irrespective of the order of the addition operations, even if overflow takes place in a sequence of operations.

A second very important feature of the 2-complement representation is that subtraction can be obtained as addition of the minuend and the 2-complement version of the subtrahend. In fact, with reference, for example, to integer numbers the addition of N_1 to the 2-complement version of N_2 as defined by (8.4) corresponds to $N_1 + 2^M - N_2$ and since the representation is modulo 2^M, this is equivalent to $N_1 - N_2$.

Thus, it is possible, by using a 2-complement arithmetic representation, to perform both addition and subtraction using only an adder. The problem is now the computation of the 2-complement version of a number. From the definitions (8.4) and (8.5) it seems that it is necessary to perform a subtraction to obtain the 2-complement. However, more efficient methods exist. For example, it is easy to see that the 2-complement of a number can be computed by complementing all the bits in its binary representation (sign included) and then adding 1 to this result.

Between the two number representations presented in the previous considerations, the fixed point one is simpler from the implementation point of view. The sum of two numbers is simple to implement and the multiplication can be obtained without overflow problems if the fixed point numbers represent fractions. The main problems for the application of this type of arithmetic are in its limited dynamic range. Hence particular care has to be taken in the normalization of the variables to avoid overflow.

By using a floating point representation, some of the problems related to the dynamic range constraints can be avoided, with at most some extra bits in the representation. However, the implementation of this type of arithmetic is more difficult and generally it is slower than the fixed point one. In fact, to add two numbers in the floating point system it is necessary first to normalize them, so that they have the same exponent, and then perform the addition. The result of addition has to be normalized again if necessary. Moreover, a floating point multiplication is really the combination of two arithmetic operations, that is, the product of the mantissas and the addition of the exponents.

It is also important to observe that in the fixed point representation, once overflow in the addition operations has been avoided through suitable normalizations of the signals, an error is introduced only in the multiplications. In the floating point representation, on the other hand, some error is also introduced in the additions, because some bits of one of the numbers are lost in the normalization process.

The increase in complexity in floating point arithmetic results in the preference of fixed point arithmetic in hardware implementations of compression-coding algorithms. In this case, the economy obtainable in the computing hardware and memory, and in addition the increase in speed possible can be more important than the increase in design work involved in (1) the choice of the best hardware structure, (2) the computation of the overflow constraints and (3) the study of the error behaviour of the structure. In software implementation on general purpose computers and minicomputers and in applications where the processing speed is not very high, a floating point implementation can give greater flexibility (Chapter 7).

Finally, we observe that in most minicomputers real numbers are represented as floating point numbers of 32 bits, 8 for the exponent (sign included) and 24 for the 2-complement mantissa. This allows the representation of 6–7 decimal digits and a good dynamic range, that is, $2^{-128} \leq N \leq 2^{127}$.

Integer numbers are generally represented as right justified fixed point numbers. It can be observed that if fixed point arithmetic is used in the implementation using a high-level language such as FORTRAN, the maximum data and coefficient length is limited by the fact that an overflow in the multiplication occurs if the sum of the bits of the two operands is greater than 15 bits (sign excluded).

Fortunately, however, most of the fixed point arithmetic units used in minicomputers compute all 32 bits that result in the multiplication of two 16-bit numbers. This allows the user to represent the variables as left justified fractions to a maximum of 15 bits plus sign and, after multiplication, to choose the 16 most significant bits of the product using a lower-level programming language. The approximation with a limited number of digits of variables, for any representation of the numbers, which are in principle continuous, has as a consequence the introduction of an error. This error depends on the number of binary digits M used in the representation, the type of representation (fixed point, floating point), the type of negative number representation and finally the method used to eliminate the digits exceeding the register length.

Two different approaches can be considered for the last operation. The first consists of simply chopping off the exceeding bits. The second consists of the approximation of the number to the nearest level, that is to the same value as in the truncation case if the ignored fraction is less than half the magnitude of the least significant bit in the representation and to the same value incremented by 1 in the other case. The first type of approximation is called *truncation*, whilst the second one is referred to as *rounding*.

Rounding is obviously more precise than truncation since the maximum error is equal to one-half the quantization step. Thus, if the number is represented by a fraction of M bits (sign excluded) the error in the approximation will be in the range

$$-\tfrac{1}{2}2^{-M} < e(n) \leq \tfrac{1}{2}2^{-M} \qquad (8.6)$$

The maximum error is greater in the truncation case, being equal to the quantization step, and its value (in sign) depends on the negative number representation. If the sign magnitude form is used, the error is then defined as the difference between the obtained value and the true value and it is between 0 and -2^{-M} if the number is positive, whereas the error is between 2^{-M} and 0 if the number is negative; that is, the error is always of opposite sign to the number. If the 2-complement representation is used then the error is not correlated with the sign of the number to be quantized but it is always negative and within the interval $(0, -2^{-M})$.

A more involved situation exists when the floating point representation is chosen. In this case the approximation (truncation or rounding) is performed only on the mantissa of the number. This means that the absolute magnitude of the error depends on the magnitude of the number, that is, in this case relative errors instead of absolute errors are important. Therefore, in the floating point case the errors introduced in the approximation are multiplicative instead of additive. Thus if a represents the value of a number to be approximated and a' the resulting floating point number, with ε defined as the relative error then we have

$$(a' - a)/a = \varepsilon \qquad (8.7)$$

and consequently

$$a' = a + \varepsilon a = a(1 + \varepsilon) \qquad (8.8)$$

If we use, for example, a rounding arithmetic the error in the mantissa is expressed by Eq. (8.6) and hence

$$-2^l(2^{-M}/2) < a' - a \leq 2^l(2^{-M}/2) \qquad (8.9)$$

if l is the value of the exponent.

A bound for ε can be obtained using (8.7) and the relation $2^{l-1} < a < 2^l$ for which the result is

$$-2^{-M} < \varepsilon \leq 2^{-M} \qquad (8.10)$$

Another aspect that must be considered in hardware (and software) implementation of data compression and error control techniques is the signal quantization. The operation of quantization can be considered as the substitution of the signal samples with the most significant M digits of their binary representation, according to the rules previously described. Hence a quantized sample $x(n)$ can be considered as represented in the form

$$x(n) = x'(n) + e(n) \qquad (8.11)$$

where $x'(n)$ is the exact value of the sample and $e(n)$ the associated error. Generally the following assumptions are considered for the error sequence $e(n)$:

(1) $e(n)$ is a stationary random process,
(2)   the probability density function of $e(n)$ is uniform over the quantization range,
(3) $e(n)$ is an uncorrelated sequence (white noise process) and
(4) $e(n)$ is uncorrelated with the sequence of exact values $x'(n)$.

Obviously these assumptions are to some extent arbitrary and it is easy to construct cases where they fail. For example, a constant signal or a sinusoidal signal sampled at a frequency which is a rational multiple of the sinusoidal frequency. In the first case all the errors $e(n)$ are equal whilst in the second case they constitute a periodic sequence; for these cases the above hypotheses are not valid. However, Bennet [2] verified that these assumptions realistically represent most of the signals which we are likely to encounter. Thus, this model for the quantization error behaviour has enormous practical value. Roughly, it can be said that the model can be used when the signal behaviour is such that it crosses several quantization steps going from one sample to the other and at the same time the number of quantization levels, or equivalently bits, in the number representation is not too small. The use of this model has the advantage of leading to a rather simple analysis of the signal quantization effects.

The probability density function has the form of Fig. 8.1a for rounding arithmetic and of Fig. 8.1b for 2-complement truncation arithmetic. The mean m and the variance σ^2 for these probability density functions are

$$m = 0, \qquad \sigma^2 = 2^{-2M}/12 \qquad (8.12)$$

for rounding, and

$$m = -2^{-(M+1)}, \qquad \sigma^2 = 2^{-2M}/12 \qquad (8.13)$$

for 2-complement truncation.

The quantization error can be conveniently measured by the ratio of the signal power S to quantization error variance (signal-to-noise ratio S/N)

$$\text{S/N} = S/\sigma^2 = 12(2^{2M}S) \qquad (8.14)$$

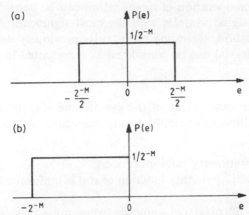

FIG. 8.1. Probability density functions: (a) rounding and (b) truncation.

Using the decibel (dB) measure we have

$$S/N_{dB} = 10\log_{10}12 + 20M\log_{10}2 + 10\log_{10}S \qquad (8.15)$$

It is interesting to observe that since $20\log_{10}2 \simeq 6$, the addition of one bit in the arithmetic increases the signal-to-noise ratio by approximately 6 dB.

The preceding exposition of the quantization process suggests some considerations about the choice of the quantization step to be used in the applications. This choice is determined by the necessary required precision, the noise present on the signal to be processed and the operation that has to be performed on the signal.

The noise present on the signal introduces an upper limit on the number of quantization steps. Obviously it does not make any sense to use a small quantization step when much noise is present on the signal, because in this case we are quantizing the noise and not the signal. It is sufficient to quantize to a level that introduces an amount of quantization noise small in comparison with the noise present on the signal.

In the opposite case, when the noise is very small, the quantization step has to be chosen so as to obtain the desired quality at the output of the processing. In fact, a degradation of the input signal quality can be caused by errors introduced in the processing. So the input signal quantization and the processing structure in terms of the algorithms employed, precision of the arithmetic used and so on have to be chosen in a way which is compatible with the necessary required accuracy at the output.

What would remain to be characterized is the contribution to the output of a processing system of the input quantization noise $e(n)$. For linear time-invariant digital systems, when applicable to data compression and error control systems, detailed analyses are available in the literature [1, 3, 4].

8.3 Overview of Digital Hardware for Data Compression and Error Control Techniques

The implementation of any data compression and error control algorithm requires memory cells, adders and multipliers as basic building blocks. The memory circuits are amongst the most developed components in semiconductor technology and several alternatives are available, the choice of which depends on several factors, for example:

(1)   the speed of operation (this is the main constraint and, in general, it determines the type of technology which is necessary to be used in the memory implementation).

(2)   the type of access (random or sequential, serial or parallel) and

(3)   the programmability of the memory.

The first requirement, which is fundamental for the choice of technology to be used and consequently the possible degree of integration, is the speed of operation, which depends on the real-time requirements of the data compression or error control systems. A wide variety of memory chips are presently available or expected in a short time [5]. The CMOS static random access memories (SRAMs) are commonly available at the 16 Kbit size, organized as 2-K × 8, 4-K × 4 and 16-K × 1 chips, with access times ranging from less than 50 ns for 16-K × 1 devices to some hundreds nanoseconds for the 2-K × 8 items. Also 64 K SRAMs are expected in CMOS technology in the near future. Faster memories are available in ECL technology generally at smaller sizes.

Dynamic RAMs that need to be refreshed periodically to maintain the stored information are available at the 64-Kbit size and are expected at the 256-Kbit size in the near future with access times of the orders of hundreds nanoseconds.

Nonvolatile memory technologies are also suited for the hardware implementation of data compression and error control systems. They offer read-only memories (ROMS), programmable read-only memories (PROMs), erasable programmable read-only memories (EPROMs) and electrically erasable programmable read-only memories (EEPROMs). They can store the constants and the fixed-value parameters and coefficients required by the data compression and error control algorithms. Their sizes range from 16 to 128 Kbit; 256 and 512-Kbit sizes are in development phase. Their typical access times are a few hundreds nanoseconds, but faster memories (tens of nanoseconds) are available or soon expected.

Furthermore, bubble memory technology seems to offer even greater storage capacity, presently expected in the range of 1 to 4 Mbit. In perspective,

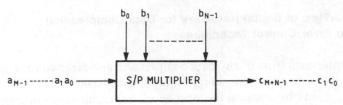

FIG. 8.2. Block-diagram of a serial–parallel multiplier.

they offer an interesting solution for processing digital images, that inherently require a lot of memory.

Shift registers are the common sequential access memories and are usually employed in data compression and error control systems. Typical shift registers have a storage capacity of hundreds to thousands of bits and clock rates up to a few megahertz. Faster shift registers are also available, generally with smaller storage capacities.

Adders and multipliers are the other main components of a digital signal processor. Both are today available in a fully intergrated-circuit form. Common parallel adders perform a 16×16 bit binary addition in about 50 ns (or less). Faster adders (ECL technology) perform 4×4 and 16×16 binary additions in about 3 and 12 ns, respectively.

Two types of binary multipliers are presently available: serial–parallel and array. A serial–parallel multiplier (Fig. 8.2) performs the binary multiplication of a number supplied in a serial form $(a_0 a_1 \cdots a_{M-1})$ by a number presented in a parallel form $(b_0 b_1 \cdots b_{N-1})$ and gives the results in a serial form $(c_0 c_1 \cdots c_{M+N-1})$. At each clock pulse the output supplies a bit of the multiplication result. Depending on the number representation, the multiplication is performed between two sign-and-magnitude numbers or between two 2-complement numbers. Presently both sign-and-magnitude and 2-complement serial–parallel multipliers are commercially available with typical clock rates ranging from 25 to 40 MHz.

The block diagram of an array multiplier is shown in Fig. 8.3. It accepts both operands in parallel form and supplies the results in the same form. Through an internal high hardware-parallelism the array multiplier is much faster than the serial–parallel one, though at the expense of an increase of the power consumption. Presently $N \times N$ array multipliers are available, with $N = 8, 12$ or 16 and typical multiplication times ranging from 40 to 160 ns.

In addition to these conventional hardware components, today's very large scale integration (VLSI) technology offers a new powerful device: the digital signal processor (DSP). The DSP is basically a programmable VLSI circuit consisting of memory devices, arithmetic and control units and

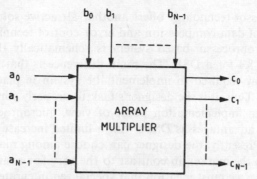

FIG. 8.3. Block-diagram of an array multiplier.

input/output (I/O) devices, all integrated on a single chip (Fig. 8.4). Through the appropriate software, the DSP is capable of performing a wide variety of processing operations including data compression and error control algorithms. By using a DSP, the designer's task is more concerned with the software design of the chosen algorithm and, to a minor extent, with hardware problems. Thus, the designer's main effort is in the algorithm optimization and is not in the hardware selection and implementation. Present DSPs are not as fast as specialized digital hardware circuits; however, even today they offer an attractive implementation alternative for many applications and their processing speed is expected to increase in the near future.

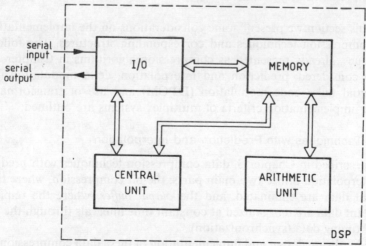

FIG. 8.4. Schematic block-diagram of a digital signal processor (DSP).

Microprocessor technology offers another attractive solution for the implementation of data compression and error control techniques. The structure of a microprocessor-based system is schematically the same as that shown in Fig. 8.4 for a DSP. The main difference is that a few integrated circuits are now required to implement the system in place of the unique chip of a DSP. Thus, it is the designer's task to properly connect the various chips. From an implementation point of view, microprocessor structures offer the same advantages as DSPs with a limited increase in the hardware design effort. Presently, the designer can choose among many microprocessor systems on the market, in contrast to the very few available DSPs.

Furthermore, we must mention that specialized integrated digital circuits are appearing on the market for specific applications. For example, 64-bit digital correlators and burst error processors have been introduced for error control coding in data transmission and storage and PCM codes are currently available in integrated form. This trend is expected to be maintained in the future, so that more and more specialized integrated circuits for data compression and error control coding will be available.

Finally, the high interest is to be outlined for special hardware implementations using charge-coupled devices (CCD), processing sampled data, with high integration implementation (especially for memories, linear filters and correlators), and surface acoustic-wave (SAW) devices, utilized for compact implementation of filters and oscillators.

8.4 Implementation of Data Compression Techniques

In this section we present some considerations on the implementation of data compression techniques and corresponding structures. The following techniques, already presented as compression algorithms in Chapter 3, are mainly considered: prediction and interpolation, delta modulation (DM), differential pulse code modulation (DPCM) and use of transformations. Further implementation criteria of multiplex systems are outlined.

8.4.1 Techniques with Prediction and Interpolation

As described in Chapter 3, data compression techniques with prediction and interpolation utilize two main parts: the bit compression, where the redundant data are eliminated, and the *output buffer*, where the remaining important data are reorganized at constant time intervals through the insertion of timing data (synchronization).

The hardware design and implementation of these data compression techniques (see also Fig. 3.2) is, in general, a not very difficult task. Standard digital circuits can be used to implement the bit-compression part, because few digital operations are involved for the evaluation of the predicted or interpolated sample (in general, low-order algorithms—such as zero- or first-order—are utilized), and for comparison with the actual incoming data sample. All bit compression could be implemented by means of a LSI or VLSI chip.

The implementation of the output buffer for a single data channel does not represent a very difficult problem. First, a suitable length for the memory is to be selected so as to avoid the bad working conditions of *overflow* and *underflow* (see Sections 3.12 and 3.13). This is done by taking into account the input data statistics and input/output data rates (design curves are available, for instance, for random (Poisson) input and constant output rates [6]). After the selection of a CMOS SRAM, an ECL RAM or a dynamic RAM can be done, according to the actual values of data rates.

The implementation of adaptive prediction algorithms (Section 3.4) is somewhat more complicated, due to the more complex relation utilized to evaluate the predicted sample which is equivalent to that of an FIR digital filter (Section 3.11) [1]. Some LSI–VLSI chips are available to implement this structure up to data rates of a few Megahertz. In the implementation of adaptive prediction algorithms the coefficient adaptation strategy is, however, conveniently realized.

8.4.2 DPCM Techniques

As described in Section 3.6, DPCM techniques utilize a prediction carried out on a suitable number of past samples. The predicted sample at a time instant t_n is subtracted from the actual input signal sample at time t_n and their difference is quantized and encoded.

The implementation complexity is, therefore, similar to the preceding adaptive prediction. Some modifications of DPCM can require slightly more complicated implementation approaches. In the asynchronous DPCM, for instance, the length of the prediction interval M (i.e., the number of past samples used by the predictor) is adaptively changed, depending on the signs and values of the past m differences between the predicted and actual samples. In this case, the main design problem is represented by the selection of the optimum or nearly optimum values of m and M.

8.4.3 DM Techniques

As outlined in Section 3.7, the block diagram of a classic DM system is relatively simple and hence its implementation with standard digital circuits or special chips does not present very difficult problems. The modifications of DM techniques, such as using variable amplitude steps or variable sampling rates, are requiring slightly more complicated approaches. For

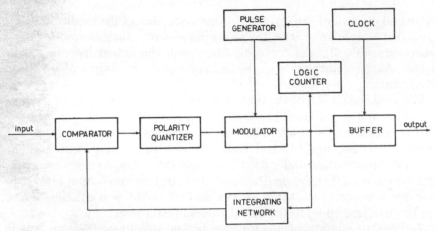

FIG. 8.5. Block-diagram of asynchronous DM systems.

example, modification of the integrating network in order to deal with variable reconstruction amplitudes or requiring a pulse generator with a variable pulse frequency connected to the DM system output through a logic counter which detects the data activity (Fig. 8.5).

It is interesting to remember that the basic data connected to all DM systems require no time data insertion, as the time information is contained in the sequence of the output samples. For the asynchronous methods (having a variable sampling rate) the sampling periods, even though not constant, are directly derived from the sequence of the output samples through the logic counter. Therefore, at the receiver another logic counter can easily determine the correct time positioning of the received pulses.

8.4.4 Techniques Using Transformations

According to the general considerations developed in Section 3.10, the block diagram for the implementation of a data compression system using transformations is of the type shown in Fig. 8.6. The input data stream, which is generally supplied serially, is first converted into a parallel form (N-point vector). The N-point vector is then mapped into another domain by applying the chosen unitary transform.

As described in Section 3.10.2, possible choices for data compression unitary transforms are the fast Fourier transform (FFT), the fast cosine transform (FCT), the fast Walsh transform (FWT), the fast Haar transform (FHT) and the Karhunen–Loéve transform (KLT). The transformation block supplies the N-point transformed vector at its output.

An appropriate compression strategy is then applied to the transformed vector to produce the final output compressed data that are supplied serially in the case of a data transmission system.

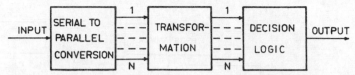

FIG. 8.6. Scheme for the implementation of a data compression system using transformations.

The serial-to-parallel conversion at the input can be easily realized by means of a serial-input parallel-output memory register. The block performing the unitary transform is, of course, the most complicated unit to be implemented. For example, when using the FFT as data transformation, complex arithmetic is necessary. Other transformations require operations on real quantities. However in general the transformation-unit computational complexity is much higher than for any other compression algorithm. The transformation unit must be generally implemented by means of a specialized hardware. However, an alternative and attractive solution for not extremely high processing speed is offered by the VLSI digital signal processor technology. For example, some digital signal processors are available or announced that perform a 32-point complex FFT in 0.7 ms or a 64-point complex FFT in 1.6 ms [7]. Their use would greatly simplify the hardware problems today associated with the implementation of transform-based compression algorithms.

The last block in Fig. 8.6 realizes the decision logic to determine which transformed data have to be retained and, for some strategies, to identify their position within the transformed vector. This block generally requires very simple logic and arithmetic and, in simple cases, no arithmetic at all. Therefore, its implementation can be easily carried out using standard memories, logic units, and, when necessary, simple arithmetic units.

8.4.5 Implementation of Multiplex Systems
Using Data Compression Techniques

In a multiplex communication system, by using data compression on many input channels, suitable care is to be reserved for the implementation of data compressors for the different channels. Two main approaches can be followed: utilize a single data compressor (or a part of that) for all data channels or use separate compression units working in parallel form [8].

Of particular interest is the case of data compression systems, using an output buffer, as with prediction–interpolation of asynchronous DM. As previously outlined, the output buffer has the important task of achieving a bandwidth compression by transmitting the output data at an average constant rate.

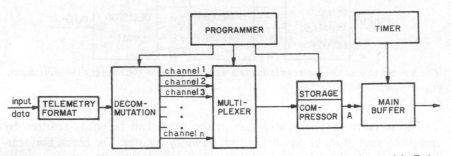

FIG. 8.7. A first approach to implement a multichannel data compression and buffering system (use of a single data compressor).

Figure 8.7 shows an example of implementation. According to the first approach, a programmer unit sends commands to the multiplexer in order to have a suitable number of samples from each channel having different data rates sent to a compressor unit for the application of the selected algorithm. The number of samples collected by the multiplexer will be such that the corresponding time intervals of the incoming data will be the same for each channel. The output of the compressor is sent to the main buffer asynchronously, while a timing unit will provide the synchronous pulses for the output.

Different algorithms can also be used with this scheme. The programmer and compressor units can be designed to select the algorithm for each channel together with the number of samples. The compression unit must also be designed with care in order to store the status of compression each time the multiplexer switches a channel off to enter the other one. A suitable memory (a few words per channel) will be used to store the current situation (status word) of each channel after the interrupts occur.

However, in this case, the scheme of Fig. 8.8 (second approach) can be more advantageous when separate compression units are used, operating on the decommutated signals, which process different numbers of samples in the same time interval, according to the sampling rates. The status words

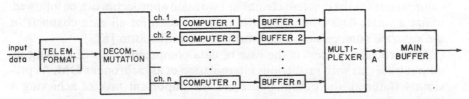

FIG. 8.8. A second approach to implement a multichannel data compression and buffering system (use of separate parallel compression units).

are stored in the compressors themselves. Small-size buffers are necessary to hold the compressed data waiting for collection by the multiplex unit, which sends the compressed data to the main buffer asynchronously.

8.5   Implementation of Error Control Techniques

In this section we present some considerations on the implementation of error control techniques for simple error detection and error correction. As a general consideration, we can outline powerful error control techniques that require quite complex implementation, especially with regard to the decoder. For this reason, until recently, it has been impractical to implement error control codes unless we have short lengths (≤ 40), constraint lengths (≤ 10 segments), or (for a block code) relatively few information digits or parity checks (≤ 10) or relatively weak error-control power (one- or two-error correction, length b burst-error correction with $b \leq 10$ or just error detection). Error control systems have been successfully used in the past, therefore, either in situations in which the error-control demands on the code are quite small (i.e., the use of Hamming single-error-correcting codes) or a feedback link is available so that error detection and retransmission techniques can be used. The exceptions have been in cases in which error correction is essential, complexity and cost are not a problem, and off-line processing is possible (i.e., deep-space probe communications, telemetry links and certain military applications) [9, 10].

The availability of LSI and VLSI integrated circuits, in conjunction with the development of various new decoding and processing algorithms, has started to change dramatically this state of affairs. The use of much longer (> 1000 digits), and therefore much more powerful, codes can be considered without loss of cost effectiveness. Relatively shorter codes can become much more effective because improved, more complex decoding algorithms can be used. Decoding delay times have been substantially reduced, due to technological advances, so that real-time decoding with data rates of more than 10 Mbit/s is possible.

In the following, some specific considerations on the implementation of some block codes and convolutional codes with implementation trends are given.

8.5.1   Block Codes

As observed earlier, the main complexity of implementation of a reasonably powerful error control code lies in the decoder. This is true also for the most part of block codes. As an example, the binary cyclic [1, 2] code with block length $n = 31$ and $k = 21$ information digits may be decoded with a 21-stage buffer shift register and a 1024-bit PROM, together with some additional logic circuitry [10]. Encoding, on the other hand, can be done with a 10-stage shift register and a few gates. For this relatively simple double-error correcting code, the ratio of decoder to encoder storage requirements is over 100:1.

In practice, for block codes, decoder complexity is roughly proportional to either the number of information digits k, or the number of check digits $c = n - k$, whichever is smaller, and depending on the decoding method used (Chapter 5) [11].

As another example, let us consider an extended Reed–Solomon code with m bits per character, block length $N = 2^m$ characters ($n = m2^m$ bits), C check characters ($c = mC$ bits), and Hamming distance $d = C + 1$. This code may be implemented for $m = 10$ ($n = 10,240$) and either $C = 32$ ($c = 320$) or $C = 8$ ($c = 80$) for throughput speeds of 10 Mbit/s or 100 Mbit/s, respectively [12]. These codes are capable of correcting $t = C/2$ character errors (for binary transmission, $C/2$ blocks of $m = 10$ bits each) or any combination of t errors and s erasures such that $(2t + s + 1) \le d$ (i.e., $2t + s \le C$). These codes have indeed very high rates: 0.969 and 0.992, respectively. For binary transmission over one-half of any burst of length $m/2 = 5$ will lie within one character, and only $1/m = \frac{1}{10}$ of bursts of length 5 will affect two characters. If the code is character interleaved to degree 2, then any burst of length $m + 1 = 11$ is corrected. Thus, if the interleaved code is a t-character error-correcting code, it is a t binary-burst correcting code. These codes can be shown to be superior to, and no more complex to realise than, long binary and multilevel BCH codes of the same parameters, particularly on bursty channels [13]. The decoders for these long Reed–Solomon codes were realised with special-purpose microprogrammable Galois field computers, using an architecture carefully matched to the hardware needs of the algebraic decoding algorithm [12]. The integrated circuit number for these decoders lies between 150 and 250; these figures would be greatly reduced by using LSI and especially VLSI circuits.

8.5.2   Convolutional Codes

Let us consider, as a typical example, the case of a convolutional coder with sequential decoding (Chapter 5). While the encoder is relatively simple to implement (shift register and few logical circuits), the main complexity again is actually connected with the decoder implementation [10].

While a minimum-distance decoder correlates the received coded sequence with all possible code sequences and then selects the sequence *nearest* to the received sequence as the one that was transmitted, a sequential decoder does not complete every correlation if it is able to decide that a sequence is so *far away* from the received sequence that it is unlikely to be the one ultimately chosen. In this way, much unnecessary computation can be avoided, and the reduced complexity of the decoder indeed compensates for the possible slight increase in the error probability. The complexity of a sequential decoder grows with the square of the constraint length. However, a basic problem with sequential decoding algorithms is that, if the distance threshold between the received sequence and the paths being searched from a given node in the tree is exceeded, then the decoder must return to the previous node and search branches from that node. If this also fails, the process of backing up and searching is repeated as many times as required. This occasionally leads to computational overload and, hence, decoding failure [9]. Ng and Goodman [14] have shown that this problem can be greatly alleviated. By making use of the linear properties of a convolutional code, it is possible to know to which node the search should back up if paths from the current node exceed the threshold. This gives an enormous savings in complexity and decoding delay, and makes minimum-distance sequential decoding a practical possibility for relatively long and powerful codes (constraint length 50 segments, rate 1/2), which could not be decoded with the Viterbi algorithm. Soft decision techniques can also be applied to this decoding algorithm [13].

8.5.3 Implementation Trends for Error Control Techniques

Taking into account the LSI–VLSI technology, the following interesting implementation trends can be outlined [10]:

(1) Minimum-distance and sequential decoding techniques are ultimately limited by the large amounts of storage required and by their relatively slow throughput speed because of the number of serial computations required. However lower complexity decoding strategies, as outlined earlier, are emerging.

(2) For high-speed, high-rate applications, long block codes (e.g., Reed–Solomon codes) are superior to convolutional codes. In particular, Reed–Solomon codes present efficient burst-error-correction capability [a (31,15) Reed–Solomon code has been adopted as the standard for the joint tactical information distribution system (JTIDS)].

(3) A concatenated block code scheme may be comparable in performance with that of an interleaved convolutional code with comparable implementation complexity (reduced complexity using a Reed–Solomon code as block code).

(4) Two main types of implementation building blocks are emerging: memory and special-purpose finite field processors. The amount of each type

required varies with the error control technique being used, but often the two blocks will need to be accessed dynamically as decoding proceeds so that they must be controlled efficiently.

(5) Due to the large amount of digital circuits required to implement a powerful code (for example, the preceding (31, 15) Reed–Solomon code requires 73 integrated circuits (16-pin) on one side of a 15 × 15 cm card with a throughput speed of about 48 Kbit/s [12]), a practical approach of implementation by means of VLSI technology could be to split the decoder into a storage block (memory VLSI is well advanced), a control block (which could be realised with a logic array) and a finite-field processor (for which a VLSI chip could be developed). Furthermore, to increase the implementation speed, limited by the interface unit, a microcode-controlled and very fast buffer/processor on one VLSI chip could be realised.

8.6   Hardware Implementation of Some Systems for Data Compression and Error Control Coding

In the following the hardware implementation of three special systems for data compression and error control coding is presented. The first system is a digital processor performing multiple filterings, bandpass analysis and spectral estimation in a compressed form. The second system is a vocoder using linear prediction algorithm to compress speech, working at 2.4 Kbit/s. The third system is a QPSK/BPSK modem containing a convolutional coding with sequential decoding, working at data rates up to 8.3 Mbit/s.

8.6.1   A Special Digital Processor for Multiple Filtering, Bandpass Analysis and Spectral Estimation

This special digital processor has three main hardware parts: the input–output unit, the digital filtering unit and the spectral estimator [15]. The system was built to process multiple input signals in the low-frequency range such as ECG–EEG in the biomedical area.

The first part has an input unit, consisting of an analog multiplexer for four input signals, a sampler and an analog-to-digital (A–D) converter giving 8 bit words (the sign enclosed). The output unit can receive up to 64 output data, which can be alternatively represented (through working mode selection) by 16 bandpass filterings for any input signal or by 4 spectral estimations in a compressed form, each spectral estimation being represented by 16 data (rms values obtained from 16 bandpass filtering) (Fig. 8.9).

The second part performs up to 64 bandpass filterings on the 4 input data, that is, 16 bandpass filterings for any input data. By considering, as maximum filtering performance, 16 filterings with 255 coefficients (Section 3.11)

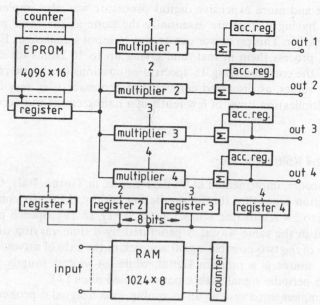

FIG. 8.9. Block-diagram of the special digital processor (digital filtering and bandpass analysis).

and a sampling frequency of 100 samples/s, a multiplication time of 0.6 μs is obtained. This time is surely compatible with the multiplication time of available fast multipliers such as *matrix multipliers*. To reduce the implementation cost, more economical multipliers of the series–parallel type have been selected with serial accumulators arranged in four processing lines (Fig. 8.9). Furthermore, there are a microprogrammed control unit (consisting of a PROM memory containing control signals with a counter reading these signals sequentially), a coefficient memory (using EPROM memories, containing up to 4096 words of 16 bits with a parallel–serial converter to interact with the other units) and an input sampled data memory (using RAM memories containing 1024 words of 8 bits, which are read and written at 4 word blocks).

The third part performs 4 spectral estimations on the 4 input signals, using the filtered data given by the second part (analysis with 16 adjacent bandpass filters). The spectral estimation is performed by evaluating the rms values of each bandpass filtering in suitable (and selectable) time intervals. A serial–parallel multiplier is used to perform the square values, giving the product results (16 bits) to a microprocessor (INTEL 8080) which performs the other requested operations (as the addition to the previously evaluated partial results).

The filtered data (bandpass analysis) and the spectral estimations can be sent to standard chart recorders, printers, magnetic tapes or video displays.

A faster and more expensive digital processor was also implemented in hardware, having a structure essentially the same as the three main parts described earlier. This processor can accept 16 input signals (e.g., ECG–EEG ones), and process them in real-time giving up to 16 bands for each input signal and the corresponding 16 spectral estimations (each one represented by 16 rms values, as discussed earlier). The processor uses very fast multipliers (multiplication times of few tenth of a nanosecond) and accumulators [16].

8.6.2 A 2.4 Kbit/s Vocoder

This vocoder, implemented at CSELT Centre in Torino, Italy, utilizes linear prediction algorithm (linear prediction coding, LPC) to compress the speech up to 2.4 Kbit/s (see also Chapter 9) [17, 18, 19]. Speech production is modeled in the same way it is generated by a time varying digital filter fed by one of the two possible signal sources: in the case of unvoiced sounds, the signal source is a random signal, while for voiced sounds, the signal source is a periodic signal with a period called *pitch* [1].

In the implemented system, an incoming speech signal is properly filtered, sampled and quantized. Samples of a proper time frame fill a suitable buffer (Fig. 8.10). When the buffer is full, its contents are dealt with by an analysis algorithm, whose output is the measurement of the characteristic parameters of speech in the corresponding time frame. These parameters are then encoded and sent to a serial output. At the receiver side, these parameters are decoded and they feed a synthesizer, whose model was assumed, as outlined earlier, for speech generation (Fig. 8.10).

Figure 8.11 shows a detailed block diagram of the LPC algorithm implemented. The most frequent computations involve:

(1) digital filtering,
(2) digital correlation computations (in pitch extraction and as a first step in LPC analysis) and
(3) matrix manipulations (as a second step in LPC analysis).

The system requirements are

(1) flexibility (programmability) and
(2) real-time capability (at suitable speed).

The first requirement (Fig. 8.12) allows algorithm variations and new system performance; this implies the choice of a programmable system. Furthermore, some important parts of the algorithm [e.g., voiced–unvoiced (VUV) decision] are intrinsically heuristics, thus requiring programming flexibility.

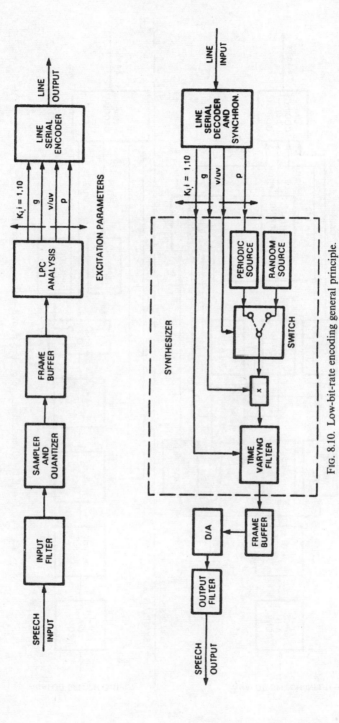

Fig. 8.10. Low-bit-rate encoding general principle.

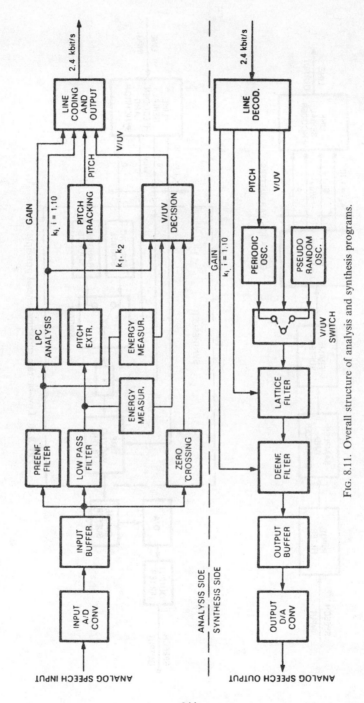

FIG. 8.11. Overall structure of analysis and synthesis programs.

244

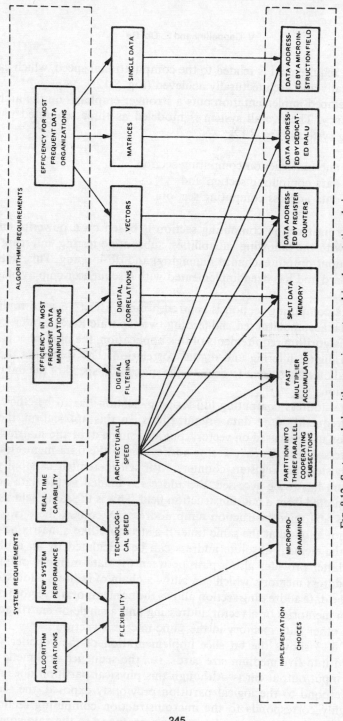

FIG. 8.12. System and algorithm requirements and implementation choices.

The second requirement is related to the computational speed, which can be technologically and architecturally achieved (Fig. 8.12).

The developed implementation puts a stronger emphasis on the architectural efficiency. The overall system is modeled as three separated parallel cooperating systems (Fig. 8.12):

(1)   the microinstruction computing section,
(2)   the data computing section and
(3)   the data address computing section.

The microinstruction computing section is based on a powerful enough sequencer with the following capabilities: subroutine testing, interrupt handling (for input/output exchange managing) and do-looping. This section is quite standard and has been implemented with a sequencer chip available in the market.

The data computing section is centred around a fast 16×16 multiplier with internal accumulator fed and feeding two separate RAMs. In fact, referring to the algorithm requirements of this application, the multiplier is heavily used in digital filtering and digital correlation. The split data memory approach allows the system to achieve the maximum speed of the data computing section.

The data address computing (do-looping) section has to be efficient for the most frequently used data organizations. In this application, the data organization used is based on vectors, but also single data and matrices have to be addressed. For an easy vector addressing in the data memories, data address registers are registers/counters with self increment capability. If a single datum has to be accessed, the address is loaded in the data address register expected from a microinstruction field. This is the same field used for forcing the next microinstruction jump address. Of course, these two situations are not allowed at the same time. If a structure like a matrix has to be accessed, the element absolute address can be calculated by an arithmetic unit. The latter provides also a path between the data memory output and the next address memory, which can allow a chain of indirect addressing. In practice, the data addressing section allows the contemporary vector addressing of data memories or a vector addressing and a single or matrix addressing of the other data memory in the same microinstruction.

Figure 8.13 shows the bit slice implementation of the vocoder system, partitioned into five medium size cards, i.e., the sequence arithmetic multiplier and input/output cards. Although this physical partition does not exactly correspond to the logical partition previously exposed, the sequence card roughly corresponds to the microinstruction computing section, the multiplier and the memory cards roughly correspond to the data computing

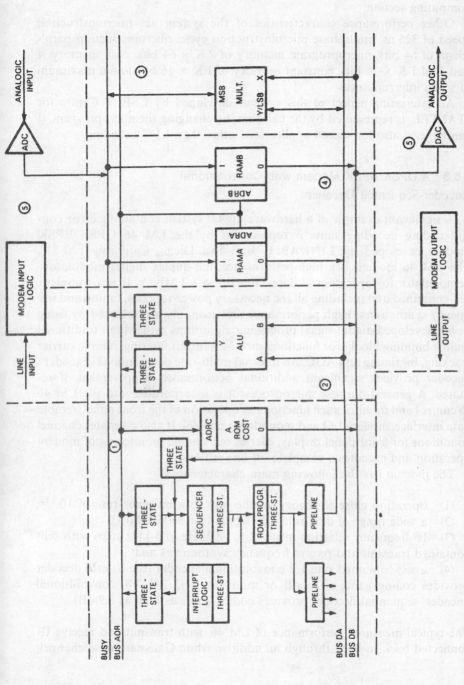

FIG. 8.13. Vocoder block-diagram and partitioning. Sequencer card, ①; arithmetic unit card, ②; multiplier card, ③; memory card, ④; input/output card, ⑤.

section and the arithmetic unit nearly corresponds to the next data address computing section.

Other performance characteristics of the system are microinstruction speed of 325 ns, multiphase microinstruction cycle, microinstruction parallelism of 64 bits, microprogram memory of 2 K × 64 bits, data memory A and B of 1 K × 16 bits, constant memory of 1 K × 16 bits and a maximum of seven interruptions.

An interesting aspect of this system, developed by CSELT Centre for ITALTEL, is represented by the fact that, by changing the microprogram, it can be used also for speech applications other than LPC vocoding.

8.6.3   A QPSK/BPSK Modem with Convolutional
Encoder-Sequential Decoder

A significant example of a hardware digital system containing error control coding–decoding units is represented by the LM 46 QPSK/BPSK modem developed by LINKABIT, Inc., San Diego, California [20, 21]. The LM 46 modem is a high-performance, full-duplex digital modulator–demodulator for operation at data rates up to 8.3 Mbit/s. It is a complete, self-contained unit including all the necessary power supplies, timing and frequency synthesizers. High performance and economy are achieved by using newly developed digital signal processing algorithms rather than traditional analog building blocks for functions such as transmit filtering, receive carrier tracking, bit timing and AGC. An internal multi-rate convolutional encoder–decoder provides significant additional performance improvement, if required. A general purpose microprocessor is incorporated into the LM 46 to control and monitor such functions as operation of the front panel, remote data interface, modem I/O and redundancy control. It also estimates channel conditions for front panel display, carries out on-line monitoring of modem operation and executes a complete off-line self-test.

The modem has the following main characteristics:

(1)   operation close to theory all the way to a bit error rate of 10^{-12},

(2)   a wide range of data rates (28 Kbit/s to 8.3604 Mbit/s),

(3)   IF frequency selection from 52 to 88 MHz in 5-kHz steps with self-contained transmit and receive frequency synthesizers and

(4)   a self-contained rate 1/2 convolutional encoder (the Viterbi decoder provides coding gains of 5.1 dB or multi-rate (1/2, 3/4, 7/8) convolutional encoder–sequential decoder provides coding gains as high as 5.9 dB).

The typical measured performance of LM 46, with transmit and receive IF connected back-to-back through an additive white Gaussian noise channel,

TABLE 8.1. Performance of the LM46 LINKABIT digital modem.

QPSK operation	No coding	Viterbi decoder		Sequential decoder		
		rate 1/2	rate 1/2	rate 3/4	rate 7/8
10^{-5}BER, 100-Kbit/s data rate	10.1	4.9	4.0	4.8	5.6
10^{-5}BER, 1.544-Mbit/s data rate	10.1	4.9^a	4.8	5.5	6.3

[a] Requires external Viterbi decoder.

is shown in Table 8.1, reporting the bit energy-to-noise ratio (E_b/N_0) required to achieve a 10^{-5} bit error rate (BER) at 100-Kbit/s and 1.544-Mbit/s data rates for different coding configurations.

References

1. Cappellini, V., Constantinides, A. G., and Emiliani, P. (1978). "Digital Filters and Their Applications." Academic Press, London.
2. Bennett, W. R. (1948). Spectra of quantized signals. *Bell Syst. Tech. J.* **27**, 446–472.
3. Oppenheim, A. V., and Schafer, R. W. (1975). "Digital Signal Processing." Prentice-Hall, Englewood Cliffs, New Jersey.
4. Rabiner, L. R., and Gold, B. (1975). "Theory and Applications of Digital Signal Processing." Prentice-Hall, Englewood Cliffs, New Jersey.
5. *Electronic Design*, August, 1982.
6. Dor, N. M. (1967). Guide to the length of buffer storage required for random (Poisson) input and constant output rates, *IEEE Trans. Electron. Comp.* **EC-16**, 683–684.
7. NEC PD7720 digital signal processor, April, 1981.
8. Benelli, G., Cappellini, V., and Lotti, F. (1980). Data compression techniques and applications, *Radio Electron. Eng.* **50** (1/2), 29–53.
9. Berlekamp, E. R. (1980). The technology of error-correcting codes, *Proc. IEEE* **68**, 564–593.
10. Farrell, P. G. (1982). Influence of LSI and VLSI technology on the design of error-correction coding systems, *Proc. IEE* **129**, 323–326.
11. Farrell, P. G. (1979). A survey of error-control codes, *in* "Algebraic Coding Theory and Applications" (G. Longo, ed.), Springer-Verlag, Berlin.
12. Berlekamp, E. R. (1979). Notes on the implementation of long RS codes and long BCH codes with high speeds and high rates, Report, Cyclotomics, Inc.
13. Goodman, R. M. F., Green, A. D., and Winfield, A. F. T. (1980). Soft-decision error-correction coding schemes for HF data transmission, *IEE Conf. Recent Adv. HF Commun. Syst. Tech.*, London, February.
14. Ng, W. H., and Goodman, R. M. F. (1978). An efficient minimum-distance decoding algorithm for convolutional error-correcting codes, *Proc. IEE* **125**, 97–103.

15. Cappellini, V., and Emiliani, P. L. (1982). A new filtering processor for ECG–EEG signals, *Proc. ISMIII, 1st,* Berlin, Federal Republic of Germany, October, pp. 195–196.
16. Cappellini, V., and Emiliani, P. L. (1983). A special digital processor for ECG–EEG filtering and analysis, *Proc. MEDINFO, 4th,* Amsterdam, The Netherlands, August, pp. 682–684.
17. Castellino, P. (1981). Speech coding at low bit rate: techniques and quality problems, *Proc. FASE, 4th,* Venice, Italy, April, pp. 19–37.
18. Ciaramella, A., Dal Degan, N., Arcella, F., and Vettori, I. (1982). Implementation of an LPC–10 vocoder, *Proc. ICC* **82**, pp. 4G.4.1–4G.4.5.
19. Ciaramella, A. (1983). Implementation of a 2.4 Kbit/s LPC vocoder. *Inter. Report* CSELT, Turin, Italy, 83.02.059.
20. Odenwalder, J. P. (1976). Error control coding handbook. Final Report LINKABIT Corp., San Diego, California, Contract F44620-76-C-0056.
21. LM46 QPSK/BPSK modem. Specifications, LINKABIT Corp., San Diego, California, 1982.

Chapter 9

Applications of Data Compression and Error Control Techniques

V. CAPPELLINI

Dipartimento di Ingegneria Elettronica
Università di Firenze
and Istituto di Ricerca sulle Onde Elettromagnetiche
Consiglio Nazionale delle Ricerche
Florence, Italy

9.1 Introduction

Historically—as already outlined in the Preface—the first applications of data compression and error control techniques were mainly reserved for *space digital telemetry* and *special ground communication links*.

Indeed the constraints of limited power aboard the rockets and spacecrafts, and the corresponding limited transmission bandwidths stimulated the first applications of simple but useful on-board data compressors (such as prediction–interpolation or variable length encoding) to reduce the great amount of data given by the different on-board sensors and measuring equipments.

Again the space research activity and exploration missions suggested the use of on-board error-control encoders (simple error-detection or error-correction to be performed by ground decoders) to counterbalance, at least in part, the communication channel constraints in the space–ground link, due essentially to the great distances between transmitting and receiving stations and to the channel noise and disturbances (such as ionosphere scintillations, Faraday rotation, solar storms, magnetic distribution variations and so on). Simple error control coders such as Hamming codes or other block codes

251

DATA COMPRESSION AND ERROR CONTROL
TECHNIQUES WITH APPLICATIONS

were mainly used. Subsequently, convolutional encoders having very simple on-board implementation (essentially shift registers with few logical circuits) and more complex ground decoders (as with threshold decoding of fixed or adaptive type or—a more sophisticated and expensive solution—with sequential decoding) were used.

Progressively, however, the applications of both coding techniques (source and channel coding) were extended to special ground communication links (as digital telemetry, data transmission), where the additional cost of implementation, connected to their use, was largely justified and compensated by the efficiency increase of higher information rate and error probability reduction.

Thus, several modems for data transmission were introducing a data compressor and/or error control coder (conversely, data decompressors and error control decoders). These modems were designed and built for data transmissions on special communication links or standard telephone lines and cables.

Through the introduction of telecommunication satellites (for telephone and television transmission) different data compression and error control coding techniques were studied and experimented with, both to reduce the bandwidth (or increase the number of signals transmitted on the same bandwidth) and to reduce error probability. These experiments were extended to ground telecommunication networks.

In particular, for voice signals different types of vocoders (audio signal compressors) were developed and tested (some practically employed in special communications, such as military links). For television images, different intraframe and interframe techniques were developed in parallel and tested, especially for reduced-quality TV transmissions (video-conference, tele-surveillance).

However, other application areas were emerging. With the large diffusion of computers and interconnections among computer systems, the practical interest of applying compression and coding techniques was increasing, due to two main reasons:

(1)   reduction of data memorized in the local computer storage systems and protection of these data (at least the most important part) from noise, disturbance or bad working conditions of the computer and

(2)   more efficient connection among computers with reduction of data to be exchanged and protection of these data in the communication channel.

The advantages of data compression were also appearing in other fields in which where the amount of data was very quickly increasing up to critical limits: remote sensing data collection and storage (as data corresponding to digitized photos or satellite images) and biomedical data (as ECG–EEG signals or images in nuclear medicine, radiography, thermography, ultrasonics and computer tomography). More recently, in the biomedical area, with the extension of telemedicine (biomedical signal and image transmission from peripheral places to central clinics or hospitals), the utility of using error control coding together with data compression has been clearly recognized and practically applied.

All of the preceding applications are now greatly expanding, due to the high technological progress of digital microelectronics, with the availability of large-scale integrated circuits (LSI, VLSI), microprocessors and array processors.

In the following sections the applications outlined in this section are presented in more detail.

9.2 Applications in Space Digital Telemetry

As already outlined in the introduction, the application of data compression and error control techniques to space digital telemetry systems can be considered as the first application actually developed. Indeed, especially in the earlier rocket or satellite experiments, the limitations and constraints due to the limited on-board power and connected transmission bandwidth were very severe. When the number of telemetry signals or the spectral extension of some signal became too large, data compression techniques were of great practical interest in order to reduce the amount of data and the bandwidth required for some specific signal.

The telemetry signals or data can be divided in two main classes:

(1) telemetry signals regarding the performance and check of on-board equipment or spacecrafts (such as power supply voltage–current, temperature, vibration, and pressure) and

(2) physical experiment data (electron density, solar energy, electric or magnetic field, photographs or images from space).

A practical problem in the application of data compression techniques to these signals (or images) is connected to their different time and frequency behaviours (see Chapter 3).

An attempt to classify different telemetry signals is given in Chapter 3 (Fig. 3.21). There are six signal classes having different behaviour: constant or nearly constant data, periodic data, slowly varying data, data resulting from the combination of periodic and slowly varying components, random data and data with bursts or spikes.

Examples of the application of some data compression algorithms (such as ZOP-floating aperture and FOP) to these typical data are shown in Section 3.14. Efficiency comparisons are also reported there. Outlined in particular are the good efficiency for several signal classes of such relatively simple algorithms as ZOP, FOP, ZOI and FOI.[†] An overall evaluation of this and other data compression algorithms, with an indication of implementation complexity, is shown in Table 9.1 in relation to different types of signals (giving the best results).

Although mainly related to the analysis of typical space telemetry signals (from ESRO 1 A satellite), the preceding considerations and results can be very useful for estimating the efficiency of data compression algorithms applied to different source signals (especially if they have a behaviour similar to the six considered classes of input data).

With regard to the application of error control coding techniques to space telemetry data, several types of codes were tested and applied. In particular BCH codes and convolutional codes found interesting applications in this field. An interesting example is represented by convolutional encoding with Viterbi decoding implemented for the SOLRAD spacecrafts [developed in 1976 by the Naval Research Laboratory (NRL)] [2]. The SOLRAD-11 experiment used a pair of spacecrafts, with the main purpose of real-time measurements of UV, x-ray and particle emission from the sun. Two satellites (11A and 11B) were rotating on the same circular orbit, 180° apart. The orbit radius was 120,000 km.; therefore, two ground stations properly placed were necessary in order to receive at least one satellite and, hence, to monitor continuously the solar activity. One ground station was implemented at Blossom Point, Maryland, while a second station was built at the Astrophysical Observatory of Arcetri in Florence.

Aboard each satellite 25 experiments were assembled to measure UV and x-ray radiation in different spectral bands of electrons, protons and heavier ions. Solar wind and transient solar events experiments were also planned. The output of all experiments was converted to digital format with a fixed structure: 12-bit words, 32-word frames and 32-frame pages. The telemetry bit rate was 102.4 bits/s. To reduce the error probability in reception at the ground stations, the digital signal was processed before the actual transmission by an on-board convolutional encoder, the output of which modulated linearly in phase the rf carrier (137.4 and 136.5 MHz for satellites 11A and 11B, respectively). Convolutional encoding was considered as the normal mode of operation, but it was possible also to transmit the unconvoluted PCM–NRZ signal through the IRIG-8 channel, as a subcarrier. A turnstile antenna was used, transmitting simultaneously both right- and left-circular polarizations.

[†] The good efficiency of the ZOP algorithm for several space telemetry signals was extensively tested and verified at Lockheed Laboratories [1].

TABLE 9.1. Overall efficiency evaluation of different data compression algorithms, with an indication of implementation complexity, considering different types of signals (giving the best results).

Algorithm	Types of signals giving the best results	Efficiency	Hardware complexity	Software complexity	Buffer requirements (words)
Power spectrum (FFT) followed by ZOP/FL	Periodic signals with few sine wave components	Good	High	Medium	$2^N(N=6,\ldots)$
Power spectrum (FFT) followed by thresholding	Narrow band and high S/N ratio signals	Good	High	Medium	$2^N(N=6,\ldots)$
Zero-order predictor floating aperture	Quiescent, nearly constant value, slowly varying data	Very good	Low	Low	1
Adaptive linear predictor (rms)	Any type; random or burst data give bad results	Good	High	Medium	4–60
Adaptive nonlinear predictors (rms)	Any type; random or burst data give bad results	Good	High	Medium	4–60
Zero-order interpolator	Quiescent, nearly constant value, slowly varying data	Very good	High	Low	1
First-order interpolator	Any type; random or burst data can give bad results	Very good	High	Low	2
Huffmann encoding	Quiescent, nearly constant value, slowly varying data	Almost good	High	Medium	$2^N(N=10,\ldots)$
Differential PCM	Slowly varying data for classical DPCM; any type for adaptive methods	Almost good	Low	Medium	2
Delta modulation	Quiescent, nearly constant value, slowly varying data	Good	Low	Medium	1–6
Run length encoding	Quiescent, nearly constant value, slowly varying data	Very good	Low	Low	1
Bit plane encoding	Quiescent, nearly constant value, slowly varying data	Good	Low	Low	$2^N(N=10,\ldots)$
Hadamard transformation	Any type	Almost good	Low	Low	$2^N(N=2,\ldots)$
Hadamard transformation followed by ZOP/FL	Any type	Very good	Low	Low	$2^N(N=2,\ldots)$

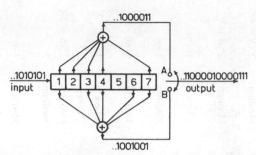

FIG. 9.1. Block diagram of the convolutional encoder with rate 1/2 and constraint length = 7.

The on-board convolutional encoder has the well-known advantages of low cost in power consumption, circuit complexity and weight. Figure 9.1 shows the block diagram of the rate 1/2, constraint length 7 convolutional encoder. It consists of a 7-stage shift register and two linear algebraic functions generated by the two patterns of connections going to the mod -2 adders. The outputs so generated are then sampled alternatively, thus giving the code symbol sequence, which is used to PM modulate the rf sinusoid carrier.

The receiving ground station, designed to accept signals with an average power of -150 dB m is shown in Fig. 9.2. A Viterbi decoding algorithm is used to correct channel errors, having the efficiency shown in Fig. 9.3, in the case of hard receiver quantization and additive white Gaussian noise (AWGN) channel (E_b is the energy per bit, N_0 is the noise spectral density and P_e is the error probability) [3].

An interesting example of the application of error control codes to space digital telemetry is represented by the GIOTTO mission to the Halley Comet. The European Space Agency (ESA) developed for this mission and other deep-space probes a sophisticated on-board encoder, consisting of a concatenated

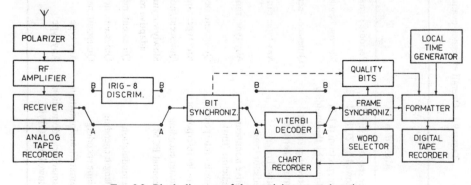

FIG. 9.2. Block diagram of the receiving ground station.

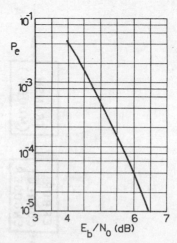

FIG. 9.3. Performance curve of the Viterbi decoder in the case of hard receiver quantization and AWGN channel; E_b is the energy per bit, N_0 = the noise spectral density and P_e = the error probability.

coding scheme with a convolutional inner-code and a Reed–Solomon outer-code including interleaving. The data of the coding scheme are as follows: convolutional code with a constraint length of 7 and a rate of 1/2 and a Reed–Solomon code with a code-word length of 255 symbols, of which 32 are data parity symbols.

Finally, the increasing interest of using data compression and error control coding techniques in the ground link between the receiving ground stations and the main Control Centre is to be pointed out for the efficient transmission of the large amount of received data (Fig. 9.4).

9.3 Speech Compression and Vocoders

One of the first applications of source coding (data compression) is surely represented by speech compression, due to the high importance of the audio signal in common life and to the interest in reducing the speech bandwidth (number of data representing it in a second) for higher communication efficiency.

Indeed many methods and techniques have been proposed, experimented with, tested and also practically used to obtain efficient voice-coders or vocoders (see also Chapters 3 and 8). To this purpose extensive studies have been developed on the audio signal: time analysis (zero-crossing, amplitude distribution and autocorrelation) and frequency analysis (bandpass analysis and short-time spectral estimation). Therefore, it was possible to know the time–frequency behaviour of vowels and consonants (the former characterized by periodic waves or pulse trains with specific main frequencies, the latter

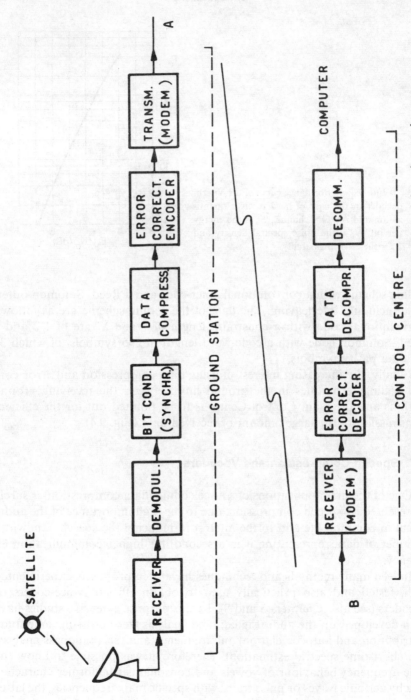

Fig. 9.4. Block diagram of a ground data-link between a receiving ground station and the main control centre.

having a more random nature with extended near-noise frequency spectra) and to define suitable models for the voice production and representation.

Let us recall the main aspects of speech generation and the characteristics of the principal sounds before describing some compression-coding techniques [4]. Speech is produced by the human vocal apparatus, in particular by excitation of an acoustic tube called the vocal tract which is terminated at one end by the vocal cords (glottis) and at the other end by the lips. An ancillary tube, the nasal tract, can be connected or disconnected to the vocal tract by the movement of the velum. The actual shape of the vocal tract is therefore determined by the position of the lips, jaw, tongue and velum.

Speech is generated in three basic ways:

(1) Voiced sounds are produced by exciting the vocal tract with quasi-periodic pulses of air flow caused by the vibration of the vocal cords.

(2) Fricative sounds are produced by forming a suitable constriction in the vocal tract and pushing air through the constriction, thereby creating turbulence which represents a noise-like source exciting the vocal tract.

(3) Plosive sounds are produced by completely closing off the vocal tract, increasing pressure and then abruptly releasing it.

All of these sources act as a wide-band excitation of the vocal tract. The vocal tract is characterized by its natural frequencies called formants, which correspond to resonances in the sound–transmission characteristics of the vocal tract.

The vocal tract can, in general, be modelled as a linear time-variant system, while in short time intervals (less than 10 ms) it can be approximated to a linear time-invariant system. In this last case, the output is the convolution of the impulse response of the vocal tract with the excitation waveform.

According to the mechanism of speech production in the human vocal apparatus described earlier, some digital models have been proposed and used for the production or simulation of speech signals.

One of the most important digital models is shown as a block diagram in Fig. 9.5. The time varying digital filter represents the vocal tract as a linear time-invariant system. As already observed, in short time intervals (less than 10 ms) the digital filter can be characterized by a fixed impulse response or by a precise set of coefficients. To represent voiced sounds, the digital filter is excited by an impulse train generator which gives a quasi-periodic impulse train in which the spacing between impulses corresponds to the fundamental period of the glottal excitation. To represent unvoiced sounds (fricative and plosive sounds), the digital filter is excited by a random number generator corresponding to a flat spectrum noise. In both cases an amplitude control, inserted before the digital filter, regulates the intensity of

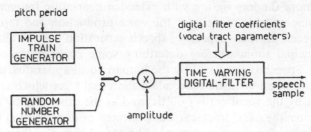

FIG. 9.5. Block diagram of a digital model for speech signal production.

the signals to reproduce the actual speech intensity. This digital speech model can give speech production with the required accuracy, just by increasing the complexity of the time-varying digital filter or by changing the pulse generation.

The preceding considerations on speech production and digital models are very important for defining speech compression methods and techniques (vocoders), studied and developed for the analysis of speech signals with the purpose of transforming and representing them in a compressed form, recovering from the compressed representation the original speech signal. Vocoders are, therefore, an economic form of transmission or storage of such signals.

Historically the first vocoder designed and tested was the Dudley channel vocoder, in which where the speech is processed by a bank of m bandpass filters (analyzer) covering the low-frequency spectrum [4]. The slowly varying envelope of each bandpass filter output is extracted through a rectifier and low-pass filter. In parallel a voice sound detector (buss–hiss detector) recognizes voiced and unvoiced sounds, while a pitch detector measures the frequency or period of the glottal excitation in voiced sounds. The short-time representation of the m-band analysis with outputs from voice sound detector and pitch detector can be economically stored locally or transmitted at a distance through a communication channel. In the system (i.e., at the receiving terminal) the m-band data are used to modulate the output of a pitch pulse generator (for voiced sounds) or a noise generator (for unvoiced sounds), the switching between the two generators being controlled by the received buss–hiss detector binary information and the fundamental period of pitch pulse generator being determined by the received pitch detector data.

A second important type of vocoder is that resulting directly from the digital speech model previously described. In the analyzer a pitch detector and a voice sound detector can be used as before, while the vocal tract parameters defining the short-time performance of the digital filter are in parallel estimated with different techniques. In the synthesis the actual system is practically very close to the structure of Fig. 9.5.

A third interesting vocoder is the linear prediction vocoder, using essentially the theory of adaptive linear prediction (ALP), described in Chapter 3, estimating the parameters for the speech signal. A detailed description of the hardware implementation of a 2.4-Kbit/s vocoder of this type—having good performance—is given in Section 8.6.2. Many other types of vocoder systems have been proposed and applied, in principal characteristics similar to the types already considered: phase vocoder, homomorphic vocoder, etc.

A particular approach is represented by the use of a compressed representation of a standard voice, by means, for instance, of speech segmentation (division in time). The so-called standard speech reproducing units (100–150 SSRU) of the language are used [5]. This solution can be useful for announcements or computer interaction.

By considering the transmission rate, from the standard rate of 64 Kbit/s (by using 8000 samples/s and 8 bits/sample), vocoder systems of the types just listed can reduce the rate to a few thousand bits per second (200–500 bits/s for SSRU transmission). Compression ratios of 10–50 can be obtained with moderate voice distortions, preserving however the speech intelligibility.

9.4 Digital Processing and Transmission of Facsimile and Television Images

In parallel with voice transmission, image transmission represents another very important application. Two main types of image transmission can be considered:

(1) transmission of time-fixed or static images (text or diagrams or photos) as in the facsimile systems and

(2) transmission of time-varying images as in the usual television systems.

9.4.1 Transmission of Static Images (Facsimile)

Let us consider first a standard A4 sheet (29.6 × 20.8 cm). To describe the written information and transmit it to the receiver, as in facsimile, an efficient method can be represented by the use of an optical reader of the written characters, connected, through a teletype or similar system, to the receiver. If the sheet contains 30 lines, each with 70 characters, there are 2100 characters in a sheet. If 7 bits are utilized for the transmission of the characters, then 14,700 bits are required for the representation of the sheet. If, however, a variable-length encoding is used, taking into account the character probabilities, a lower number of bits is required (as an example, for the English language, a mean word-length, equal to the source entropy, of 4.2 bits/character is the result, with 8800 bits required to represent the sheet).

A more economic system can scan the sheet (assumed to be black characters on a white background) with 1200 lines (at least 4 lines/mm are required) and represent each line with 800 equidistant space samples (points). Each sample being of binary value, there are 960,000 bits required to represent the whole sheet (an amount quite greater than the previous one). A little more efficient coding is obtained through the representation of the lengths of black or white point sequences by means of variable-word-length coding: mean values of 0.3–0.4 bits/point are sufficient. By using the variations of the preceding sequences line-by-line (comparing one with the following one) and suitable encoding of these variations, mean values of 0.1–0.2 bits/point are obtained.

In the case of a black-and-white photo to be transmitted (telephoto), the number of data required is quite higher. Let us consider a telephoto of 13 × 18 cm. To have sufficient spatial resolution, 8.6 lines/mm are required and therefore 1500 lines, 1100 samples/line, is the result. The overall amount of data, by representing the gray-level of each sample with 7 bits, is therefore 11.5 Mbits (by using a transmission with 4800 bits/s, 40 minutes are required for the transmission of a complete photo). By means of data compression techniques such as DPCM with variable-word-length coding (see Section 3.5) a mean word-length of 2–3 bits/sample is obtained and by means of digital transformations (see Section 3.11) a value of 1–2 bits/sample can be reached.

9.4.2   Transmission of Time-varying Images (Television)

For a good reproduction of movement, image sequences are required at a sufficient rate. In the European TV standard, for instance, 25 images/s is used. By using 625 lines/image and 8 bits/sample, transmission rates of 50 Mbit/s are obtained.

To reduce these high values, the analysis of two subsequent images can be done in such a way as to take into account, for instance, only the parts that actually moved in the transition from one image to the subsequent one (interframe techniques). The DPCM techniques can be used for this purpose. Through variable word-length coding, mean word-lengths of 2–2.5 bits/sample are obtained, thus reducing the transmission rate to 10–20 Mbit/s.

A suitable encoding (as with prediction-interpolation or, more efficiently, with digital transformations, see Chapter 3) can be performed in each single image (intraframe techniques). By combining interframe and intraframe techniques, lower bit rates (2–10 Mbit/s) are obtained, at the expense of higher complexity and cost.

An interesting approach to reduce redundancy in TV images, by means of inter–intra-frame coding, is based on movement compensation. The coding consists essentially in determining for each pixel the prediction model (spatial, temporal) and transmitting, when necessary, the quantized differences and the prediction model changes [6].

In the case of videotelephone or teleconference systems, due to the lower number of image points in movement from one image to another, and by using DPCM techniques with variable-word-length encoding, 0.9–1 bit/sample is sufficient. If information about image moving objects or parts is suitably used, values of 0.4–0.5 bit/sample are reached. For instance, for an object translation, the shift and direction values can be sent to the receiver, which will reconstruct gray levels of moved image parts. Transmission rates on the order of a few megabits per second are thus obtained. Error control coding techniques (block or convolutional codes) with low redundancy and good efficiency can be very useful to protect compressed image data against channel noise and disturbances (see Chapter 5).

9.5 Applications to Space Digital Commmunications

After the application of data compression and error control techniques to space digital telemetry, applications to space digital communications through a satellite started and expanded. The main differences from the space digital telemetry are here represented by two aspects:

(1) greater bit rate required (i.e., to exchange telephone or TV signals) and
(2) more knowledge on the space channel properties (in general, with stationary satellites, the space channel is with fixed distance and its performance is *a priori* more known).

An interesting example of error control coding system for digital satellite and space communication links is represented by the LV7017B Convolutional Encoder Viterbi Decoder of LINKABIT Inc., San Diego, California [7,8]. It works at data rates from 32 Kbit/s to 10 Mbit/s, which can be externally clocked, with no hardware changes, and assures a 5-dB reduction in the required E_b/N_0 for a 10^{-5}-bit error rate compared to uncoded PSK modulation on a Gaussian noise channel with code rate 1/2 (over 4 dB with code rate 3/4). Therefore LV7017B, when used in conjunction with a BPSK or QPSK modem, significantly reduces the E_b/N_0 required to achieve a given error rate.

Another system by LINKABIT is the LS2017 Convolutional Encoder–
Sequential Decoder working up to 12 Mbit/s (rate 7/8), improving modem
efficiency in digital satellite and space communication links. At 10^{-7}-bit error
rate a savings of 4.9 dB is obtained compared to uncoded modulation.

It is important to outline that the decibel savings just indicated can be
translated, with great advantages, into reduced satellite power (EIRP) or
lower values of G/T (gain to temperature ratio) in receiver terminals (smaller
antenna size or less costly low-noise amplifiers). Therefore, in most cases, the
reduction will result in considerable initial and operational cost savings for
the terminal and/or space segments of the satellite communication system.

A specific example of application is represented by the *maritime satellite
systems*. Figure 9.6 shows the block diagram of a typical maritime satellite
system (as planned by ESA). Encoded data are sent from ground communication networks to ships in navigation through the satellite repeater and vice
versa [9].

Furthermore, high-speed data transmissions through satellite links (with
speeds higher than those in recommendation X.1, CCITT) are appearing of
great interest. In particular a satellite multiservice system is planned, using
European satellites ECS and Telecom 1. This system can offer high-speed

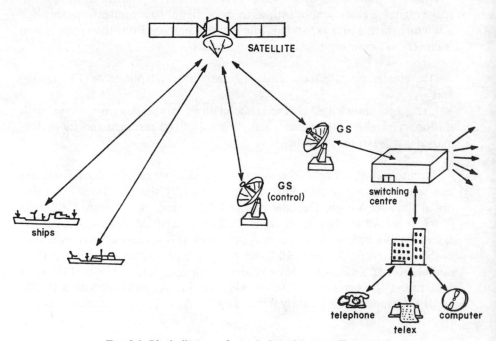

FIG. 9.6. Block diagram of a typical maritime satellite system.

data communication among computers (file transfer) and integrated transmission (service) of voice–data, the fast facsimile and videoconference.

9.6 Applications to Data Transmission
and Digital Communication Systems

With the evolution of digital devices and systems and the increasing need for the exchange of information (data, speech and images) from one place to another, the interest and utility of sending binary data through usual telephone lines and channels has expanded greatly in the last decade.

Conventional telephone-line data transmission systems communicate about 1600–2400 data per second with a probability of error of the order of 10^{-4}–10^{-5}. The errors which occur in these systems are attributed primarily to impulse noise bursts, which do not appear very frequently, and to channel dropouts. With data rates in this (conventional) range, the error rate can be reduced virtually to zero, without a substantial rate reduction, by the simple procedure of using straightforward detect and repeat or block coding techniques.

An interesting example of the use of error control coding techniques for efficient low-rate data transmission is represented by the time-division telemetering and supervisory control modular system (TIC 1000, TIC 1000/4), developed by Telettra SpA, Milano, Italy. The system comprises one or more centrally located master stations and one or more remote stations, with either one-way or two-way transfer of information. The system works at telegraph transmission speed (50–2400 bauds), handling (by a line governor) up to 1000 messages. The messages exchanged between the remotes and the master consist of 10 information bits plus 5 check bits. A cyclic code (15, 10), derived from the Bose–Chaudhuri code (15, 11), is utilized [10, 11].

For substantially higher data rates (greater than 2400 data/s) the situation changes. Random noise and intersymbol interference (delay distortion) are no longer negligible and introduce signaling anomalies that require error correction. Convolutional codes with threshold or sequential decoding have been used to this purpose (see also Chapter 5).

An interesting example along this line is represented by the QPSK/BPSK Modem of LINKABIT Inc., San Diego, California (see Section 8.6.3), containing a rate 1/2 convolutional encoder—Viterbi decoder providing coding gains of 5.1 dB and a multi-rate (1/2, 3/4, 7/8) convolutional encoder—sequential decoder with coding gains as high as 5.9 dB. The modem can operate in a wide range of data rates, up to 8.3604 Mbit/s.

Digital speech communications (in particular digital telephony) are now of great importance. The interest of source coding is here connected to the data rate or bandwidth reduction. From the standard 64 Kbit/s (corresponding to 8000 samples/s each having 8 bits) several reduced rates techniques have been tested and applied, going down to 32 Kbit/s and 16 Kbit/s with usual techniques and to a few thousand bits per second with special vocoders (see Chapters 3, 8 and Section 9.3).

Digital TV communications (see Section 9.4) have started and developed lately, due to the large bandwidth of video signal (in broadcast TV the NTSC color video signal is sampled at 10.7 MHz—3 times the color subcarrier frequency—and each sample is quantized to 8 bits (256 levels), resulting in a bit rate of 85.6 Mbit/s). Data compression or redundancy reduction techniques have been extensively studied and applied to video signal (see also Chapter 3 and Section 9.4) for the specific purpose of reducing the bandwidth and data rate values.

Interframe and intraframe compression techniques have been applied with success. Suitable compression techniques (see Section 9.4) can reduce the data rate to 20 Mbit/s for broadcast-quality systems or to 2–5 Mbit/s for videotelephone or teleconferencing applications.

Finally, an important aspect in the communication field is represented by the introduction of suitable systems (transmultiplexers), interconnecting time-division (TDM) systems with frequency-division (FDM) systems.[†] This permits the application in the TDM part (as PCM format) of data compression and error control techniques, increasing the efficiency of the overall analog–digital communication system [4, 12].

9.7   Applications to Computer Systems and Networks

An extraordinary progress of computer systems, due to the digital technology innovations, has been taking place. Standard computers, minicomputers, microprocessors and array-processors have been expanding in many application areas (digital signal–image processing, communications, radar, biomedicine and remote sensing).

The interest in applying source and channel coding concepts and properties to the computer system itself, is connected for several important reasons:

(1)   Reduction of the number of data (source coding) inside the computer system is, in any case, useful for a more efficient use of it. This can be con-

---

[†] An interesting practical example is represented by the TMX 262 transmultiplexer, developed by the TRT, Paris, which performs the conversion of two PCM 30-channel streams (2.048 Mbit/s) into one FDM standard supergroup (312–552 kHz band) and vice versa. This conversion facilitates the introduction of digital equipment into an analog telephone network (coexistence of analog and digital systems) [13].

sidered not only for the input–output data (processed data), but also for the programs representing the operations to be performed (compact software packages).

(2) Protection of data from noise or disturbances (channel coding) inside the computer system and its peripheral units is very important, especially for data of high relevance (processed data and programs).

As for the source coding aspect, besides the use of the described techniques (Chapters 3, 6) for the input–output data, of special interest is the research for compact programs, that is programs represented in a compressed form (hence, reducing the memory cost) or using compact languages (increasing the processing speed as well as reducing the memory cost). The research of these last topics is in progress, in particular for special applications (as digital signal–image processing, recognition of moving objects and robotics) [14].

As far as the channel coding aspect is concerned, it can be observed that very simple error control coding is used in computer systems, ever since the first implementations. In general, a simple parity-check gives the possibility of detecting some errors in the computer operation. This approach is frequently used in storage or memory units (cards, paper tapes, magnetic tapes and disks). More efficient coding techniques have also been studied, tested and used especially for important data storage. An interesting example is represented by the use of convolutional coding with probabilistic decoding (maximum likelihood decoding (MLD), use of Viterbi algorithm) in digital magnetic recording systems. As a result of computer simulation, the MLD method gains approximately 2.5 dB in S/N compared with the bit-by-bit detection method and the error rate is reduced by a factor of 50 to 300 in the raw error rates in the 10^{-3}–10^{-4} range [15].

9.8 Applications to Biomedicine

Electronic techniques were widely introduced in the biomedicine field, to increase the efficiency of diagnosis and care. In particular, digital electronic techniques have been expanding in this new field for the advantages of higher precision, reliability and flexibility and possibility of automatic or semi-automatic control and supervision by computer systems. Source coding techniques are of great interest and practical importance for efficient processing of biomedical signals and images.

Data compression techniques can reduce the amount of data representing biomedical signals or images, with the advantage of reducing the requested memory capacity and cost and the transmission bandwidth (i.e., the possibility of transmitting data regarding a larger number of patients). Techniques giving high compression ratios (with the eventual loss of some information) can be useful for representation of the most significant characteristics of biomedical signals and images, as sufficient for the wide mass screening on many patients or large population groups. Techniques assuring no information loss (with the higher compatible compression ratios) are required for accurate diagnosis or single patient examinations in the care phase.

9.8.1 Data Compression Application to Biomedical Signals

Most of the data compression techniques described in Chapter 3 can be useful to this purpose, i.e., use of digital filtering, spectral estimation and prediction–interpolation. Some practical examples are given next [16].

Figure 9.7a shows the application of the zero-order prediction (ZOP) algorithm to an ECG signal, while Fig. 9.7b shows its efficiency, measured by the compression ratio (Ca) and errors (peak and rms errors) as a function of the normalized aperture (or amplitude tolerance).

As we can see from Fig. 9.7, up to an aperture equal to 2% the ECG reconstructed signal is practically the same as the original one, while going up to an aperture equal to 10% the reconstructed signal is an approximation (of lower fidelity at higher aperture values) of the original signal. These last cases, having obviously higher compression ratios, can be useful for mass screening.

Another example of data compression of ECG signals, now using the FFT algorithm with different threshold values (eliminating some transformed data), is shown in Fig. 9.8. The distortion is negligible up to a threshold value equal to 5% (compression ratio $\simeq 10$)

As was observed in Chapter 3, a pre-digital filtering, before the application of data compression, can be very useful in reducing noise and disturbances, hence increasing the efficiency of the data compression algorithms used.

An example of this processing procedure is shown in Fig. 9.9, relating to the use of a FIR digital filter before a ZOP algorithm. The effects of channel noise and errors on ECG compressed data are analysed in Chapter 6.

9.8.2 Data Compression Application to Biomedical Images

The techniques described in Chapter 3 can be used for biomedical image data compression, whose amount is increasing in an impressive way. As examples, for blood cell analysis 15 million images were processed in the U.S. alone in 1982, while for x-ray images (excluding those in dentistry) 1 million images were processed in the U.S. alone in 1980.

All one-dimensional data compression techniques (prediction–interpolation, variable length encoding) can also be applied to biomedical image

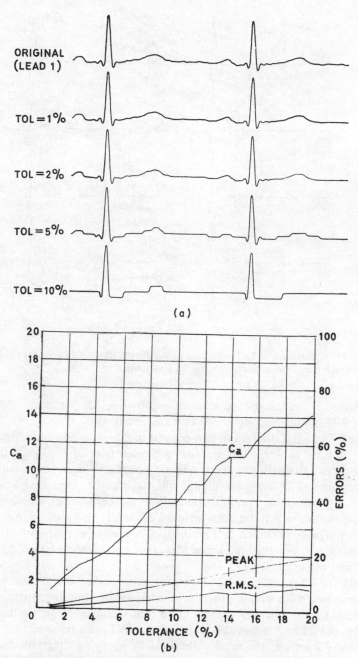

FIG. 9.7. Application of zero-order prediction (ZOP) algorithm with floating tolerance to an ECG signal. (a) Reconstructed waveforms and (b) performance curves.

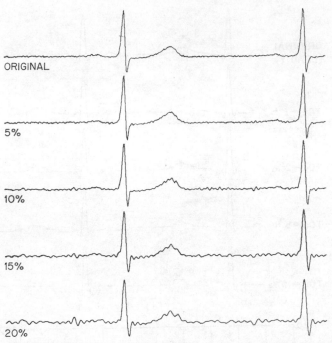

ORIGINAL

5%

10%

15%

20%

FIG. 9.8. Application of FFT algorithm with different threshold values (applied on transformed data) to an ECG signal: reconstructed waveforms.

processing, if the images are scanned line-by-line. Of particular interest are use of 2-D digital filtering and 2-D transformations.

The 2-D digital filtering of low-pass or bandpass type represents by itself a sort of data compression, because a limited part of the space frequency spectrum is extracted, requiring a lower number of data to be maintained. Furthermore, 2-D low-pass digital filtering can be used as a useful pre-processing, before the eventual application of other compression algorithms, because the smoothed data can be more efficiently compressed. An example, to this purpose, is shown in Fig. 9.10: on the right the smoothed image is appearing, without the high space frequency components (essentially due to noise and disturbances) [17, 18].

With regard to the use of 2-D transformations, they are in general applied in connection with simple procedures, such as thresholding, variable length encoding and prediction–interpolation (see Chapter 3). In particular, fast Fourier (FFT) and fast Walsh transforms (FWT) can be used.

Table 9.2 reports the results obtained by applying different transformations (Fourier, Hadamard, Haar) in fast form with thresholding to nuclear medicine images (scintigraphies). The main data compression efficiency parameters are the compression ratio (CR), peak and rms errors. As

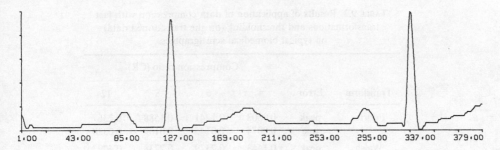

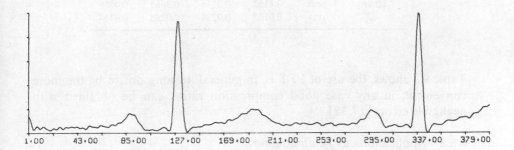

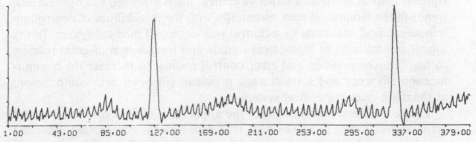

FIG. 9.9. Application of a pre-digital filtering, before the application of data compression (ZOP with floating tolerance) to an ECG signal.

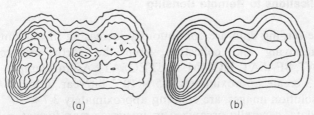

FIG. 9.10. Application of a 2-D FIR digital filtering of low-pass type to a biomedical scintigraphy: (a) original image and (b) processed image (iso-contour displays).

TABLE 9.2. Results of application of data compression with fast
transformations and thresholding (on the transformed data)
on typical biomedical scintigraphies.

Transform	Error	Compression ratio (CR)			
		4	6	8	12
Fourier	peak	0.0803	0.1241	0.1588	0.2367
	rms	0.0074	0.0145	0.0169	0.0320
Walsh	peak	0.1443	0.2329	0.2738	0.4093
	rms	0.0171	0.0229	0.0278	0.0361
Haar	peak	0.1132	0.3111	0.3665	0.4656
	rms	0.0165	0.0234	0.0285	0.0364

Table 9.2 shows, the use of FFT is, in general, turning out to be the more convenient; in any case good compression ratios can be obtained with negligible errors [17, 18].

9.8.3 Applications to Telemedicine

The transmission of biomedical signals and images from one place (peripheral clinical units) to another (a central main hospital) has opened new trends in the biomedical area, essentially with the possibilities of controlling remote medical situations by a central well-equipped medical system. In the digital transmission of biomedical signals and images it is of great interest to use data compression and error control coding, to increase the communication efficiency and solve storage problems (through data compression) at the main receiving central system.

Figure 9.11 shows an example of the application of data compression and error control coding to ECG signal. It is clear how the compressed–uncoded signal is strongly changed by channel noise, while with suitable coding the original signal is restored at the receiving terminal (see also Section 6.4).

9.9 Applications to Remote Sensing

Remote sensing data are continuously increasing in amount due to the ground receiving and collection from the earth resource satellites (LANDSAT, SEASAT, HCMM, METEOSAT). As an example, LANDSAT 1, 2 and 3 create approximately 1.5×10^{13} bit/year. LANDSAT D, with higher-resolution images, are creating approximately 3.7×10^{15} bits/year.

These data, generally organized in image or map format, related to the observed earth region, are to be stored for subsequent processing and utiliza-

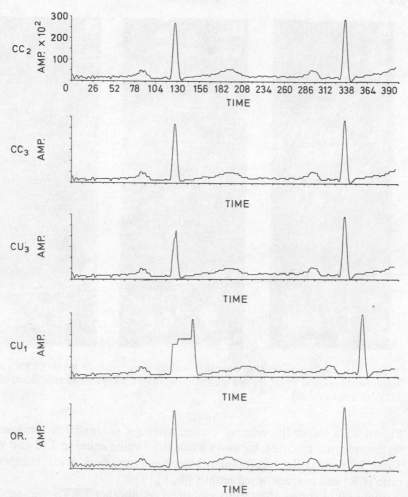

FIG. 9.11. Example of application of data compression and error control coding to an ECG signal (for the symbols, see Section 6.4).

tion (in general, for many years). In terms of processing, for instance, the EROS facilities in the U.S during 1980 received and processed for civilian applications 26×10^3 LANDSAT scenes.

Big storage problems are, therefore, emerging. Data compression techniques can solve, at least in part, these problems (further compressed data can be more easily classified for final interpretation). The techniques described in Chapter 3 can be used.

Figure 9.12 shows the application of zero-order interpolation (ZOI) with floating tolerance to ERTS-1 satellite images (of a region near Rome, Italy).

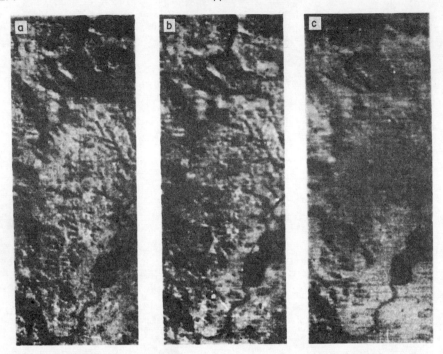

FIG. 9.12. Application of ZOI algorithm with floating tolerance to an ERTS-1 satellite image: (a) the original image, (b) and (c), the reconstructed images [tolerance values equal to 3.12% (b) and 9.37% (c)].

Figure 9.12a shows the original image, while the reconstructed images (Fig. 9.12b and c) are reported, by using a tolerance value equal to 3.12 and 9.37%. Table 9.3 reports the results for other cases [rms, peak error, compression ratio (CR) and average word length [L_m] [19].

Figure 9.13 shows the results obtained on another ERTS-1 image (from another region near Rome, Italy), by using a fast Walsh transform (FWT) with variable-word-length coding. The transformed image is divided into several equal squares (4 × 4) and a minimum-word-length coding (a bit number sufficient to represent the maximum absolute value in the square plus 1 bit for the sign) is performed for each of them.

The reconstructed image corresponds to the value of $q/N = 6.25\%$ (q is the quantization value of transformed data, and N the dimension of the processed image). Table 9.4 shows numerical results for this and two other cases.

From the tests, it is clear how the FWT techniques give higher efficiency (greater compression ratios with comparable error values) than the simpler ZOI or similar algorithms.

TABLE 9.3. Results obtained by applying the ZOI
algorithm with floating tolerance to an ERTS-1
satellite image.[a]

Δ (%)	RMSE (%)	PE (%)	CR	L_m (bits/sample)
3.12	2.32	3.12	1.60	3.12
6.25	4.11	6.25	3.03	1.65
9.37	5.60	9.37	5.02	0.99
12.50	7.04	12.50	7.68	0.65
15.62	8.37	15.62	11.49	0.43

[a] Δ = floating tolerance value; RSME = rms error;
PE = peak error; CR = compression ratio; L_m = mean
word length.

Another example of the application of data compression with transformations is shown in Fig. 9.14. The discrete cosine transform (DCT, relation (3.39), implemented in a fast way, FCT) is applied to a LANDSAT C image of a south Italy region, near the Sele river, with thresholding compression of transformed data representing image square sub-blocks of 16×16 data. In Fig. 9.14a the original image is presented, while in Fig. 9.14b the reconstructed one is shown (threshold = 0.5% of maximum value, CR = 2.75, rms error = 0.95%) [20]. The resulting overall efficiency is quite good as with FWT techniques. The FWT and FCT compression techniques represent, therefore, suitable approaches for compressing remote sensing images, as given by earth resource satellites.

TABLE 9.4. Results obtained by applying the FWT
with variable-word-length coding to an ERTS-1
satellite image.[a]

q/N (%)	RMSE (%)	PE (%)	CR	L_m (bits/sample)
0.78	0.87	6.25	1.25	3.95
3.12	3.50	15.62	2.13	2.35
6.25	5.62	28.12	3.85	1.30

[a] The transformed image is divided into 4×4 equal squares; q = quantization value of the transform coefficient; N = number of rows and columns of the processed image; other variables are defined in Table 9.3.

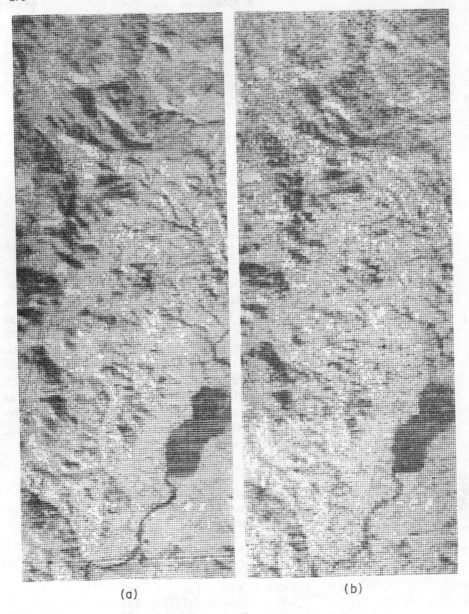

(a) (b)

FIG. 9.13. Application of FWT transform with variable-word-length encoding to an ERTS-1 satellite image: (a) original image, $L_M = 5$ bits/sample and (b) reconstructed image, $L_M = 1.30$ bits/sample.

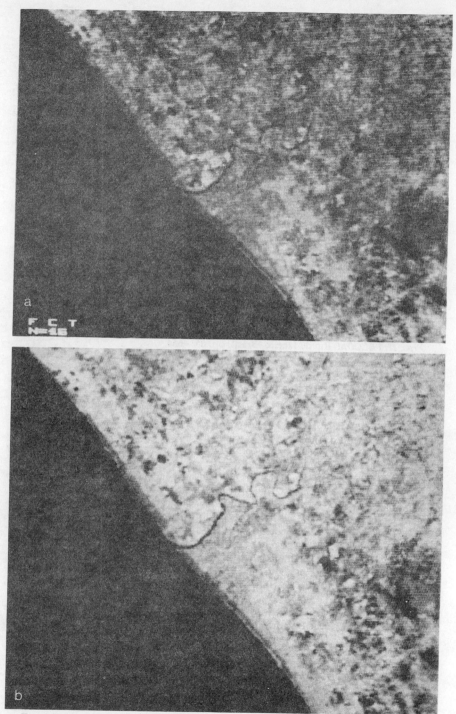

FIG. 9.14. Application of FCT transform with thresholding to a LANDSAT C image. (a) Original image and (b) reconstructed image.

References

1. PCM telemetry data compression study, phase 1. NASA Contract NAS 5-9729, October, 1965.
2. Gregory, W. H. (1974). Technology spawning new data on the sun, *Aviat. Week Space Technol.* January, 1974.
3. Andreoni, R., Barletti, R., Cappellini, V., Gabbanini, A., Lotti, F., Pampaloni, P., Sprocchetti, R., and Tofani, G. (1976). Receiving ground station for the Solrad-11 project, *Proc. Convegno sullo Spazio, 16th*, Roma, March, pp. 237–244.
4. Cappellini, V., Constantinides, A. G., and Emiliani, P. (1978). "Digital Filters and Their Applications." Academic Press, London.
5. Francini, G. L., and DeBiasi, G. B. (1968). Study of a system of minimal speech-reproducing units for Italian speech. *J. Acoust. Soc. Am.* **43**, 1282–1286.
6. Brofferio, S., Cafforio, C., Rocca, F., and Ruffino, U. (1975). A dynamic programming approach to video coding using movement compensation, *Proc. Conf. Digital Signal Processing*, Florence, pp. 158–169.
7. Odenwalder, J. P. (1976). Error control coding handbook. Final Report LINKABIT Corp., San Diego, California, Contract F44620-76-C-0056.
8. LM46 QPSK/BPSK modem. Specifications, LINKABIT Corp., San Diego, California, 1982.
9. Bertini, S., and Cappellini, V. (1980). Some aspects of maritime satellite communications, *Proc. INTELCOM*, Rio de Janeiro, Brasil, pp. 653–656.
10. Telemetering and supervisory control systems—TC1000. Telettra SpA, Milano, June, 1979.
11. Supervisory control systems—TC1000/04. Telettra SpA, Milano, September, 1982.
12. Scheuermann, H., and Gockler, N. (1981). A comprehensive survey of digital transmultiplexing method. *Proc. IEEE*, **69**, 1419–1450.
13. Transmultiplexer—TMX-262. Specifications, TRT, Paris, 1982.
14. Eastwood, M. A. (1983). CAD and languages for robotics, *Proc. NATO Adv. Study Inst. Robotics Artif. Intell.*, Castelvecchio Pascoli–Lucca, Italy, June–July, p. 19.
15. Kobayashi, H. (1970). Application of probabilistics decoding to digital magnetic recording systems, *IBM Res. Rep.* **RC 2986**, Yorktown Heights, New York, August.
16. Benelli, G., Cappellini, V., and Lotti, F. (1980). Data compression techniques and applications, *Radio Electron. Eng.* **50**, 29–53.
17. Cappellini, V. (1977). Some digital techniques for biomedical signal and image processing, *Elektrotehnika, Proc. Symposium Medicine and Techniques*, Zagreb, Yugoslavia, pp. 283–285.
18. Cappellini, V., and Venetsanopoulos, A. N. (1983). Two-dimensional digital filters with application to biomedical image processing, *Proc. Congresso Brasileiro de Engenhoria Biomedica, 8th*, Florianópolis, Brasil, November.
19. Cappellini, V., Chini, A., and Lotti, F. (1976). Some data compression methods for processing the image received from earth resource satellites. Proc. Convegno sullo Spazio, *16th*, March, pp. 33–43.
20. Cappellini, V., and Del Re, E. (1984). Image data compression by the Discrete Cosine Transform. Department Electrical Engineering Report, University of Florence, Florence, November, 1984.

Appendix 1

Finite Fields: A Brief Survey

A.1 Definition of Field

A *field* is an algebraic structure in which two operations are defined, called the sum and product, which verify the familiar properties of the corresponding operations between real or complex numbers. A formal definition of a field is given later in this section; preliminarily, however, it is convenient to define (commutative) groups.[†]

DEFINITION 1   A *group* $(G,)$ is a nonempty set G on which an operation called product is defined which verifies ($a, b, c, \ldots$ are elements of G):

(1) $(ab)c = a(bc)$ for any triple a, b, c
(2) $ab = ba$ for any couple a, b
(3) $1a = a = a1$ for a suitable group element denoted by 1
(4) any element a has an inverse, denoted by a^{-1}, such that $aa^{-1} = a^{-1}a = 1$

The element 1 in (3) is called the *unity* of the group; it can be proved that unity is unique. Also the inverse a^{-1} of any a is unique.

Sometimes the operation in a group is called *sum* instead of product; then the group axioms (1) to (4) become:

(1′) $(a + b) + c = a + (b + c)$
(2′) $a + b = b + a$
(3′) $0 + a = a = a + 0$
(4′) $-a + a = a - a = 0$

In this case the group is called *additive*, whereas axioms (1)–(4) define a *multiplicative* group. Note that the special element in (3′) is now denoted by 0

[†] From now on all groups will be assumed to be commutative, i.e., to verify property (2) of Definition 1.

and called the *zero* of the group; the inverse of a is denoted by $-a$; also note that $a + -a$ is written in short as $a - a$.

DEFINITION 2   A *field* $(F, +,)$ is a set F on which two operations, sum and product, are defined which verify

(1) $(F, +)$ is an additive group
(2) $(F - \{0\}, \cdot)$ is a multiplicative group
(3) $a(b + c) = ab + ac$, for any triple a, b, c

Obvious examples of fields are the fields of rational, real or complex numbers. A whole class of finite fields is obtained by considering, for any prime p, Z_p, or rather $Z_p(+,)$, the field of integers modulo p. The elements of Z_p, $0, 1, \ldots, p - 1$, are all possible remainders obtained by dividing an integer number by p. To perform operations in Z_p we add or multiply in the usual way, divide the result by p and keep the remainder.

This is called operating "modulo p". For $p = 2$ we have the smallest fields of all, the binary field Z_2, whose elements are 0 and 1. Finite fields, called also *Galois fields* in honour of Evariste Galois (1811–1832), are of particular concern to us. Before turning to them, we need to digress and discuss (abstract) polynomials.

A.2   Polynomials Over a Field

The coefficients of a polynomial can be chosen in any field, since to operate on polynomials we need only to operate on their coefficients. The polynomials in the variable x[†] with coefficients in a field F form an algebraic structure which is poorer than a field because condition (4) of Definition 2 does not hold for the product between polynomials. Such a structure is called a *ring*. Examples of *rings* are the ring of integer numbers (positive and negative), any field and the ring of polynomials with coefficients on a field.

The Euclidean algorithm of division carries over to abstract polynomials. This suggests the possibility of constructing new fields in the same way as the fields Z_p are constructed from the ring Z of integers. To construct Z_p we must first fix the prime p. In our case we fix an *irreducible polynomial*, that is a polynomial which does not factor in polynomials of (positive) lower degree. Let $F(x)$ be the ring of polynomials $f(x)$ with coefficients in the field F; fix a polynomial $\Phi(x)$ of degree r. Let $F(x)|_{\Phi(x)}$ be the set of all possible remainders when a polynomial in $F(x)$ is divided by $\Phi(x)$, that is the set of all polynomials of degree $< r$. Sum and product are performed in

---

† Note that x is simply a convenient symbol. Here we do not consider polynomials as functions. The polynomial $x^3 + x + 1$ might also be written as $(1, 0, 1, 1)$.

$F(x)|_{\Phi(x)}$ modulo $\Phi(x)$. It can be proved that (1) $F(x)|_{\Phi(x)}$ is always a ring and (2) $F(x)|_{\Phi(x)}$ is a field if and only if (iff) $\Phi(x)$ is irreducible.

EXAMPLE 1   Take the real polynomials, i.e., $F = R$, and take the irreducible real polynomial $x^2 + 1$. Then $R(x)|x^2 + 1$ is the field of complex numbers (simply write $ax + b$ as $aj + b$, j being the imaginary unity; also note that $x^2 + 1$ is reducible when considered as a complex polynomial).[†]

EXAMPLE 2   Take now the polynomials over the Galois field Z_p and assume that $\Phi(x)$ is an irreducible polynomial (over Z_p) of degree r. Then $Z_p(x)|_{\Phi(x)}$ is itself a Galois field. Its order (number of elements) is clearly p^r.

The last example shows that it is important to know how many irreducible polynomials there are over Z_p. Fortunately we can prove that for any Galois field of order q, GF(q) say, and for any positive integer number r there exists at least a polynomial with coefficient in GF(q) which is irreducible over GF(q). As a consequence, for any prime p and any integer $r \geq 1$ there exists at least a Galois field GF(q) of order $q = p^r$. This statement will be strengthened in the next section.

A.3   The Multiplicative Structure of Galois Fields

From now on we restrict our attention to Galois fields. We have seen that any Z_p (p prime) is a Galois field and that $Z_p(x)|_{\Phi(x)} = $ GF(q) ($\Phi(x)$ irreducible over Z_p) is also a Galois field. Now, all Galois fields are, essentially, of these two types.

PROPOSITION 1   The order of a Galois field is of the form p^r, p prime; up to isomorphisms there is only one Galois field of order $q = p^r$, GF(q), say.

"Up to isomorphisms" means that two Galois fields of the same order differ only in the "name" of their elements. More formally: there is a one-to-one mapping f between them (the isomorphism) preserving both operations:

$$f(a + b) = f(a) + f(b), f(ab) = f(a)f(b)$$

However, it is not always convenient to consider the elements of GF(q) as polynomial remainders, since this representation becomes too cumbersome if, e.g., we use the elements of GF(q) as coefficients for other polynomials.

Now a more detailed description will be given of a Galois field, starting with its multiplicative substructure. Assume that α is a nonzero element in

---

† Therefore, when saying that a polynomial is irreducible we must specify in what field this claim is made.

GF(q). It is easily proved that the powers of α from a subgroup[†] of the multiplicative group $GF(q) - \{0\}$. This subgroup has a cyclic structure in the sense that it is isomorphic with the additive group Z_n for a suitable n. More precisely, n is the smallest positive integer such that $\alpha^n = 1$. Then the distinct elements of the subgroup are $\alpha^0 = 1, \alpha^1, \alpha^2, \ldots, \alpha^{n-1}$; the isomorphism is obtained by setting $f(\alpha^s) = s$, $0 \le s < n$. Moreover, $\alpha^s = \alpha^t$ iff $s \equiv t(\bmod n)$.

The number n is called the *order* of α, and α is called a primitive nth root of unity. Clearly the only element of order 1 is the unity 1. The greatest possible order for an element α is $q - 1$, then the powers of α generate all nonzero elements of $GF(q)$ and α is called a *primitive* element of the field. It is a remarkable result of the theory that primitive elements always exist.

PROPOSITION 2   The number of primitive elements in a field $GF(q)$ is $\Phi(q - 1)$, Φ being the Euler function. (For any positive integer n, $\Phi(n)$ is the number of positive integers less than n which are relatively prime to n. A convenient formula is $\Phi(n) = n\prod_i[1 - (1/p_i)]$, with $\prod_i p_i^{r_i}$ being the decomposition of n into its prime factors and $\Phi(1) = 1$.)

For example, the number of primitive elements in $GF(9) = GF(3^2)$ is $\Phi(8) = 8(1 - \frac{1}{2}) = 4$; for $GF(8) = GF(2^3)$, $\Phi(7) = 6$ $[\Phi(p) = p - 1$ if p is prime]. If α is a primitive element of $GF(q)$, all the nonzero elements have the form α^s, $0 \le s \le q - 2$, and multiplication reduces to addition of the exponents modulo $q - 1$. It is easily proved that the order of any nonzero element β of $GF(q)$ divides $q - 1$, so that $\beta^{q-1} = 1$. This implies that the q field elements, including 0 , satisfy the equation $x^q = x$, and are, therefore, *all* the solutions of this equation over any superfield containing $GF(q)$.

PROPOSITION 3   The elements of $GF(q)$ are q solutions of the equation $x^{q^n} = x$, n a positive integer. There are no other solutions for $n = 1$.

Proposition 3 gives the factorization of $x^q - x = x(x^{q-1} - 1)$ as $x(x - 1)(x - \alpha)(x - \alpha^2) \cdots (x - \alpha^{q-2})$. We shall pursue the question of factorizing $x^n - 1$ for any value of n. Let $d|n$ mean "d divides n".

PROPOSITION 4   Assume that the order of α is n. Then

$$x^n - 1 = \prod_{d\,:\,d|n} \prod_{\beta\,:\,\text{ord}(\beta)=d} (x - \beta)$$

the products being taken over all factors d of n and over all field elements β of order d.

---

† A subgroup of a group is a subset of a group which is itself a group; in particular a subgroup is "closed" in the sense that operations between subgroup elements do not take out of the subgroup.

The polynomial

$$Q^{(d)}(x) = \prod_{\beta:\, \mathrm{ord}(\beta)=d} (x - \beta)$$

is called a *cyclotomic polynomial*. Hence, the factorization of Proposition 4 can be written as

$$x^n - 1 = \prod_{d:\, d\mid n} Q^{(d)}(x)$$

The cyclotomic polynomial $Q^{(n)}(x)$ is given by the polynomial formula:

$$Q^{(n)}(x) = \prod_{d:\, d\mid n} (x^d - 1)^{\mu(n/d)} = \prod_{d:\, d\mid n} (x^{n/d} - 1)^{\mu(d)}$$

where $\mu(\cdot)$ is the Möbius function, which is defined as:

$$\mu(d) = \begin{cases} 1 & \text{for} \quad d = 1, \\ (-1)^k & \text{if} \quad d \text{ is the product of } k \text{ distinct primes,} \\ 0 & \text{otherwise.} \end{cases}$$

For example,

$$Q^{(4)}(x) = (x - 1)^{\mu(4)}(x^2 - 1)^{\mu(2)}(x^4 - 1)^{\mu(1)} = (x^2 - 1)^{-1}(x^4 - 1) = x^2 + 1$$

Note that this formula works for *any* field.

A.4 The Additive Structure of Galois Fields

We now consider the interplay of the additive and the multiplicative structure of Galois fields. A Galois field $\mathrm{GF}(q) = \mathrm{GF}(p^r)$ contains a subfield, called the *integer subfield*, which is isomorphic to Z_p. The isomorphism is obtained by associating the integer r, $0 \le r < p$, to the field element $1 + 1 + \cdots + 1$ (r times).

Actually we shall identify the field element $1 + 1 + \cdots + 1$ (r times) with r, so that $Z_p \subseteq \mathrm{GF}(p^r)$. The prime number p is called the *characteristic* of $\mathrm{GF}(p^r)$. A consequence of Proposition 3 is that the integers of the fields $\mathrm{GF}(p^r)$ are the solutions of the equation $x^p = x$. Note that in a field of characteristic 2 sum and subtraction coincide because $1 = -1$. More generally, $p\alpha = 0$ in any field of characteristic p.

A convenient formula is given by the following.

PROPOSITION 5   If $\alpha_1, \alpha_2, \ldots, \alpha_n$ are elements of a field of characteristic p and if q is a power of p, then

$$\left(\sum_{i=1}^n \alpha_i \right)^q = \sum_{i=1}^n \alpha_i^q$$

(The cross products cancel.)

For example, in a field of characteristic 2, $(a + b)^2 = a^2 + b^2, (a + b)^4 = a^4 + b^4, (a + b)^8 = a^8 + b^8$ and so forth. We said that $Z_p = \mathrm{GF}(p)$ is a subfield of $\mathrm{GF}(p^r)$ for any r. Also, $\mathrm{GF}(q)$ is a subfield of $\mathrm{GF}(q^r)$ for any r and no other subfield of $\mathrm{GF}(q^r)$ has order q. More generally, $\mathrm{GF}(q^j)$ is a subfield of $\mathrm{GF}(q^k)$ if and only if j divides k. Therefore, the Galois fields of a given characteristic have a very neat lattice structure when ordered by inclusion.

Often, we need the following setting: a field $\mathrm{GF}(q^k)$ is given and the subfield $\mathrm{GF}(q)$ is fixed to provide coefficients for certain polynomials. In such a context, $\mathrm{GF}(q)$ is called the *ground (sub)field*, and its elements are called *ground elements*. Often the ground field is the integer subfield $Z_p = \mathrm{GF}(p)$. The formula of Proposition 5 can be used to prove the following proposition.

PROPOSITION 6   Let $f(x)$ be a polynomial where coefficients are ground elements. Let ω, $\omega \in \mathrm{GF}(q^k)$, be a solution of the equation $f(x) = 0$; then ω^{q^s} is a solution of the same equation for any integer s. If the order of ω is n, then the elements $\omega, \omega^q, \omega^{q^2}, \ldots, \omega^{q^{m-1}}$ are distinct and no other distinct element exists. Here m in the smallest positive integer such that $q^m \equiv 1$ modulo n.

The element $\omega, \omega^q, \omega^{q^2}, \ldots, \omega^{q^{m-1}}$ of Proposition 6 are called *conjugates* (with respect to the ground subfield). Proposition 6 states that if a ground polynomial has a root of order n, then it has at least m conjugate roots. As a matter of fact there is a ground polynomial $f(x)$ which has no other roots.

PROPOSITION 7   Let ω be an element of order n of $\mathrm{GF}(q^k)$ and let m be the same as in Proposition 6. Then the coefficients of the polynomial of degree $m f(x) = \Pi_{i=0}^{m-1} (x - \omega^{q^i})$ are ground elements. Moreover, $f(x)$ is irreducible over $\mathrm{GF}(q)$.

Although $f(x)$ does not factor into a product of ground polynomials of lower degree, it does factor into linear terms over $\mathrm{GF}(q^r)$. Any ground polynomial which has a root ω has all the conjugate elements $\omega^q, \omega^{q^2}, \ldots, \omega^{q^{m-1}}$ as roots and, therefore, is a multiple of $f(x)$; for this reason the latter is called the *minimal polynomial* of ω (with respect to the ground subfield); its degree m is also called the *degree* of ω with respect to the ground subfield. Proposition 6 shows the relation existing between the order and the degree of a field element ω. The algebraic structure of fields is clarified by the following proposition.

PROPOSITION 8   If the degree of ω is m, the polynomials in ω of degree less than m and with ground coefficients are all distinct and form a subfield of order q^m. (A polynomial in $\omega, f(\omega) = a_t \omega^t + a_{t-1} \omega^{t-1} + \cdots + a_0$, is an element of $\mathrm{GF}(q^k)$ which is obtained from $f(x)$, x an indeterminate, when x is replaced by ω).

We still need a few facts.

PROPOSITION 9   The polynomial $x^{q^k} - x$ factors into the product of all monic polynomials irreducible over GF(q) whose degree divides k. (A monic polynomial is one whose leading coefficient is one.)

PROPOSITION 10   Assume $f(x)$ is a polynomial of degree m irreducible over GF(q). Then GF(q^m) contains m roots of $f(x)$. Therefore, $f(x)$ factors linearly in GF(q^m).

The purport of the theory is properly appreciated in algebraic coding.

Appendix 2

Computer Programs for the Implementation of Data Compression and Error Control Techniques

The following programs can be used for processing data using compression–decompression and/or coding–decoding techniques. The programs are written in FORTRAN IV language. They are given in form of subroutines and the calling statements as well as most of the symbols used are in agreement with the examples and flowcharts described in Sections 7.3–7.5. and in Section 7.7.

286

DATA COMPRESSION AND ERROR CONTROL
TECHNIQUES WITH APPLICATIONS

```
C         ZERO ORDER PREDICTOR (FLOATING APERTURE)
C         ---------------------------------------------
C         Comprimes the vector 'SOURC' onto 'COUT' inserting time iden
C
C         The odd components of 'COUT' will contain data and the even
C         components the time identification
C
C         SOURC  =   Compressed input signal
C         NINP   =   Number of input points
C         TOL    =   Tolerance value
C         COUT   =   Compressed output signal + time insertion
C         NTS    =   Number of output samples after compression
C
C**************************************************************************
C
          SUBROUTINE  CZOP(SOURC,NINP,TOL,COUT,NTS)
          DIMENSION SOURC(1),COUT(1)
          IC=0
          IS=0
10        IF(IS-NINP) 11,21,21
11        IS=IS+1
          IC=IC+1
          REF=SOURC(IS)
          COUT(IC)=SOURC(IS)
          CS=0.
          DO 15 JZ=1,NINP
          CS=CS+1.
          IS=IS+1
          IF(IS-NINP) 13,13,17
13        IF(ABS(SOURC(IS)-REF)-TOL)15,15,17
15        CONTINUE
          CS=CS+1
          GOTO 19
17        IS=IS-1
19        IC=IC+1
          COUT(IC)=CS-1.
          GOTO 10
21        NTS=IC
          RETURN
          END
```

```
C          ZERO ORDER PREDICTOR (FIXED APERTURE)
C          -------------------------------------
C          Comprimes the vector 'SOURC' onto 'COUT' inserting time ident.
C
C          The odd components of 'COUT' will contain data and the even
C          components the time identification
C
C          SOURC  =  Compressed input signal
C          NINP   =  Number of input points
C          TOL    =  Tolerance value
C          COUT   =  Compressed output signal + time insertion
C          NTS    =  Number of output samples after compression
C
C****************************************************************************
C
           SUBROUTINE   CZOPX(SOURC,NINP,TOL,COUT,NTS)
           DIMENSION SOURC(1),COUT(1)
           IC=0
           IS=0
           DT=2.*TOL
10         IF(IS-NINP) 11,21,21
11         IS=IS+1
           IC=IC+1
           REF=AINT(SOURC(IS)/ DT) *DT+TOL
           COUT(IC)=SOURC(IS)
           CS=0.
           DO 15 JZ=1,NINP
           CS=CS+1.
           IS=IS+1
           IF(IS-NINP) 13,13,17
13         IF(ABS(SOURC(IS)-REF)-TOL)15,15,17
15         CONTINUE
           CS=CS+1.
           GOTO 19
17         IS=IS-1
19         IC=IC+1
           COUT(IC)=CS-1.
           GOTO 10
21         NTS=IC
           RETURN
           END
```

```
C       ZERO ORDER INTERPOLATOR
C       ------------------------
C       Comprimes the vector 'SOURC' onto 'COUT' inserting time ident
C
C       The odd components of 'COUT' will contain data and the even
C       components the time identification
C
C       SOURC  =  Compressed input signal
C       NINP   =  Number of input points
C       TOL    =  Tolerance value
C       COUT   =  Compressed output signal + time insertion
C       NTS    =  Number of output samples after compression
C
C************************************************************************?
C
        SUBROUTINE CZOI(SOURC,NINP,TOL,COUT,NTS)
C       Set maximum number of compressed samples to 255
        DATA TOP / 255./
        DIMENSION SOURC(1),COUT(1)
        NTS=0
        CS=0.
        I=1
1       TMAX=SOURC(I)+TOL
        TMIN=SOURC(I)-TOL
        IF(I-NINP) 3,37,37
3       IP1=I+1
        DO 35 K=IP1,NINP
        ALPHA=SOURC(K)+TOL
        BETA=SOURC(K)-TOL
        IF(ALPHA-TMAX) 11,12,12
12      IF(TMAX-BETA) 11,15,15
15      IF(BETA-TMIN) 11,26,26
11      IF(TMAX-ALPHA) 13,14,14
14      IF(ALPHA-TMIN) 13,16,16
16      IF(TMIN-BETA) 13,27,27
13      IF(ALPHA-TMAX) 17,18,18
18      IF(TMIN-BETA) 17,29,29
17      IF(TMAX-ALPHA) 21,19,19
19      IF(BETA-TMIN) 21,28,28
21      COUT(NTS+1)=(TMAX+TMIN)/2.
        COUT(NTS+2)=CS
        CS=0.
        I=K
        NTS=NTS+2
        GOTO 1
26      TMIN=BETA
        GOTO 29
27      TMAX=ALPHA
        GOTO 29
28      TMAX=ALPHA
        TMIN=BETA
29      IF(CS-TOP) 35,21,21
35      CS=CS+1.
37      COUT(NTS+1)=(TMAX+TMIN)/2.
        COUT(NTS+2)=CS
        NTS=NTS+2
        RETURN
        END
```

```
C         FIRST ORDER INTERPOLATOR  -  DISJOINED LINE SEGMENT
C         ---------------------------------------------------------
C         Comprimes the vector 'SOURC' onto 'COUT' inserting time ident.
C
C         The first two components of 'CINP' will contain data, the
C         third component the time identification ,and so on.
C
C         SOURC  =  Compressed input signal
C         NINP   =  Number of input points
C         TOL    =  Tolerance value
C         COUT   =  Compressed output signal + time insertion
C         NTS    =  Number of output samples after compression
C
C*************************************************************************
C
          SUBROUTINE CFOID(SOURC,NINP,TOL,COUT,NTS)
          DIMENSION SOURC(1),COUT(1)
          I=1
          NTS=0
          CS=0.
12        NTS=NTS+1
          COUT(NTS)=SOURC(I)
          TMAX=SOURC(I+1)+TOL
          TMIN=SOURC(I+1)-TOL
          IP2=I+2
          DO 92 K=IP2,NINP
          ALPHA=SOURC(I)+(SOURC(K)-SOURC(I)+TOL)/FLOAT(K-I)
          BETA=SOURC(I)+(SOURC(K)-SOURC(I)-TOL)/FLOAT(K-I)
          IF(ALPHA-TMAX) 10,20,20
20        IF(TMAX-BETA) 10,50,50
50        IF(BETA-TMIN) 10,86,86
10        IF(TMAX-ALPHA) 30,40,40
40        IF(ALPHA-TMIN) 30,60,60
60        IF(TMIN-BETA) 30,87,87
30        IF(ALPHA-TMAX) 70,80,80
80        IF(TMIN-BETA) 70,89,89
70        IF(TMAX-ALPHA) 85,81,81
81        IF(BETA-TMIN) 85,88,88
85        COUT(NTS+1)=(TMAX+TMIN)/2.
          COUT(NTS+2)=CS
          NTS=NTS+2
          CS=0.
          I=K
          IF(I-NINP+1) 12,84,84
84        DO 91 J=I,NINP
          NTS=NTS+1
91        COUT(NTS)=SOURC(J)
          COUT(NTS+1)=0.
          GOTO 93
86        TMIN=BETA
          GOTO 89
87        TMAX=ALPHA
          GOTO 89
88        TMAX=ALPHA
          TMIN=BETA
89        CS=CS+1.
92        CONTINUE
          COUT(NTS+1)=(TMAX+TMIN)/2.
          COUT(NTS+2)=CS
          NTS=NTS+2
93        CONTINUE
          RETURN
          END
```

```
C          ZERO ORDER DECOMPRESSION
C          ------------------------
C          Reconstructed output for Z.O.P. compressors
C
C          Decomprimes the compressed input vector 'CINP' onto 'ROUT'
C
C          The odd components of 'CINP' must contain data and the even
C          components the time identification
C
C          CINP  =  Compressed input signal
C          NINP  =  Number of input points
C          ROUT  =  Reconstructed output signal
C          NOUT  =  Number of output points
C
C*********************************************************************
C
           SUBROUTINE RZOPI(CINP,NINP,ROUT,NOUT)
           DIMENSION CINP(1),ROUT(1)
           JS=0
           DO 2 JC=1,NINP,2
           JS=JS+1
           ROUT(JS)=CINP(JC)
           IF(CINP(JC+1)) 3,2,3
3          N=CINP(JC+1)
           DO 1 J=1,N
           JS=JS+1
1          ROUT(JS)=ROUT(JS-1)
2          CONTINUE
           NOUT=JS
           RETURN
           END
```

```
C          FIRST ORDER DECOMPRESSION
C          --------------------------
C          Reconstructed output for F.O.I.-Disjoined Line Segment
C
C          Decomprimes the compressed input vector 'CINP' onto 'ROUT'
C
C          The first two components of 'CINP' must contain data, the
C          third component the time identification ,and so on.
C
C          CINP  =  Compressed input signal
C          NINP  =  Number of input points
C          ROUT  =  Reconstructed output signal
C          NOUT  =  Number of output points
C
C*********************************************************************
C
          SUBROUTINE RFOID(CINP,NINP,ROUT,NOUT)
          DIMENSION CINP(1),ROUT(1)
          NOUT=0
          DO 7 I=1,NINP,3
          IF(I+2-NINP) 1,1,8
1         ROUT(NOUT+1)=CINP(I)
          ROUT(NOUT+2)=CINP(I+1)
          NOUT=NOUT+2
          IF(CINP(I+2)) 7,7,3
3         D=ROUT(NOUT)-ROUT(NOUT-1)
          K=CINP(I+2)+1.E-5
          DO 5 L=1,K
          NOUT=NOUT+1
5         ROUT(NOUT)=ROUT(NOUT-1)+D
7         CONTINUE
          RETURN
8         DO 9 J=I,NINP
          NOUT=NOUT+1
9         ROUT(NOUT)=CINP(J)
          RETURN
          END


C          COMPRESSION BY HADAMARD TRANSFORM
C          ---------------------------------
C          The input signal is transformed by a 4x4 Hadamard matrix and the
C          output is compressed by a zero order predictor, floating apertur
C
C          SOURC =  input vector
C          NINP  =  number of input points
C          TOL   =  tolerance value for ZOP
C          COUT  =  compressed output vector
C          NTS   =  number of output points
C
C          Subroutines required:   HAD1, CZOP
C
C*********************************************************************
C
          SUBROUTINE CZHAD(SOURC,NINP,TOL,COUT,NTS)
          CALL HAD1(SOURC,COUT,NINP)
          DO 1 J=1,NINP
1         SOURC(J)=COUT(J)
          CALL CZOP(SOURC,NINP,TOL,COUT,NTS)
          RETURN
          END
```

```
C          DIRECT HADAMARD TRANSFORM    -  "HAD1"
C          ---------------------------------------
C
C          HADIN    =   input vector
C          HDOUT    =   output vector
C          NTOT     =   number of samples
C
C          HAD is a  Hadamard matrix of order 4
C
C*****************************************************************************
C
           SUBROUTINE HAD1(HADIN,HDOUT,NTOT)
           DIMENSION HADIN(1),HDOUT(1),HAD(4,4)
           DATA HAD /5*1.,-1.,1.,-1.,2*1.,2*-1.,1.,2*-1.,1/
           NPTS=NTOT/4
           NTOT=NPTS*4
           DO 1 I=1,NTOT,4
           K=I/4+1
           DO 1 J=1,4
           L=K+(J-1)*NPTS
           HDOUT(L)=0.
           DO 1 M=1,4
           IM=I+M
           HDOUT(L)=HDOUT(L)+HAD(J,M)*HADIN(IM-1)
1          CONTINUE
           RETURN
           END


C          HADAMARD TRANSFORM FOLLOWED BY ZOP  -  DECOMPRESSION
C          ----------------------------------------------------
C
C          CINP   =   compressed input signal
C          NINP   =   number of input points
C          ROUT   =   reconstructed signal
C          NOUT   =   number of output points
C
C          Subroutines required:    HAD2
C
C*****************************************************************************
C
           SUBROUTINE RZHAD(CINP,NINP,ROUT,NOUT)
           DIMENSION CINP(1),ROUT(1)
C   unpack CINP onto ROUT
           JS=0
           DO 5 JC=1,NINP,2
           JS=JS+1
           ROUT(JS)=CINP(JC)
           IF(CINP(JC+1)) 1,5,1
1          JJ=CINP(JC+1)+1.E-5
           DO 3 J=1,JJ
           JS=JS+1 .
3          ROUT(JS)=ROUT(JS-1)
5          CONTINUE
           NOUT=JS
           DO 7 J=1,NOUT
7          CINP(J)=ROUT(J)
C   inverse Hadamard transform
           CALL HAD2(CINP,ROUT,NOUT)
           RETURN
           END
```

293

```
C         INVERSE HADAMARD TRANSFORM    -   "HAD2"
C         ---------------------------------------
C
C         HADIN  =   input vector
C         HDOUT  =   output vector
C         NTOT   =   number of samples
C
C         RHAD is a normalized Hadamard matrix of order 4
C
C***********************************************************************
C
          SUBROUTINE HAD2(HADIN,HDOUT,NTOT)
          DIMENSION HADIN(1),HDOUT(1),RHAD(4,4)
          DATA RHAD /5*.25,-.25,.25,-.25,2*.25,2*-.25,.25,2*-.25,.25/
          NPTS=NTOT/4
          DO 1 I=1,NPTS
          DO 1 J=1,4
          K=J+(I-1)*4
          HDOUT(K)=0.
          DO 1 L=1,4
          M=I+(L-1)*NPTS
          HDOUT(K)=HDOUT(K)+RHAD(J,L)*HADIN(M)
1         CONTINUE
          RETURN
          END


C         CODEC   -   ENCODING/DECODING
C         -----------------------------
C
C         This subroutine performs the encoding operation if utilized
C         at the transmitter and the syndrome computation if utilized
C         at the receiver
C
C***********************************************************************
C
          SUBROUTINE CODEC(COD,S,N1,M,K,IQ,IND)
          INTEGER COD(1),H(4,15),S(1)
          DO 1 I=1,M
1         S(I)=0
          DO 2 I=1,N1
          IF(COD(I).NE.0) GOTO 2
          DO 3 II=1,M
3         S(II)=S(II)+H(II,I)
2         CONTINUE
          DO 4 I=1,M
4         S(I)=MOD(S(I),IQ)
          IF(IND.EQ.0) GOTO 5
          DO 6 I=1,M
6         COD(I+K)=IQ-S(I)
5         RETURN
          END
```

Appendix 3

Computer Programs for the Simulation of a Digital Communication System Including Data Compression and Error Control Techniques

The simulation of a digital communication system is described in detail in Chapter 7. Examples of the FORTRAN IV lists are reported in the following for two subroutines simulating channel noise generation (symbols are in agreement with those given in Sections 7.7 and 7.8).

For the simulation of some data compression and/or error control techniques, to be enclosed in the digital communication system, the programs in Appendix 2 can be used.

(Continued)

```
C         RANDOM NUMBER GENERATOR
C         -----------------------
C         Generation of uniformly distributed random real
C         numbers between 0 and 1.0
C
C   NOTE:  'nnn' is a positive integer not longer than the
C          length of the internal representation of integer
C          numbers expressed in bits
C
C****************************************************************
C
          SUBROUTINE RAND(NC01,R)
          DATA  KB/ nnn /
          M=2**KB
          IA=2**(KB/2)+3
          RX=FLOAT(M)
          NC01=NC01*IA
          NC01=NC01-(NC01/M)*M
          RC=FLOAT(NC01)
          R=RC/RX
          RETURN
          END


C         NORMALLY DISTRIBUTED REAL NUMBER GENERATOR
C         ------------------------------------------
C
C         Starting from uniformly distributed
C         numbers, computes two normally distributed
C         real numbers Y1,Y2
C
C         Subroutine required:   RAND
C
C         NC01 is an integer positive number to start
C         the RAND routine
C
C****************************************************************
C
          SUBROUTINE GAUSS(Y1,Y2,NC01)
          CALL RAND(NC01,R)
          SR=R
          CALL RAND(NC01,R)
          BR=R
          A=SQRT(-2.*ALOG(SR))
          B=6.28318530*BR
          Y1=A*COS(B)
          Y2=A*SIN(B)
          RETURN
          END
```

Index

A

Access, memory, 229
Accumulator, 246
Adder, 230
Addition, 224, 226
Algorithm
  prediction-interpolation, 35-42
  steepest descent, 40
  Viterbi, 130, 133, 239, 249, 263, 265, 267
Alphabet
  channel input, 96
  channel output, 96
  input and output, 5
  primary and secondary, 15
Amplitude distribution, 257
Analog-to-digital (A-D) converter, 240
Applications
  biomedicine, 267-272
  communication systems, 265-266
  computer systems and networks, 266-267
  data transmission, 265-266
  facsimile and television, 261-263
  remote sensing, 272-277
  space digital communications, 263-265
  space digital telemetry, 253-257
  speech compression and vocoders, 257-261
Arithmetics, 222
Autocorrelation, 257

B

Bahl-Chien code, 147, 149
Bandpass analysis, 240-241

Bandwidth
reduction, 252, 266
transmission, 34, 214, 267
Bayes's rule, 6, 134
Berlekamp algorithm, 122
Binary arithmetics, 222
Binoid code, 142
Biomedical signal and image, 267-268
Biomedicine, 266-268
Block code, 237
Blood cell, 268
Bose-Chaudhuri-Hocquenghem (BCH)
  code, 119-124, 169, 210, 238, 254, 265
Broadcast television, 266
Buffer, 35, 65, 232, 235-236
  fullness sensor, 65
  overflow, 65
  underflow, 65
Burst, 91, 93
  cluster, 144
  distribution, 95
  error, 149
  error correction, 115, 130, 139, 144, 237
  noise, 265
  phased, 139-140
  trapping (BT) technique, 150
Burton code, 141
Buss-hiss detector, 260

C

Capacity, 5, 9
  binary symmetric channel (BSC), 87, 89-90

297